Since 1905, when the Special Theory of Relativity was first published, there has been a vast gap between Einstein's scientific eminence and public understanding of just what he did. Many persons still think of Einstein as a kind of mathematical surrealist, rather than as the discoverer of cosmic laws that have changed man's conception of physical reality. They do not realize that Relativity, over and above its scientific import, represents a radical new philosophical outlook.

THE UNIVERSE AND DR. EINSTEIN

The fascinating report by a gifted journalist which has become essential reading for students and the general public alike.

"Everybody who has a mind, or who imagines he is a thinker, should understand this much of Relativity as a minimum."

—Philip Wylie

BANTAM
SCIENCE
AND
MATHEMATICS

The Universe and Dr. Einstein

by Lincoln Barnett

Revised Edition
Foreword by Albert Einstein

THE UNIVERSE AND DR. EINSTEIN
*A Bantam Book / published by arrangement with
William Morrow and Company, Inc.*

PRINTING HISTORY

William Morrow edition published October 1948

2nd printing ... February 1949	5th printing ... February 1950
3rd printing ... February 1949	6th printing ..... August 1950
4th printing .... May 1949	7th printing ...... April 1952

8th printing .... July 1952

William Morrow Second Revised edition published February 1957

2nd printing .... May 1957	5th printing..........June 1963
3rd printing ...... April 1959	6th printing........ July 1965
4th printing .... June 1961	7th printing.....September 1966

Science Book Club edition published July 1957

Bantam Science and Mathematics edition published May 1968

*Bantam Books are published by Bantam Books, Inc., a subsidiary
of Grosset & Dunlap, Inc. Its trade-mark, consisting of the words
"Bantam Books" and the portrayal of a bantam, is registered in the
United States Patent Office and in other countries. Marca Registrada.
Bantam Books, Inc., 271 Madison Avenue, New York, N.Y. 10016.*

TO

J. K. B. AND L. H. B.

Acknowledgment

FOR THEIR HELP AND ADVICE IN THE PREPARATION OF this book I wish to thank Dr. Allen G. Shenstone and Dr. Valentin Bargmann of the Department of Physics, Princeton University; Dr. Hermann Weyl of the Institute for Advanced Study, Princeton, N. J.; and Dr. H. P. Robertson of the California Institute of Technology.

I also wish to express my appreciation to Dr. Harlow Shapley of the Harvard Observatory, who read the original manuscript and made valuable suggestions and criticisms, with particular reference to the sections dealing with astronomy.

I owe my very special gratitude to Dr. William W. Havens, Jr., of the Department of Physics, Columbia University, who read and checked both the original manuscript, prior to its publication in *Harper's* magazine, and the expanded version that appears here; and who patiently and cordially contributed his time and knowledge to the solution of many difficulties presented by the exposition of this material.

Foreword By Albert Einstein

ANYONE WHO HAS EVER TRIED TO PRESENT A RATHER abstract scientific subject in a popular manner knows the great difficulties of such an attempt. Either he succeeds in being intelligible by concealing the core of the problem and by offering to the reader only superficial aspects or vague allusions, thus deceiving the reader by arousing in him the deceptive illusion of comprehension; or else he gives an expert account of the problem, but in such a fashion that the untrained reader is unable to follow the exposition and becomes discouraged from reading any further.

If these two categories are omitted from today's popular scientific literature, surprisingly little remains. But the little that is left is very valuable indeed. It is of great importance that the general public be given an opportunity to experience—consciously and intelligently—the efforts and results of scientific research. It is not sufficient that each result be taken up, elaborated, and applied by a few specialists in the field. Restricting the body of knowledge to a small group deadens the philosophical spirit of a people and leads to spiritual poverty.

Lincoln Barnett's book represents a valuable contribution to popular scientific writing. The main ideas of the theory of relativity are extremely well presented. Moreover, the present state of our knowledge in physics is aptly characterized. The author shows how the growth of our factual knowledge, together with the striving for a unified theoretical conception comprising all empirical data, has led to the present situation which is characterized—notwithstanding all successes—by an uncertainty concerning the choice of the basic theoretical concepts.

Princeton, New Jersey
September 10, 1948

CARVED IN THE WHITE WALLS OF THE RIV-
erside Church in New York, the figures of six hundred great men of the ages—saints, philosophers,
kings—stand in limestone immortality, surveying
space and time with blank imperishable eyes. One
panel enshrines the geniuses of science, fourteen of
them, spanning the centuries from Hippocrates,
who died around 370 B.C., to Albert Einstein, who
died in 1955. In this whole sculptured gallery of
the illustrious dead, Einstein is the only one who
shook the world within the memory of most living
men.

It is equally noteworthy that of the thousands of
people who worship weekly at Manhattan's most
spectacular Protestant church, probably 99 per cent
would be hard pressed to explain why Einstein's
image is there. It is there because a generation ago,
when the iconography of the church was being
planned, Dr. Harry Emerson Fosdick wrote letters
to a group of the nation's leading scientists asking
them to submit lists of the fourteen greatest names
in scientific history. Their ballots varied. Most of
them included Archimedes, Euclid, Galileo, and
Newton. But on every list appeared the name of
Albert Einstein.

The vast gap that has persisted for more than fifty

years—since 1905, when the Theory of Special Relativity was first published—between Einstein's scientific eminence and public understanding of it is the measure of a gap in American education. To-day most newspaper readers know vaguely that Einstein had something to do with the atomic bomb; beyond that his name is simply a synonym for the abstruse. While his theories form part of the body of modern science, many of them are not yet part of the modern curriculum. It is not surprising there-fore that many a college graduate still thinks of Einstein as a kind of mathematical surrealist rather than as the discoverer of certain cosmic laws of im-mense importance in man's slow struggle to under-stand physical reality. He may not realize that Relativity, over and above its scientific import, comprises a major philosophical system which aug-ments and illumines the reflections of the great epistemologists—Locke, Berkeley, and Hume. Con-sequently he has very little notion of the vast, arcane, and mysteriously ordered universe in which he dwells.

Dr. Einstein, long professor emeritus at the In-stitute for Advanced Study in Princeton, spent the last years of his life working on a problem which had baffled him for more than a quarter of a cen-tury. This was his Unified Field Theory, which attempted to set forth in one series of mutually consistent equations the physical laws governing two of the fundamental forces of the universe, gravitation and electromagnetism. The significance of this task can be appreciated only when one realizes that most of the phenomena of our external world seem to be produced by these two primordial forces. Until a hundred years ago electricity and magnetism —while known and studied since early Greek times —were regarded as separate quantities. But the experiments of Oersted and Faraday in the nineteenth century showed that a current of electricity is always surrounded by a magnetic field, and conversely that under certain conditions magnetic forces can induce electrical currents. From these experiments came the discovery of the electromagnetic field through which light waves, radio waves, and all other electromagnetic disturbances are propagated in space.

Thus electricity and magnetism may be considered as aspects of a single force. Save for gravitation and the newly discovered, little understood meson forces which appear to hold the various parts of the atomic nucleus together, nearly all other forces in the material universe—frictional forces, chemical forces which hold atoms together in molecules, cohesive forces which bind larger particles of matter, elastic forces which cause bodies to maintain their shape—are of electromagnetic origin; for all of these involve the interplay of matter, and all matter is composed of atoms which in turn are composed of electrical particles. Yet the similarities between gravitational and electromagnetic phenomena are very striking. The planets spin in the gravitational field of the sun; electrons swirl in the electromagnetic field of the atomic nucleus. The earth, moreover, is a big magnet—a peculiar fact which is apparent to anyone who has ever used a compass. The sun also has a magnetic field. And so have all the stars.

Although many attempts have been made to identify gravitational attraction as an electromagnetic effect, all have failed. Einstein thought he had succeeded in 1929 and published a unified field theory which he later rejected as inadequate. His new theory, completed in the final days of 1949, was far more ambitious; for it promulgated a set of universal laws designed to encompass not only the boundless gravitational and electromagnetic fields of interstellar space but also the tiny, terrible field inside the atom. Whether the whole grand objective of a Unified Field Theory will be realized only many more months or years of mathematical and experimental work can determine. But in its vast cosmic picture, when fully revealed, the abyss between macrocosmos and microcosmos—the very big and the very little—will surely be bridged, and the whole complex of the universe will resolve into a homogeneous fabric in which matter and energy are indistinguishable and all forms of motion from the slow wheeling of the galaxies to the wild flight of electrons become simply changes in the structure and concentration of the primordial field.

Since the aim of science is to describe and explain the world we live in, such a theory would, by thus defining the manifold of nature within the terms of a single harmonious theory, attain its loftiest goal. The meaning of the word "explain," however, suffers a contraction with man's every step in quest of reality. Science cannot yet really "explain" electricity, magnetism, and gravitation; their effects can be measured and predicted, but of their ultimate nature no more is known to the modern scientist than to Thales of Miletus, who first speculated on the electrification of amber around 585 B.C. Most contemporary physicists reject the notion that man can ever discover what these mysterious forces "really" are. Electricity, Bertrand Russell says, "is not a thing, like St. Paul's Cathedral; it is a way in which things behave. When we have told how things behave when they are electrified, and under what circumstances they are electrified, we have told all there is to tell." Until recently scientists would have scorned such a thesis. Aristotle, whose natural science dominated Western thought for two thousand years, believed that man could arrive at an understanding of ultimate reality by reasoning from *self-evident principles*. It is, for example, a self-evident principle that everything in the universe has its proper place, hence one can deduce that objects fall to the ground because that's where they belong, and smoke goes up because that's where *it* belongs. The goal of Aristotelian science was to explain *why* things happen. Modern science was born when Galileo began trying to explain *how* things happen and thus originated the method of controlled experiment which now forms the basis of scientific investigation.

Out of Galileo's discoveries and those of Newton in the next generation there evolved a mechanical universe of forces, pressures, tensions, oscillations, and waves. There seemed to be no process of nature which could not be described in terms of ordinary experience, illustrated by a concrete model or predicted by Newton's amazingly accurate laws of mechanics. But before the turn of the past century certain deviations from these laws became apparent; and though these deviations were slight, they were of such a fundamental nature that the whole edifice of Newton's machine-like universe began to topple. The certainty that science can explain *how* things happen began to dim about twenty years ago. And right now it is a question whether scientific man is in touch with "reality" at all—or can ever hope to be.

THE FACTORS THAT FIRST LED PHYSICISTS to distrust their faith in a smoothly functioning mechanical universe loomed on the inner and outer horizons of knowledge—in the unseen realm of the atom and in the fathomless depths of intergalactic space. To describe these phenomena quantitatively, two great theoretical systems were developed between 1900 and 1927. One was the Quantum Theory, dealing with the fundamental units of matter and energy. The other was Relativity, dealing with space, time, and the structure of the universe as a whole.

Both are now accepted pillars of modern physical thought. Both describe phenomena in their fields in terms of consistent, mathematical relationships. They do not answer the Newtonian "how" any more than Newton's laws answered the Aristotelian "why." They provide equations, for example, that define with great accuracy the laws governing the radiation and propagation of light. But the actual mechanism by which the atom radiates light and by which light is propagated through space remains one of nature's supreme mysteries. Similarly the laws governing the phenomenon of radioactivity enable scientists to predict that in a given quantity of uranium a certain number of atoms will disintegrate in a certain length of time. But just which atoms will decay and how they are selected for doom are questions that man cannot yet answer.

In accepting a mathematical description of nature, physicists have been forced to abandon the ordinary world of our experience, the world of sense perceptions. To understand the significance of this retreat it is necessary to step across the thin line that divides physics from metaphysics. Questions involving the relationship between observer and reality, subject and object, have haunted philosophical thinkers since the dawn of reason. Twenty-three centuries ago the Greek philosopher Democritus wrote: "Sweet and bitter, cold and warm as well as all the colors, all these things exist but in opinion and not in reality; what really exists are unchangeable particles, atoms, and their motions in empty space." Galileo also was aware of the purely subjective character of sense qualities like color, taste, smell, and sound and pointed out that "they can no more be ascribed to the external objects than can the tickling or the pain caused sometimes by touching such objects."

The English philosopher John Locke tried to penetrate to the "real essence of substances" by drawing a distinction between what he termed the primary and secondary qualities of matter. Thus he considered that shape, motion, solidity, and all geometrical properties were real or primary qualities, inherent in the object itself; while secondary qualities, like colors, sounds, tastes, were simply projections upon the organs of sense. The artificiality of this distinction was obvious to later thinkers.

"I am able to prove," wrote the great German

mathematician, Leibnitz, "that not only light, color, heat, and the like, but motion, shape, and extension too are mere apparent qualities." Just as our visual sense, for example, tells us that a golf ball is white, so vision abetted by our sense of touch tells us that it is also round, smooth, and small—qualities that have no more reality, independent of our senses, than the quality which we define by convention as white.

Thus gradually philosophers and scientists arrived at the startling conclusion that since every object is simply the sum of its qualities, and since qualities exist only in the mind, the whole objective universe of matter and energy, atoms and stars, does not exist except as a construction of the consciousness, an edifice of conventional symbols shaped by the senses of man. As Berkeley, the archenemy of materialism, phrased it: "All the choir of heaven and furniture of earth, in a word all those bodies which compose the mighty frame of the world, have not any substance without the mind. . . . So long as they are not actually perceived by me, or do not exist in my mind, or that of any other created spirit, they must either have no existence at all, or else subsist in the mind of some Eternal Spirit." Einstein carried this train of logic to its ultimate limits by showing that even space and time are forms of intuition, which can no more be divorced from consciousness than can our concepts of color, shape, or size. Space has no objective reality except as an order or arrangement of the objects we perceive in it, and time has no independent existence apart from the order of events by which we measure it.

These philosophical subtleties have a profound

bearing on modern science. For along with the philosophers' reduction of all objective reality to a shadow-world of perceptions, scientists became aware of the alarming limitations of man's senses. Anyone who has ever thrust a glass prism into a sunbeam and seen the rainbow colors of the solar spectrum refracted on a screen has looked upon the whole range of visible light. For the human eye is sensitive only to the narrow band of radiation that falls between the red and the violet. A difference of a few one hundred thousandths of a centimeter in wave length makes the difference between visibility and invisibility. The wave length of red light is .00007 cm. and that of violet light .00004 cm.

But the sun also emits other kinds of radiation. Infrared rays, for example, with a wave length of .00008 to .032 cm. are just a little too long to excite the retina to an impression of light, though the skin detects their impact as heat. Similarly ultraviolet rays with a wave length of .00003 to .000001 cm. are too short for the eye to perceive but can be recorded on a photographic plate. Photographs can also be made by the "light" of X-rays which are even shorter than ultraviolet rays. And there are other electromagnetic waves of lesser and greater frequency—the gamma rays of radium, radio waves, cosmic rays—which can be detected in various ways and differ from light only in wavelength. It is evident, therefore, that the human eye fails to respond to most of the "lights" in the world, and that what man can perceive of the reality around him is distorted and enfeebled by the limitations of his organ of vision. The world would appear far different to him if his eye were sensitive, for example, to X-rays.

The electromagnetic spectrum reveals the narrow range of radiation visible to man's eye. From the standpoint of physics, the only difference between radio waves, visible light, and such high-frequency forms of radiation as X-rays and gamma rays lies in their wave length. But out of this vast range of electromagnetic radiation, extending from cosmic rays with wave lengths of only one trillionth of a centimeter up to infinitely long radio waves, the human eye selects only the narrow band indicated in white on the above chart. Man's preceptions of the universe in which he dwells are thus restricted by the limitations of his visual sense. Wave lengths are indicated on the chart by the denary system: i.e. 10^3 centimeters equals $10 \times 10 \times 10$ equals 1,000; and 10^{-3} equals $1/10 \times 1/10 \times 1/10$ equals 1/1,000.

Realization that our whole knowledge of the universe is simply a residue of impressions clouded by our imperfect senses makes the quest for reality seem hopeless. If nothing has existence save in its being perceived, the world should dissolve into an anarchy of individual perceptions. But a curious order runs through our perceptions, as if indeed there might be an underlayer of objective reality which our senses translate. Although no man can ever know whether his sensation of red or of Middle C is the same as another man's, it is nevertheless possible to act on the assumption that everyone sees colors and hears tones more or less alike.

This functional harmony of nature Berkeley, Descartes, and Spinoza attributed to God. Modern physicists who prefer to solve their problems without recourse to God (although this seems to become more difficult all the time) emphasize that nature mysteriously operates on mathematical principles. It is the mathematical orthodoxy of the universe that enables theorists like Einstein to predict and discover natural laws simply by the solution of equations. But the paradox of physics today is that with every improvement in its mathematical apparatus the gulf between man the observer and the objective world of scientific description becomes more profound.

It is perhaps significant to man that in terms of simple magnitude he is the mean between macrocosm and microcosm. Stated crudely this means that a super-giant red star (the largest material body in the universe) is just as much bigger than man as an electron (one of the tiniest of physical entities) is smaller. It is not surprising, therefore, that the prime mysteries of nature dwell in those realms farthest removed from sense-imprisoned man, nor that science, unable to describe the extremes of reality in the homely metaphors of classical physics should content itself with noting such mathematical relationships as may be revealed.

3

THE FIRST STEP IN SCIENCE'S RETREAT from mechanical explanation toward mathematical abstraction was taken in 1900, when Max Planck put forth his Quantum Theory to meet certain problems that had arisen in studies of radiation. It is common knowledge that when heated bodies become incandescent they emit a red glow that turns to orange, then yellow, then white as the temperature increases. Painstaking efforts were made during the past century to formulate a law stating how the amount of radiant energy given off by such heated bodies varied with wave length and temperature. All attempts failed until Planck found by mathematical means an equation that satisfied the results of experiment. The extraordinary feature of his equation was that he was forced to make the assumption that radiant energy is emitted not in an unbroken stream but in discontinuous bits or portions which he termed *quanta.*

Planck had no other evidence for such an assumption, for no one knew anything (then or now) of the actual mechanism of radiation. But to fit the observed facts he had to conclude that each quantum carries an amount of energy given by the equation, $E = h\nu$, where ν is the frequency of the radiation and *h* is Planck's Constant, a small but inexorable number (roughly .00000000000000000000000006624) which has since proved to be one of the most fundamental constants in nature. In any process of radiation the amount of emitted energy divided by the frequency is always equal to *h*. Although Planck's Constant has dominated the computations of atomic physics for half a century, its magnitude cannot be explained any more than the magnitude of the speed of light can be explained. Like other universal constants it is simply a mathematical fact for which no explanation has been given. Sir Arthur Eddington once observed that any true law of nature is likely to seem irrational to rational man; hence Planck's quantum principle, he thought, is one of the few real natural laws science has revealed.

The far-reaching implications of Planck's conjecture did not become apparent till 1905, when Einstein, who almost alone among contemporary physicists appreciated its significance, carried the Quantum Theory into a new domain. Planck had believed he was simply patching up the equations of radiation. But Einstein postulated that all forms of radiant energy—light, heat, X-rays—actually travel through space in separate and discontinuous quanta. Thus the sensation of warmth we experience when sitting in front of a fire results from the bombardment of our skin by innumerable quanta of radiant heat. Similarly sensations of color arise from the bombardment of our retinas by light quanta which differ from each other just as the frequency v varies in the equation $E = hv$

Einstein substantiated this idea by working out a

law accurately defining a puzzling phenomenon known as the photoelectric effect. Physicists had been at a loss to explain the fact that when a beam of pure violet light is allowed to shine upon a metal plate the plate ejects a shower of electrons. If light of lower frequency, say yellow or red, falls on the plate, electrons will again be ejected but at reduced velocities. The vehemence with which the electrons are torn from the metal depends only on the

METAL PLATE

The photoelectric effect was interpreted by Einstein in 1905. When light falls on a metal plate, the plate ejects a shower of electrons. This phenomenon cannot be explained by the classic wave theory of light. Einstein deduced that light is not a continuous stream of energy but is composed of individual particles of bundles of energy which he called *photons*. When a photon strikes an electron the resulting action is analogous to the impact of billiard balls, as shown in the simplified conception above.

color of the light and not at all on its intensity. If the light source is removed to a considerable distance and dimmed to a faint glow the electrons that pop forth are fewer in number but their velocity is undiminished. The action is instantaneous even when the light fades to imperceptibility.

Einstein decided that these peculiar effects could be explained only by supposing that all light is composed of individual particles or grains of energy which he called *photons*, and that when one of them hits an electron the resulting action is comparable to the impact of two billiard balls. He reasoned further that photons of violet, ultraviolet, and other forms of high frequency radiation pack more energy than red and infrared photons, and that the velocity with which each electron flies from the metal plate is proportional to the energy content of the photon that strikes it. He expressed these principles in a series of historic equations which won him the Nobel Prize and profoundly influenced later work in quantum physics and spectroscopy. Television and other applications of the photoelectric cell have sprung from Einstein's Photoelectric Law.

In thus adducing an important new physical principle Einstein uncovered at the same time one of the deepest and most troubling enigmas of nature. No one doubts today that all matter is made up of atoms which in turn are composed of even smaller building blocks called electrons, neutrons, and protons. But Einstein's notion that light too may consist of discontinuous particles clashed with a far more venerable theory that light is made up of waves.

There are indeed certain phenomena involving light that can only be explained by the wave theory. For example the shadows of ordinary objects like buildings, trees and telegraph poles appear sharply defined; but when a very fine wire or hair is held between a light source and a screen it casts no distinct shadow whatsoever, suggesting that light rays have bent around it just as waves of water bend around a small rock. Similarly a beam of light passing through a round aperture projects a sharply-defined disk upon a screen; but if the aperture is reduced to the size of a pinhole, then the disk becomes ribbed with alternating concentric bands of light and darkness, somewhat like those of a conventional target. This phenomenon is known as diffraction and has been compared with the tendency of ocean waves to bend and diverge on passing through the narrow mouth of a harbor. If instead of one pinhole, two pinholes are employed very close together and side by side, the diffraction patterns merge in a series of parallel stripes. Just as two wave systems meeting in a swimming pool will reinforce each other when crest coincides with crest and annul each other when the crest of one wave meets the trough of another, so in the case of the adjacent pinholes the bright stripes occur where two light waves reinforce each other and the dark stripes where two waves have interfered. These phenomena—diffraction and interference—are strictly wave characteristics and would not occur if light were made up only of individual corpuscles. More than two centuries of experiment and theory assert that light *must* consist of waves. Yet Einstein's Photoelectric Law shows that light *must* consist of photons.

This fundamental question—is light waves or is it particles?—has been answered only by asserting

that it must be both. The dual character of light
is, however, only one aspect of a deeper and more
remarkable duality which pervades all nature.

A further hint of this strange dualism came in
1925, when a young French physicist named Louis
de Broglie suggested that phenomena involving the
interplay of matter and radiation could best be understood by regarding electrons not as individual
particles but as systems of waves. This audacious
concept flouted two decades of quantum research
in which physicists had built up rather specific ideas
about the elementary particles of matter. The atom
had come to be pictured as a kind of miniature solar
system composed of a central nucleus surrounded
by varying numbers of electrons (1 for hydrogen,
92 for uranium) revolving in circular or elliptical
orbits. The electron was less vivid. Experiments
showed that all electrons had exactly the same mass
and the same electrical charge, so it was natural to
regard them as the ultimate foundation stones of the
universe. It also seemed logical at first to picture
them simply as hard elastic spheres. But little by little, as investigation progressed, they became more
capricious, defiant of observation and measurement.
In many ways their behavior appeared too complex
for any material particle. "The hard sphere," declared the British physicist, Sir James Jeans, "has
always a definite position in space; the electron apparently has not. A hard sphere takes up a very
definite amount of room; an electron—well it is
probably as meaningless to discuss how much room
an electron takes up as it is to discuss how much
room a fear, an anxiety, or an uncertainty takes up."

Shortly after de Broglie had his vision of "matter waves" a Viennese physicist named Schrödinger developed the same idea in coherent mathematical form, evolving a system that explained quantum phenomena by attributing specific wave functions to protons and electrons. This system, known as "wave mechanics," was corroborated in 1927 when two American scientists, Davisson and Germer, proved by experiment that electrons actually do exhibit wave characteristics. They directed a beam of electrons upon a metal crystal and obtained diffraction patterns analogous to those produced when light is passed through a pinhole.* Their measurements indicated, moreover, that the wave length of an electron is of the precise magnitude predicted by de Broglie's equation, $\lambda = h/mv$, where v is the velocity of the electron, m is its mass, and h is Planck's Constant. But further surprises were in store. For subsequent experiments showed that not only electrons but whole atoms and even molecules produce wave patterns when diffracted by a crystal surface, and that their wave lengths are exactly what de Broglie and Schrödinger forecast. And so all the basic units of matter—what J. Clerk Maxwell called "the imperishable foundation stones of the universe"—gradually shed their substance. The old-fashioned spherical electron was reduced to an undulating charge of electrical energy, the atom to a system of superimposed waves. One could only conclude that all matter is made of waves and we live in a world of waves.

*A crystal, because of the even and orderly arrangement of its component atoms and the closeness of their spacing, serves as a diffraction grating for very short wave lengths, such as those of X-rays.

The paradox presented by waves of matter on the one hand and particles of light on the other was resolved by several developments in the decade before World War II. The German physicists, Heisenberg and Born, bridged the gap by developing a new mathemathical apparatus that permitted accurate description of quantum phenomena either in terms of waves *or* in terms of particles as one wished. The idea behind their system had a profound influence on the philosophy of science. They maintained it is pointless for a physicist to worry about the properties of a single electron; in the laboratory he works with beams or showers of electrons, each containing billions of individual particles (or waves); he is concerned therefore only with mass behavior, with statistics and the laws of probability and chance. So it makes no practical difference whether individual electrons are particles or systems of waves—in aggregate they can be pictured either way. For example, if two physicists are at the seashore one may analyze an ocean wave by saying, "Its properties and intensity are clearly indicated by the positions of its crest and its trough"; while the other may observe with equal accuracy, "The section which you term a crest is significant simply because it contains more molecules of water than the area you call a trough." Analogously Born took the mathematical expression used by Schrödinger in his equations to denote wave function and interpreted it as a "probability" in a statistical sense. That is to say he regarded the intensity of any part of a wave as a measure of the probable distribution of particles at that point. Thus he dealt with the phenomena of diffraction, which hitherto only the wave theory could explain, in terms of the *probability* of certain corpuscles—light quanta or electrons—following certain paths and arriving at certain places. And so "waves of matter" were reduced to "waves of probability." It no longer matters how we visualize an electron or an atom or a probability wave. The equations of Heisenberg and Born fit any picture. And we can, if we choose, imagine ourselves living in a universe of waves, a universe of particles, or as one facetious scientist has phrased it, a universe of "wavicles."

4

WHILE QUANTUM PHYSICS THUS DEFINES with great accuracy the mathematical relationships governing the basic units of radiation and matter, it seems to obscure our picture of the true nature of both. Most modern physicists, however, consider it rather naïve to speculate about the true nature of anything. They are "positivists"—or "logical empiricists"—who contend that a scientist can do no more than report his observations. And so if he performs two experiments with different instruments and one seems to reveal that light is made up of particles and the other that light is made up of waves, he must accept both results, regarding them not as contradictory but as complementary. By itself neither concept suffices to explain light, but together they do. Both are necessary to describe reality and it is meaningless to ask which is really true. For in the abstract lexicon of quantum physics there is no such word as "really."

It is futile, moreover, to hope that the invention of more delicate tools may enable man to penetrate much farther into the microcosm. There is an indeterminacy about all the events of the atomic universe which refinements of measurement and observation can never dispel. The element of caprice in atomic behavior cannot be blamed on man's coarse-grained implements. It stems from the very nature of things, as shown by Heisenberg in 1927 in a famous statement of physical law known as the "Principle of Uncertainty." To illustrate his thesis Heisenberg pictured an imaginary experiment in which a physicist attempts to observe the position and velocity* of a moving electron by using an immensely powerful supermicroscope. Now, as has already been suggested, an individual electron appears to have no definite position or velocity. A physicist can define electron behavior accurately enough so long as he is dealing with great numbers of them. But when he tries to locate a particular electron in space the best he can say is that a certain point in the complex superimposed wave motions of the electron group represents the *probable* position of the electron in question. The individual electron is a blur—as indeterminate as the wind or a sound wave in the night—and the fewer the electrons with which the physicist deals, the more indeterminate his findings. To prove that this indeterminacy is a symptom not of man's immature science but of an ultimate barrier of nature, Heisenberg presupposed that the imaginary microscope used by his imaginary physicist is optically capable of magnifying by a hundred billion diameters—i.e., enough to bring an object the size of an electron within the range of human visibility. But now a further difficulty is encountered. For inasmuch as an electron is smaller than a light wave, the physicist can "illuminate" his subject only by using radiation of

---

* In physics the term "velocity" connotes direction as well as speed.

shorter wave length. Even X-rays are useless. The electron can be rendered visible only by the high-frequency gamma rays of radium. But the photo-electric effect, it will be recalled, showed that photons of ordinary light exert a violent force on electrons; and X-rays knock them about even more roughly. Hence the impact of a still more potent gamma ray would prove disastrous.

The Principle of Uncertainty asserts therefore that it is impossible with any of the principles now known to science to determine the position and the velocity of an electron at the same time—to state confidently that an electron is "right here at this spot" and is moving at "such and such a speed." For by the very act of observing its position, its velocity is changed; and, conversely, the more accurately its velocity is determined, the more indefinite its position becomes. And when the physicist computes the mathematical margin of uncertainty in his measurements of an electron's position and velocity he find it is always a function of that mysterious quantity—Planck's Constant, h.

Quantum physics thus appears to shake two pillars of the old science, causality and determinism. For by dealing in terms of statistics and probabilities it abandons all idea that nature exhibits an inexorable sequence of cause and effect between individual happenings. And by its admission of margins of uncertainty it yields up the ancient hope that science, given the present state and velocity of every material body in the universe, can forecast the history of the universe for all time. One by-product of this surrender is a new argument for the existence of free will. For if physical events are indeterminate and the future is unpredictable, then perhaps the unknown quantity called "mind" may yet guide man's destiny among the infinite uncertainties of a capricious universe. Another conclusion of greater scientific importance is that in the evolution of quantum physics the barrier between man, peering dimly through the clouded windows of his senses, and whatever objective reality may exist has been rendered almost impassable. For whenever he attempts to penetrate and spy on the "real" objective world, he changes and distorts its workings by the very process of his observation. And when he tries to divorce this "real" world from his sense perceptions he is left with nothing but a mathematical scheme. He is indeed somewhat in the position of a blind man trying to discern the shape and texture of a snowflake. As soon as it touches his fingers or his tongue it dissolves. A wave electron, a photon, a wave of probability, cannot be visualized; they are simply symbols useful in expressing the mathematical relationships of the microcosm.

To the question, why does modern physics employ such esoteric methods of description, the physicist answers: because the equations of quantum physics define more accurately than any mechanical model the fundamental phenomena beyond the range of vision. In short, *they work*, as the calculations which hatched the atomic bomb spectacularly proved. The aim of the practical physicist, therefore, is to enunciate the laws of nature in ever more precise mathematical terms. Where the nineteenth century physicist envisaged electricity as a fluid and, with this metaphor in mind, evolved the laws that generated our present electrical age, the twentieth century physicist tries to avoid metaphors. He knows that electricity is not a physical fluid, and he knows that such pictorial concepts as "waves" and "particles," while serving as guideposts to new discovery, must not be accepted as accurate representations of reality. In the abstract language of mathematics he can describe how things behave though he does not know—or need to know—what they are.

Yet there are present-day physicists to whom the void between science and reality presents a challenge. Einstein more than once expressed the hope that the statistical method of quantum physics would prove a temporary expedient. "I cannot believe," he wrote, "that God plays dice with the world." He repudiated the positivist doctrine that science can only report and correlate the results of observation. He believed in a universe of order and harmony. And he believed that questing man may yet attain a knowledge of physical reality. To this end he looked not within the atom, but outward to the stars, and beyond them to the vast drowned depths of empty space and time.

5

Chess

IN HIS GREAT TREATISE *On Human Understanding* philosopher John Locke wrote three hundred years ago: "A company of chessmen standing on the same squares of the chessboard where we left them, we say, are all in the same place or unmoved: though perhaps the chessboard has been in the meantime carried out of one room into another. . . . The chessboard, we also say, is in the same place if it remain in the same part of the cabin, though perhaps the ship which it is in sails all the while; and the ship is said to be in the same place supposing it kept the same distance with the neighboring land, though perhaps the earth has turned around; and so chessmen and board and ship have every one changed place in respect to remoter bodies."

Embodied in this little picture of the moving but unmoved chessmen is one principle of relativity—relativity of position. But this suggests another idea—relativity of motion. Anyone who has ever ridden on a railroad train knows how rapidly another train flashes by when it is traveling in the opposite direction, and conversely how it may look almost motionless when it is moving in the same direction. A variation of this effect can be very deceptive in an enclosed station like Grand Central Terminal in New York. Once in a while a train gets under way so gently that passengers feel no recoil whatever. Then if they happen to look out the window and see another train slide past on the next track, they have no way of knowing which train is in motion and which is at rest; nor can they tell how fast either one is moving or in what direction. The only way they can judge their situation is by looking out the other side of the car for some fixed body of reference like the station platform or a signal light. Sir Isaac Newton was aware of these tricks of motion, only he thought in terms of ships. He knew that on a calm day at sea a sailor can shave himself or drink soup as comfortably as when his ship is lying motionless in harbor. The water in his basin, the soup in his bowl, will remain unruffled whether the ship is making five knots, 15 knots, or 25 knots. So unless he peers out at the sea it will be impossible for him to know how fast his ship is moving or indeed if it is moving at all. Of course if the sea should get rough or the ship change course abruptly, then he will sense his state of motion. But granted the idealized conditions of a glass-calm sea and a silent ship, nothing that happens below decks—no amount of observation or mechanical experiment performed *inside* the ship—will disclose its velocity through the sea. The physical principle suggested by these considerations was formulated by Newton in 1687. "The motions of bodies included in a given space," he wrote, "are the same among themselves, whether that space is at rest or moves uniformly forward in a straight line." This is known as the Newtonian or Galilean Relativity Principle. It can also be phrased in more general terms: mechanical laws which are valid in one place are equally valid in any other place which moves uniformly relative to the first.

The philosophical importance *universal philosophy* of this principle lies in what it says about the universe. Since the aim of science is to explain the world we live in, as a whole and in all its parts, it is essential to the scientist that he have confidence in the harmony of nature. He must believe that physical laws revealed to him on earth are in truth universal laws. Thus in relating the fall of an apple to the wheeling of the planets around the sun Newton hit upon a universal law. And although he illustrated his principle of relative motion by a ship at sea, the ship he actually had in mind was the earth. For all ordinary purposes of science the earth can be regarded as a stationary system. We may say if we choose that mountains, trees, houses, are at rest, and animals, automobiles, and airplanes move. But to the astrophysicist, the earth, far from being at rest, is whirling through space in a giddy and highly complicated fashion. In addition to its daily rotation about its axis at the rate of 1000 miles an hour, and its annual revolution about the sun at the rate of 20 miles a second, the earth is also involved in a number of other less familiar gyrations. Contrary to popular belief the moon does not revolve around the earth; they revolve around each other—or more precisely, around a common center of gravity. The entire solar system, moreover, is moving within the local star system at the rate of 13 miles a second; the local star system is moving within the Milky Way at the rate

motl of universe

of 200 miles a second; and the whole Milky Way is drifting with respect to the remote external galaxies at the rate of 100 miles a second—and all in different directions!

Although he could not then know the full complexity of the earth's movements, Newton was nevertheless troubled by the problem of distinguishing relative motion from true or "absolute" motion in a confusingly busy universe. He suggested that "in the remote regions of the fixed stars or perhaps far beyond them, there may be some body absolutely at rest," but admitted there was no way of proving this by any celestial object within man's view. On the other hand it seemed to Newton that space itself might serve as a fixed frame of reference to which the wheeling of the stars and galaxies could be related in terms of absolute motion. He regarded space as a physical reality, stationary and immovable; and while he could not support this conviction by any scientific argument, he nevertheless clung to it on theological grounds. For to Newton space represented the divine omnipresence of God in nature.

In the next two centuries it appeared probable that Newton's view would prevail. For with the development of the wave theory of light scientists found it necessary to endow empty space with certain mechanical properties—to assume, indeed, that space was some kind of substance. Even before Newton's time the French philosopher, Descartes, had argued that the mere separation of bodies by distance proved the existence of a medium between them. And to eighteenth and nineteenth century physicists it was obvious that if light consisted of waves, there must be some medium to support them, just as water propagates the waves of the sea and air transmits the vibrations we call sound. Hence when experiments showed that light can travel in a vacuum, scientists evolved a hypothetical substance called "ether" which they decided must pervade all space and matter. Later on Faraday propounded another kind of ether as the carrier of electric and magnetic forces. When Maxwell finally identified light as an electromagnetic disturbance the case for the ether seemed assured.

A universe permeated with an invisible medium in which the stars wandered and through which light traveled like vibrations in a bowl of jelly was the end product of Newtonian physics. It provided a mechanical model for all known phenomena of nature, and it provided the fixed frame of reference, the absolute and immovable space, which Newton's cosmology required. Yet the ether presented certain problems, not the least of which was that its actual existence had never been proved. To discover once and for all whether there really was any such thing as ether, two American physicists, A. A. Michelson and E. W. Morley, performed a classic experiment in Cleveland in the year 1881.

The principle underlying their experiment was quite simple. They reasoned that if all space is simply a motionless sea of ether, then the earth's motion through the ether should be detectable and measurable in the same way that sailors measure the velocity of a ship through the sea. As Newton pointed out, it is impossible to detect the movement of a ship through calm waters by any mechanical experiment performed *inside* the ship. Sailors ascertain a ship's speed by throwing a log overboard and watching the unreeling of the knots on the log line. Hence to detect the earth's motion through the ether sea, Michelson and Morley threw a "log" overboard, and the log was a beam of light. For if light really is propagated through the ether, then its velocity should be affected by the ether stream arising from the earth's movement. Specifically a light ray projected in the direction of the earth's movement should be slightly retarded by the ether flow, just as a swimmer is retarded by a current when going upstream. The difference would be

The Michelson-Morley interferometer consisted of an arrangement of mirrors, so designed that a beam transmitted from a light source (above left) was divided and sent in two directions at the same time. This was done by a mirror, A, the *face* of

slight, for the velocity of light (which was accurately determined in 1849) is 186,284 miles a second, while the velocity of the earth in its orbit around the sun is only 20 miles a second. Hence a light ray sent *against* the ether stream should travel at the rate of 186,264 miles a second, while one sent *with* the ether stream should be clocked at 186,304 miles a second. With these ideas in mind Michelson and Morley constructed an instrument of such great delicacy that it could detect a variation of even a fraction of a mile per second in the enormous velocity of light. This instrument, which they called an "interferometer" consisted of a group of mirrors so

---

which was only thinly silvered, so that part of the beam was permitted to pass through to mirror C (right) and the remainder reflected at right angles toward mirror B. Mirrors B and C then reflected the rays back to mirror A where, reunited, they proceeded to an observing telescope T. Since the beam ACT had to pass three times through the thickness of glass behind the reflecting face of mirror A, a clear glass plate of equal thickness was placed between A and B to intercept beam ABT and compensate for this retardation. The whole apparatus was rotated in different directions so that the beams ABT and ACT could be sent with, against, and at right angles to the postulated ether stream. At first it might appear that a trip "downstream," for example from B to A, should compensate in time for an "upstream" trip from A to B. But this is not so. To row a boat one mile upstream and another mile downstream takes longer than rowing two miles in still water or across current, even with allowance for drift. Had there been any acceleration or retardation of either beam by the ether stream, the optical apparatus at T would have detected it.

arranged that a light beam could be split in two and flashed in different directions at the same time. The whole experiment was planned and executed with such painstaking precision that the result could not be doubted. And the result was simply this: there was no difference whatsoever in the velocity of the light beams regardless of their direction.

The Michelson-Morley experiment confronted scientists with an embarrassing alternative. On the one hand they could scrap the ether theory which had explained so many things about electricity, magnetism, and light. Or if they insisted on retaining the ether they had to abandon the still more venerable Copernican theory that the earth is in motion. To many physicists it seemed almost easier to believe that the earth stood still than that waves—light waves, electromagnetic waves—could exist without a medium to sustain them. It was a serious dilemma and one that split scientific thought for a quarter century. Many new hypotheses were advanced and rejected. The experiment was tried again by Morley and by others, with the same conclusion; the apparent velocity of the earth through the ether was zero.

6

Among those who pondered the enigma of the Michelson-Morley experiment was a young patent office examiner in Berne, named Albert Einstein. In 1905, when he was just twenty-six years old, he published a short paper suggesting an answer to the riddle in terms that opened up a new world of physical thought. He began by rejecting the ether theory and with it the whole idea of space as a fixed system or framework, absolutely at rest, within which it is possible to distinguish absolute from relative motion. The one indisputable fact established by the Michelson-Morley experiment was that the velocity of light is unaffected by the motion of the earth. Einstein seized on this as a revelation of universal law. If the velocity of light is constant regardless of the earth's motion, he reasoned, it must be constant regardless of the motion of any sun, moon, star, meteor, or other system moving anywhere in the universe. From this he drew a broader generalization, and asserted that the laws of nature are the same for all uniformly moving systems. This simple statement is the essence of Einstein's Special Theory of Relativity. It incorporates the Galilean Relativity Principle which stated that mechanical laws are the same for all uniformly moving systems. But its phrasing is more comprehensive; for Einstein was thinking not only of mechanical laws but of the laws governing light and other electromagnetic phenomena. So he lumped them together in one fundamental postulate: all the phenomena of nature, all the laws of nature, are the same for all systems that move uniformly relative to one another.

On the surface there is nothing very startling in this declaration. It simply reiterates the scientist's faith in the universal harmony of natural law. It also advises the scientist to stop looking for any absolute, stationary frame of reference in the universe. The universe is a restless place: stars, nebulae, galaxies, and all the vast gravitational systems of outer space are incessantly in motion. But their movements can be described only with respect to each other, for in space there are no directions and no boundaries. It is futile moreover for the scientist to try to discover the "true" velocity of any system by using light as a measuring rod, for the velocity of light is constant throughout the universe and is unaffected either by the motion of its source or the motion of the receiver. Nature offers no absolute standards of comparison; and space is—as another great German mathematician, Leibnitz, clearly saw two centuries before Einstein—simply "the order or relation of things among themselves." Without things occupying it, it is nothing.

Along with absolute space, Einstein discarded the concept of absolute time—of a steady, unvarying, inexorable universal time flow, streaming from the infinite past to the infinite future. Much of the obscurity that has surrounded the Theory of Relativity stems from man's reluctance to recognize that sense of time, like sense of color, is a form of perception. Just as there is no such thing as color without an eye to discern it, so an instant or an hour or a day is nothing without an event to mark it. And just as space is simply a possible order of material objects, so time is simply a possible order of events. The subjectivity of time is best explained in Einstein's own words. "The experiences of an individual," he says, "appear to us arranged in a series of events; in this series the single events which we remember appear to be ordered according to the criterion of 'earlier' and 'later.' There exists, therefore, for the individual, an I-time, or subjective time. This in itself is not measurable. I can, indeed, associate numbers with the events, in such a way that a greater number is associated with the later event than with an earlier one. This association I can define by means of a clock by comparing the order of events furnished by the clock with the order of the given series of events. We understand by a clock something which provides a series of events which can be counted."

By referring our own experiences to a clock (or a calendar) we make time an objective concept. Yet the time intervals provided by a clock or a calendar are by no means absolute quantities imposed on the entire universe by divine edict. All the clocks ever used by man have been geared to our solar system. What we call an hour is actually a measurement in space—an arc of 15 degrees in the apparent daily rotation of the celestial sphere. And what we call a year is simply a measure of the earth's progress in its orbit around the sun. An inhabitant of Mercury, however, would have very different notions of time. For Mercury makes its trip around the sun in 88 of our days, and in that same period rotates just once on its axis. So on Mercury a year and a day amount to the same thing. But it is when science ranges beyond the neighborhood of the sun that all our terrestrial ideas of time become meaningless. For Relativity tells us there is no such thing as a fixed interval of time independent of the system to which it is referred. There is indeed no such thing as simultaneity, there is no such thing as "now," independent of a system of reference. For example a man in New York may telephone a friend in London, and although it is 7:00 P.M. in New York and midnight in London, we may say that they are talking "at the same time." But that is because they are both residents of the same planet, and their clocks are geared to the same astronomical system. A more complicated situation arises if we try to ascertain, for example, what is happening on the star Arcturus "right now." Arcturus is 38 light years away. A light year is the distance light travels in one year, or roughly six trillion miles. If we should try to communicate with Arcturus by radio "right now" it would take 38 years for our message to reach its destination and another 38 years for us to receive a reply.* And when we look at Arcturus and say that we see it "now," in 1957, we are actually seeing a ghost—an image projected on our optic nerves by light rays that left their source in 1919. Whether

---

* *Radio waves travel at the same speed as light waves.*

Arcturus even exists "now" nature forbids us to know until 1995.

Despite such reflections it is difficult for earth-bound man to accept the idea that *this very instant* which he calls "now" cannot apply to the universe as a whole. Yet in the Special Theory of Relativity Einstein proves by an unanswerable sequence of example and deduction that it is nonsense to think of events taking place simultaneously in unrelated systems. His argument unfolds along the following lines.

To begin with one must realize that the scientist, whose task it is to describe physical events in objective terms, cannot use subjective words like "this," "here," and "now." For him concepts of space and time take on physical significance only when the relations between events and systems are defined. And it is constantly necessary for him, in dealing with matters involving complex forms of motion (as in celestial mechanics, electrodynamics, etc.) to relate the magnitudes found in one system with those occurring in another. The mathematical laws which define these relationships are known as laws of transformation. The simplest transformation may be illustrated by a man promenading on the deck of a ship: if he walks forward along the deck at the rate of 3 miles an hour and the ship moves through the sea at the rate of 12 miles an hour, then the man's velocity with respect to the sea is 15 miles an hour; if he walks aft his velocity relative to the sea is of course 9 miles an hour. Or as a variation one may imagine an alarm bell ringing at a railway crossing. The sound waves produced by the bell spread away through the surrounding air at the rate of 400 yards a second. A railroad train speeds toward the crossing at the rate of 20 yards a second. Hence the velocity of the sound relative to the train is 420 yards a second so long as the train is approaching the alarm bell and 380 yards a second as soon as the train passes the bell. This simple addition of velocities rests on obvious common sense, and has indeed been applied to problems of compound motion since the time of Galileo. Serious difficulties arise, however, when it is used in connection with light.

In his original paper on Relativity, Einstein emphasized these difficulties with another railway incident. Again there is a crossing, marked this time by a signal light which flashes its beam down the track at 186,284 miles a second—the constant velocity of light, denoted in physics by the symbol c. A train steams toward the signal light at a given velocity v. So by the addition of velocities one concludes that the velocity of the light beam relative to the train is c plus v when the train moves toward the signal light, and c minus v as soon as the train passes the light. But this result conflicts with the findings of the Michelson-Morley experiment which demonstrated that the velocity of light is unaffected either by the motion of the source or the motion of the receiver. This curious fact has also been confirmed by studies of double stars which revolve around a common center of gravity. Careful analysis of these moving systems has shown that the light from the approaching star in each pair reaches earth at precisely the same velocity as the light from the receding star. Since the velocity of light is a universal constant it cannot in Einstein's railway problem be affected by the velocity of the train. Even if we imagine that the train is racing toward the signal light at a speed of 10,000 miles a second, the principle of the constancy of the velocity of light tells us that an observer aboard the train will still clock the speed of the oncoming light beam at precisely 186,284 miles a second, no more, no less.

The dilemma presented by this situation involves much more than a Sunday morning newspaper puzzle. On the contrary it poses a deep enigma of nature. Einstein saw that the problem lay in the irreconcilable conflict between his belief in (1) the constancy of the velocity of light, and (2) the principle of the addition of velocities. Although the latter appears to rest on the stern logic of mathematics (i.e., that two plus two makes four), Einstein recognized in the former a fundamental law of nature. He concluded, therefore, that a new transformation rule must be found to enable the scientist to describe the relations between moving systems in such a way that the results satisfy the known facts about light.

Einstein found what he wanted in a series of equations developed by the great Dutch physicist, H. A. Lorentz, in connection with a specific theory of his own. Although its original application is of interest now chiefly to scientific historians, the Lorentz transformation lives on as part of the mathematical framework of Relativity. To understand what it says, however, it is first necessary to perceive the flaws in the old principle of the addition of velocities. These flaws Einstein pointed out by means of still another railway anecdote. Once again he envisaged a straight length of track, this time with an observer sitting on an embankment beside it. A thunderstorm breaks, and two bolts of lightning strike the track simultaneously at separate points,

A and B. Now, asks Einstein, what do we mean by "simultaneously"? To pin down this definition he assumes that the observer is sitting precisely half way between A and B, and that he is equipped with an arrangement of mirrors which enable him to see A and B at the same time without moving his eyes. Then if the lightning flashes are reflected in the observer's mirrors at precisely the same instant, the two flashes may be regarded as simultaneous. Now a train roars down the track, and a second observer is sitting precariously perched atop one of the cars with a mirror apparatus just like the one on the embankment. It happens that this moving observer finds himself directly opposite the observer on the embankment at the precise instant the lightning bolts hit A and B. The question is: will the lightning flashes appear simultaneous to him? The answer is: they will not. For if his train is moving away from lightning bolt B and toward lightning bolt A, then it is obvious that B will be reflected in his mirrors a fraction of a second later than A. Lest there be any doubt about this, one may imagine temporarily that the train is moving at the impossible rate of 186,284 miles a second, the velocity of light. In that event flash B, traveling at precisely the same velocity as flash A, will never be reflected in the mirrors at all because it will never be able to overtake the train. So the observer on the train will assert that only one lightning bolt struck the track. And whatever the speed of the train may be the moving observer will always insist that the lightning flash ahead of him has struck the track first. Hence the lightning flashes which are simultaneous relative to the stationary observer are *not* simultaneous relative to the observer on the train.

The paradox of the lightning flashes thus dramatizes one of the subtlest and most difficult concepts in Einstein's philosophy: the relativity of simultaneity. It shows that man cannot assume that his subjective sense of "now" applies to all parts of the universe. For, Einstein points out, "every reference body (or coordinate system) has its own particular time; unless we are told the reference body to which the statement of time refers, there is no meaning in a statement of the time of an event." The fallacy in the old principle of the addition of velocities lies therefore in its tacit assumption that the duration of an event is independent of the state of motion of the system of reference. In the case of the man pacing the deck of a ship, for example, it was assumed that if he walked three miles in one hour as timed by a clock on the moving ship, his rate would be just the same timed by a stationary clock anchored somehow in the sea. It was further assumed that the distance he traversed in one hour would have the same value whether it was measured relative to the deck of the ship (the moving system) or relative to the sea (the stationary system). This constitutes a second fallacy in the addition of velocities—for distance, like time, is a relative concept, and there is no such thing as a space interval independent of the state of motion of the system of reference.

Einstein asserted, therefore, that the scientist who wishes to describe the phenomena of nature in terms that are consistent for all systems throughout the universe must regard measurements of time and distance as variable quantities. The equations comprising the Lorentz transformation do just that. They preserve the velocity of light as a universal constant, but modify all measurements of time and distance according to the velocity of each system of reference.*

---

* The Lorentz transformation relates distances and times observed on moving systems with those observed on systems relatively at rest. Suppose, for example, that a system, or reference body, is moving in a certain direction, then according to the old principle of the addition of velocities, a distance or length x', measured with respect to the moving system along the direction of motion, is related to length x, measured with respect to a relatively stationary system, by the equation $x' = x \pm vt$, where v is the velocity of the moving system and t is the time. Dimensions y' and z', measured with respect to the moving system at right angles to x' and at right angles to each other (i.e., height and breadth), are related to dimensions y and z on the relatively stationary system by $y' = y$, and $z' = z$. And finally a time interval t', clocked with respect to the moving system, is related to time interval t, clocked with respect to the relatively stationary system, by $t' = t$. In other words, distances and times are not affected, in classical physics, by the velocity of the system in question. But it is this presupposition which leads to the paradox of the lightning flashes. The Lorentz transformation reduces the distances and times observed on moving systems to the conditions of the stationary observer, keeping the velocity of light c

So although Lorentz had originally developed his equations to meet a specific problem, Einstein made them the basis of a tremendous generalization, and to the edifice of Relativity another axiom: the laws of nature preserve their uniformity in all systems when related by the Lorentz transformation. Stated thus, in the abstract language of mathematics the significance of this axiom can scarcely be apparent to the layman. But in physics an equation is never a pure abstraction; it is simply a kind of shorthand expression which the scientist finds convenient to describe the phenomena of nature. Sometimes it is also a Rosetta Stone in which the theoretical physicist can decipher secret realms of knowledge. And so by deduction from the message written in the equations of the Lorentz transformation, Einstein discovered a number of new and extraordinary truths about the physical universe.

---

a constant for all observers. Here are the equations of the Lorentz transformation which have supplanted the older and evidently inadequate relationships cited above:

$$x' = \frac{x - vt}{\sqrt{1 - (v^2/c^2)}}$$
$$y' = y$$
$$z' = z$$
$$t' = \frac{t - (v/c^2)x}{\sqrt{1 - (v^2/c^2)}}$$

It will be noted that, as in the old transformation law, dimensions y' and z' are unaffected by motion. It will also be seen that if the velocity of the moving system v is small relative to the velocity of light c, then the equations of the Lorentz transformation reduce themselves to the relations of the old principle of the addition of velocities. But as the magnitude of v approaches that of c, then the values of x' and t' are radically changed.

7

expt once had

THESE TRUTHS CAN BE DESCRIBED IN VERY concrete terms. For once he had evolved the philosophical and mathematical bases of Relativity, Einstein had to bring them into the laboratory, where abstractions like time and space are harnessed by means of clocks and measuring rods. And so translating his basic ideas about time and space into the language of the laboratory, he pointed out some hitherto unsuspected properties of clocks and rods. For example: a clock attached to any moving system runs at a different rhythm from a stationary clock; and a measuring rod attached to any moving system changes its length according to the velocity of the system. Specifically the clock slows down as its velocity increases, and the measuring rod shrinks in the direction of its motion. These peculiar changes have nothing to do with the construction of the clock or the composition of the rod. The clock can be a pendulum clock, a spring clock, or an hour glass. The measuring rod can be a wooden ruler, a metal yardstick, or a ten-mile cable. The slowing of the clock and the contraction of the rod are not mechanical phenomena; an observer riding along with the clock and the measuring rod would not notice these changes. But a stationary

56

observer, i.e., stationary relative to the moving system, would find that the moving clock has slowed down with respect to his stationary clock, and that the moving rod has contracted with respect to his stationary units of measurement.

This singular behavior of moving clocks and yardsticks accounts for the constant velocity of light. It explains why all observers in all systems everywhere, regardless of their state of motion, will always find that light strikes their instruments and departs from their instruments at precisely the same velocity. For as their own velocity approaches that of light, their clocks slow down, their yardsticks contract, and all their measurements are reduced to the values obtained by a relatively stationary observer. The laws governing these contractions are defined by the Lorentz transformation and they are very simple: the greater the speed, the greater the contraction. A yardstick moving with 90 per cent the velocity of light would shrink to about half its length; thereafter the rate of contraction becomes more rapid; and if the stick should attain the velocity of light, it would shrink away to nothing at all. Similarly a clock traveling with the velocity of light would stop completely. From this it follows that nothing can ever move faster than light, no matter what forces are applied. Thus Relativity reveals another fundamental law of nature: *the velocity of light is the top limiting velocity in the universe.*

At first meeting these facts are difficult to digest but that is simply because classical physics assumed, unjustifiably, that an object preserves the same dimensions whether it is in motion or at rest and that a clock keeps the same rhythm in motion and at rest. Common sense dictates that this must be so. But as Einstein has pointed out, common sense is actually nothing more than a deposit of prejudices laid down in the mind prior to the age of eighteen. Every new idea one encounters in later years must combat this accretion of "self-evident" concepts. And it is because of Einstein's unwillingness ever to accept any unproven principle as self-evident that he was able to penetrate closer to the underlying realities of nature than any scientist before him. Why, he asked, is it any more strange to assume that moving clocks slow down and moving rods contract, than to assume that they don't? The reason classical physics took the latter view for granted is that man, in his everyday experience, never encounters velocities great enough to make these changes manifest. In an automobile, an airplane, even in a V-2 rocket, the slowing down of a watch is immeasurable. It is only when velocities approximate that of light that relativistic effects can be detected. The equations of the Lorentz transformation show very plainly that at ordinary speeds the modification of time and space intervals amounts practically to zero. Relativity does not therefore contradict classical physics. It simply regards the old concepts as limiting cases that apply solely to the familiar experiences of man.

Einstein thus surmounts the barrier reared by man's impulse to define reality solely as he perceives it through the screen of his senses. Just as the Quantum Theory demonstrated that elementary particles of matter do not behave like the larger particles we discern in the coarse-grained world of our perceptions, so Relativity shows that we cannot foretell the phenomena accompanying great velocities from the sluggish behavior of objects visible to man's indolent eye. Nor may we assume that the laws of Relativity deal with exceptional occurrences; on the contrary they provide a comprehensive picture of an incredibly complex universe in which the simple mechanical events of our earthly experience are the exceptions. The present-day scientist, coping with the tremendous velocities that prevail in the fast universe of the atom or with the immensities of sidereal space and time, finds the old Newtonian laws inadequate. But Relativity provides him in every instance with a complete and accurate description of nature.

Whenever Einstein's postulates have been put to test, their validity has been amply confirmed. Remarkable proof of the relativistic retardation of time intervals came out of an experiment performed by H. E. Ives of the Bell Telephone Laboratories in 1936. A radiating atom may be regarded as a kind of clock in that it emits light of a definite frequency and wave-length which can be measured with great precision by means of a spectroscope. Ives compared the light emitted by hydrogen atoms moving at high velocities with that emitted by hydrogen atoms at rest, and found that the frequency of vibration of the moving atoms was reduced in exact accordance with the predictions of Einstein's equations. Someday science may devise a far more interesting test of the same principle. Since any periodic motion serves to measure time, the human heart, Einstein has pointed out, is also a kind of clock. Hence, according to Relativity, the heart-beat of a person traveling with a velocity close to that of light would be relatively slowed, along with his respiration and all other physiological processes. He would not notice this retardation because his watch would slow down in the same degree. But judged by a stationary timekeeper he would "grow old" less rapidly.

8

I<small>N ORDER TO DESCRIBE</small> <small>THE MECHANICS OF</small> the physical universe, three quantities are required: time, distance, and mass. Since time and distance are relative quantities one might guess that the mass of a body also varies with its state of motion. And indeed the most important practical results of Relativity have arisen from this principle—the relativity of mass.

In its popular sense, "mass" is just another word for "weight." But as used by the physicist, it denotes a rather different and more fundamental property of matter: namely, resistance to a change of motion. A greater force is necessary to move or stop a freight car than a velocipede; the freight car resists a change in its motion more stubbornly than the velocipede because it has greater mass. In classical physics the mass of any body is a fixed and unchanging property. Thus the mass of a freight car should remain the same whether it is at rest on a siding, rolling across country at 60 miles an hour, or hurtling through outer space at 60,000 miles a second. But Relativity asserts that the mass of a moving body is by no means constant, but increases with its velocity relative to an observer. The old physics failed to discover this fact simply because man's senses and instruments are too crude to note the infinitesimal increases of mass produced by the feeble accelerations of ordinary experience. They become perceptible only when bodies attain velocities relatively close to that of light. (This phenomenon, incidentally, does not conflict with the relativistic contraction of length. One is tempted to ask: how can an object become smaller and at the same time get heavier? The contraction, it should be noted, is only in the direction of motion; width and breadth are unaffected. Moreover mass is not merely "heaviness" but resistance to a change in motion.)

Einstein's equation giving the increase of mass with velocity is similar in form to the other equations of Relativity but vastly more important in its consequences:

$$m = \frac{m_o}{\sqrt{1 - v^2/c^2}}$$

Here m stands for the mass of a body moving with velocity v, m_o for its mass when at rest, and c for the velocity of light. Anyone who has ever studied elementary algebra can readily see that if v is small, as are all the velocities of ordinary experience, then the difference between m_o and m is practically zero. But when v approaches the value of c then the increase of mass becomes very great, reaching infinity when the velocity of the moving body reaches the velocity of light. Since a body of infinite mass would offer infinite resistance to motion the conclusion is once again reached that no material body can travel with the speed of light.*

* See Appendix.

Of all aspects of Relativity the principle of increase of mass has been most often verified and most fruitfully applied by experimental physicists. Electrons moving in powerful electrical fields and beta particles ejected from the nuclei of radioactive substances attain velocities ranging up to 99 per cent that of light. For atomic physicists concerned with these great speeds, the increase of mass predicted by Relativity is no arguable theory but an empirical fact their calculations cannot ignore. In fact the mechanics of the proton-synchroton and other new super-energy machines must be designed to allow for the increasing mass of particles as their speed approaches the velocity of light, in order to make them operate at all.

By further deduction from his principle of Relativity of mass, Einstein arrived at a conclusion of incalculable importance to the world. His train of reasoning ran somewhat as follows: since the mass of a moving body increases as its motion increases, and since motion is a form of energy (kinetic energy), then the increased mass of a moving body comes from its increased energy. In short, energy has mass! By a few comparatively simple mathematical steps, Einstein found the value of the equivalent mass m in any unit of energy E and expressed it by the equation $m = E/c^2$. Given this relation a high school freshman can take the remaining algebraic step necessary to write the most important and certainly the most famous equation in history: $E = mc^2$.

The part played by this equation in the development of the atomic bomb is familiar to most newspaper readers. It states in the shorthand of physics that the energy contained in any particle of matter is equal to the mass of that body multiplied by the square of the velocity of light, the proper units being chosen in each case. This extraordinary relationship becomes more vivid when its terms are translated into concrete values: i.e., one kilogram of coal (about two pounds), if converted *entirely* into energy, would yield 25 billion kilowatt hours of electricity or as much as all the power plants in the U.S. could generate by running steadily for two months.

$E = mc^2$ provides the answer to many of the long-standing mysteries of physics. It explains how radioactive substances like radium and uranium are able to eject particles at enormous velocities and to go on doing so for millions of years. It explains how the sun and all the stars can go on radiating light and heat for billions of years; for if our sun were being consumed by ordinary processes of combustion, the earth would have died in frozen darkness eons ago. It reveals the magnitude of the energy that slumbers in the nuclei of atoms, and forecasts how many grams of uranium must go into a bomb in order to destroy a city. Finally it discloses some fundamental truths about physical reality. Prior to Relativity scientists had pictured the universe as a vessel containing two distinct elements, matter and energy— the former inert, tangible, and characterized by a property called mass, and the latter active, invisible, and without mass. But Einstein showed that mass and energy are equivalent: the property called mass is simply concentrated energy. In other words matter is energy and energy is matter, and the distinction is simply one of temporary state.

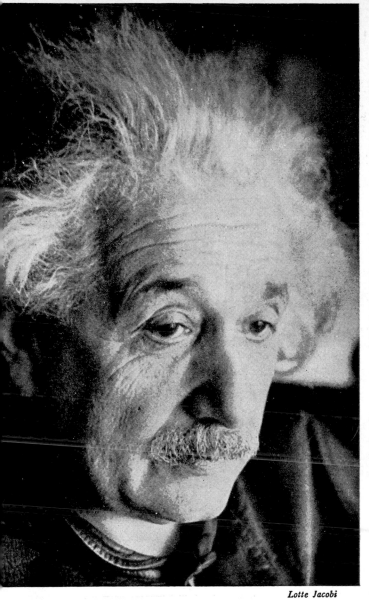

Lotte Jacobi

DR. ALBERT EINSTEIN

Yerkes Observatory, 10-inch Bruce Refractor

The Milky Way which girdles our heavens with a band of pearly light is actually a vast ocean of suns, star fields, clusters, and clouds, composing the galaxy within which our immediate star system moves. Our sun, far from being the center of the universe, is not even the center of our galaxy, but rides on the periphery 30,000 light years from the galactic nucleus. The dark areas suggesting rents in the stellar canopy through which one peers into the void, are actually obscuring masses of opaque matter, dust clouds, whose significance is discussed on pages 104-105.

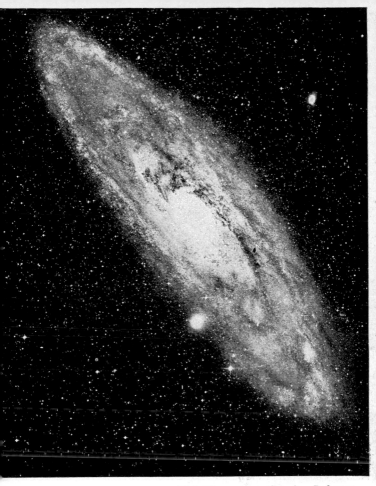

Lick Observatory, Crossley Reflector

The great Andromeda galaxy is a giant star system similar in shape and structure to our own Milky Way. Although it can be seen with the naked eye as a faint luminescence in the constellation Andromeda, it is 700,000 light years away. Yet it is the nearest of all the island universes that wheel in the depths of space. Its diameter is 60,000 light years. To an observer situated in this galaxy, our Milky Way would look very much like this. The smaller nebulosities near by are minor members of the super-galactic cluster that encompasses the Andromeda spiral, our Milky Way, and the Magellanic Clouds.

Mount Wilson Observatory, 60-inch Reflector

The Pegasus quintet comprises a galactic supersystem—a cluster of galaxies—each member an island universe composed, like our Milky Way, of hundreds of millions of stars. Note how the interpenetrating effects of gravitation have distorted several of its members. So deeply sunk in space are these galaxies that the light by which this photograph was made took 22 million years to traverse the stupendous reaches between its origins and earth. The immensity of the universe can be comprehended only when one realizes that as our solar system is to the Milky Way, so our Milky Way is to the systems of outer space. For an account of what these remote galaxies tell astronomers about the cosmos, see pages 99 ff.

In the light of this broad principle many puzzles of nature are resolved. The baffling interplay of matter and radiation which appears sometimes to be a concourse of particles and sometimes a meeting of waves, becomes more understandable. The dual role of the electron as a unit of matter and a unit of electricity, the wave electron, the photon, waves of matter, waves of probability, a universe of waves —all these seem less paradoxical. For all these concepts simply describe different manifestations of the same underlying reality, and it no longer makes sense to ask what any one of them "really" is. Matter and energy are interchangeable. If matter sheds its mass and travels with the speed of light we call it radiation or energy. And conversely if energy congeals and takes on a different form we call it matter. Heretofore science could only note their ephemeral properties and relations as they touched the perceptions of earth-bound man. But since July 16, 1945 man has been able to transform one into the other. For on that night at Alamogordo, New Mexico, man for the first time transmuted a substantial quantity of matter into the light, heat, sound, and motion which we call energy.

Yet the fundamental mystery remains. The whole march of science toward the unification of concepts—the reduction of all matter to elements and then to a few types of particles, the reduction of "forces" to the single concept "energy," and then the reduction of matter *and* energy to a single basic quantity—leads still to the unknown. The many questions merge into one, to which there may never be an answer: what is the essence of this mass-energy substance, what is the underlying stratum of physical reality which science seeks to explore?

Thus Relativity, like the Quantum Theory, draws man's intellect still farther away from the Newtonian universe, firmly rooted in space and time and functioning like some great, unerring, and manageable machine. Einstein's laws of motion, his basic principles of the relativity of distance, time, and mass, and his deductions from these principles comprise what is known as the Special Theory of Relativity. In the decade following the publication of this original work, he expanded his scientific and philosophical system into the General Theory of Relativity, through which he examined the mysterious force that guides the whirling of the stars, comets, meteors, and galaxies, and all the moving systems of iron, stone, vapor, and flame in the immense inscrutable void. Newton called this force "universal gravitation." From his own concept of gravitation Einstein attained a view of the vast architecture and anatomy of the universe as a whole.

THE NONMATHEMATICIAN," SAYS ALBERT
Einstein, "is seized by a mysterious shuddering
when he hears of 'four-dimensional' things, by a
feeling not unlike that awakened by thoughts of the
occult. And yet there is no more commonplace
statement than that the world in which we live is a
four-dimensional space-time continuum."

A nonmathematician might question Einstein's
use of the term "commonplace" in this connection.
Yet the difficulty lies more in the wording than the
ideas. Once the meaning of the word "continuum"
is properly grasped Einstein's picture of the universe
as a four-dimensional space-time continuum—and
this is the view that underlies all modern concep-
tions of the universe—becomes perfectly clear. A
continuum is something that is continuous. A ruler,
for example, is a one-dimensional space continuum.
Most rulers are divided into inches and fractions,
scaled down to one-sixteenth of an inch.

But it is possible to imagine a ruler calibrated to a
millionth or a billionth of an inch. In theory there is
no reason why the steps from point to point should
not be even smaller. The distinguishing characteristic of a continuum is that the interval separating

any two points may be divided into an infinite number of arbitrarily small steps.

A railroad track is a one-dimensional space continuum, and on it the engineer of a train can describe his position at any time by citing a single co-ordinate point—i.e., a station or a milestone. A sea captain, however, has to worry about two dimensions. The surface of the sea is a two-dimensional continuum and the co-ordinate points by which a sailor fixes his position in his two-dimensional continuum are latitude and longitude. An airplane pilot guides his plane through a three-dimensional continuum, hence he has to consider not only longitude and latitude, but also his height above the ground. The continuum of an airplane pilot constitutes space as we perceive it. In other words, the space of our world is a three-dimensional continuum.

To describe any physical event involving motion, however, it is not enough simply to indicate position in space. It is necessary to state also how position changes in time. Thus to give an accurate picture of the operation of a New York-Chicago express, one must mention not only that it goes from New York to Albany to Syracuse to Cleveland to Toledo to Chicago, but also the times at which it touches each of those points. This can be done either by means of a timetable or a visual chart. If the miles between New York and Chicago are plotted horizontally on a piece of ruled paper and the hours and minutes are plotted vertically, then a diagonal line properly drawn across the page illustrates the progress of the train in a two-dimensional space-time continuum. This type of graphic representation is familiar to most newspaper readers; a stock market chart, for example, pictures financial events in a two-dimensional dollar-time continuum. In the same way the flight of an airplane from New York to Los

The westbound run of a New York-Chicago express pictured in a two-dimensional space-time continuum.

Angeles can best be pictured in a four-dimensional space-time continuum. The fact that the plane is at latitude x, longitude y, and altitude z means nothing to the traffic manager of the airline unless the time co-ordinate is also given. So time is the fourth dimension. And if one wishes to envisage the flight as a whole, as a physical reality, it cannot be broken down into a series of disconnected take-offs, climbs, glides, and landings. Instead it must be thought of as a continuous curve in a four-dimensional space-time continuum.

Since time is an impalpable quantity it is not possible to draw a picture or construct a model of a four-dimensional space-time continuum. But it can be imagined and it can be represented mathematically. And in order to describe the stupendous reaches of the universe beyond our solar system, beyond the clusters and star clouds of the Milky Way, beyond the lonely outer galaxies burning in the void, the scientist must visualize it all as a continuum in three dimensions of space and one of time. In our minds we tend to separate these dimensions; we have an awareness of space and an awareness of time. But the separation is purely subjective; and as the Special Theory of Relativity showed, space and time separately are relative quantities which vary with individual observers. In any objective description of the universe, such as science demands, the time dimension can no more be detached from the space dimension than length can be detached from breadth and thickness in an accurate representation of a house, a tree, or Betty Grable. According to the great German mathematician, Herman Minkowski, who developed the mathematics of the space-time continuum as a convenient medium for expressing the principles of Relativity, "space and time separately have vanished into the merest shadows, and only a sort of combination of the two preserves any reality."

It must not be thought, however, that the space-time continuum is simply mathematical construction. The world *is* a space-time continuum; all reality exists both in space and in time, and the two are indivisible. All measurements of time are really measurements in space, and conversely measurements in space depend on measurements of time. Seconds, minutes, hours, days, weeks, months, seasons, years, are measurements of the earth's position in space relative to the sun, moon, and stars. Similarly latitude and longitude, the terms whereby man defines his spatial position on earth, are measured in minutes and seconds, and to compute them accurately one must know the time of day and the day of the year. Such "landmarks" as the Equator, the Tropic of Cancer, or the Arctic Circle are simply sundials which clock the changing seasons; the Prime Meridian is a co-ordinate of daily time; and "noon" is nothing more than an angle of the sun.

Even so, the equivalence of space and time becomes really clear only when one contemplates the stars. Among the familiar constellations, some are "real" in that their component stars comprise true gravitational systems, moving in an orderly fashion relative to one another; others are only apparent—their patterns are accidents of perspective, created by a seeming adjacency of unrelated stars along the line of sight. Within such optical constellations one may observe two stars of equal brightness and assert that they are "side by side" in the firmament, whereas in actuality one may be 40 light years and the other 400 light years away.

Obviously the astronomer has to think of the universe as a space-time continuum. When he peers through his telescope he looks not only outward in space but backward in time. His sensitive cameras can detect the glimmer of island universes 500 million light years away—faint gleams that began their journey at a period of terrestrial time when the first vertebrates were starting to crawl from warm Paleozoic seas onto the young continents of Earth. His spectroscope tells him, moreover, that these huge outer systems are hurtling into limbo, away from our own galaxy, at incredible velocities ranging up to 35,000 miles a second. Or, more precisely, they *were* receding from us 500 million years ago. Where they are "now," or whether they even exist "now," no one can say. If we break down our picture of the universe into three subjective dimensions of space and one of local time, then these galaxies have no objective existence save as faint smudges of ancient enfeebled light on a photographic plate. They attain physical reality only in their proper frame of reference, which is the four-dimensional space-time continuum.

In man's brief tenancy on earth he egocentrically orders events in his mind according to his own feelings of past, present, and future. But except on the reels of one's own consciousness, the universe, the objective world of reality, does not "happen"—it simply exists. It can be encompassed in its entire majesty only by a cosmic intellect. But it can also be represented symbolically, by a mathematician, as a four-dimensional space-time continuum. An understanding of the space-time continuum is requisite to a comprehension of the General Theory of Relativity and of what it says about gravitation, the unseen force that holds the universe together and determines its shape and size.

10 ———————————————

IN THE SPECIAL THEORY OF RELATIVITY, Einstein studied the phenomenon of motion and showed that there appears to be no fixed standard in the universe by which man can judge the "absolute" motion of the earth or of any other moving system. Motion can be detected only as a change of position with respect to another body. We know for example that the earth is moving around the sun at the rate of twenty miles a second. The changing seasons suggest this fact. But until four hundred years ago men thought the shifting position of the sun in the sky revealed the sun's movement around the earth; and on this assumption ancient astronomers developed a perfectly practical system of celestial mechanics which enabled them to predict with great accuracy all the major phenomena of the heavens. Their supposition was a natural one, for we can't *feel* our motion through space; nor has any physical experiment ever proved that the earth actually is in motion. And though all the other planets, stars, galaxies, and moving systems in the universe are ceaselessly, restlessly changing position, their movements are observable only with respect to one another. If all the objects in the universe were removed save one, then no one could say whether that one remaining object was at rest or hurtling through the void at 100,000 miles a second. Motion is a relative state; unless there is some system of reference to which it may be compared, it is meaningless to speak of the motion of a single body.

Shortly after publishing the Special Theory of Relativity, however, Einstein began wondering if there is not indeed one kind of motion which may be considered "absolute" in that it can be detected by the physical effect it exerts on the moving system itself—without reference to any other system. For example, an observer in a *smoothly* running train is unable to tell by experiments performed inside the train whether he is in motion or at rest. But if the engineer of the train suddenly applies the brakes or jerks open the throttle, he will then be made aware, by the resulting jolt, of a change in his velocity. And if the train rounds a turn, he will know by the outward tug of his own body, resisting a change of direction, that the train's course has been altered in a certain way. Therefore, Einstein reasoned, if only one object existed in the entire universe—the earth for example—and it suddenly began to gyrate irregularly, its inhabitants would be uncomfortably aware of their motion. This suggests that nonuniform motion, such as that produced by forces and accelerations, may be "absolute" after all. It also suggests that empty space can serve as a system of reference within which it is possible to distinguish absolute motion.

To Einstein, who held that space is emptiness and motion is relative, the apparently unique character of nonuniform motion was profoundly disturbing. In the Special Theory of Relativity he had taken as his premise the simple assertion that the laws of nature are the same for all systems moving *uniformly* relative to one another. And as a steadfast believer in the universal harmony of nature he refused to believe that any system in a state of nonuniform motion must be a uniquely distinguished system in which the laws of nature are different. Hence as the basic premise of his General Theory of Relativity, he stated: the laws of nature are the same for all systems regardless of their state of motion. In developing this thesis he worked out new laws of gravitation which upset most of the concepts that had shaped man's picture of the universe for three hundred years.

Einstein's springboard was Newton's Law of Inertia which, as every schoolboy knows, states that "every body continues in its state of rest, or of uniform motion in a straight line, unless it is compelled to change that state by forces impressed thereon." It is inertia, therefore, which produces our peculiar sensations when a railroad train suddenly slows down or speeds up or rounds a curve. Our body wants to continue moving uniformly in a straight line, and when the train impresses an opposing force upon us the property called inertia tends to resist that force. It is also inertia which causes a locomotive to wheeze and strain in order to accelerate a long train of freight cars.

But this leads to another consideration. If the cars are loaded the locomotive has to work harder and burn more coal than if the cars are empty. To his Law of Inertia Newton therefore added a second law stating that the amount of force necessary to accelerate a body depends on the mass of the body; and that if the same force is applied to two bodies of different masses, then it will produce a greater acceleration in the smaller body than in the bigger one. This principle holds true for the whole range of man's everyday experience—from pushing a baby carriage to firing a cannon. It simply generalizes the obvious fact that one can throw a baseball farther and faster than one can throw a cannonball.

There is, however, one peculiar situation in which there appears to be no connection between the acceleration of a moving body and its mass. The baseball and the cannonball attain exactly the same rate of acceleration when they are *falling*. This phenomenon was first discovered by Galileo, who proved by experiment that, discounting air resistance, bodies all fall at precisely the same rate regardless of their size or composition. A baseball and a handkerchief fall at different speeds only because the handkerchief offers a larger surface to air resistance. But objects of comparable shape, such as a marble, a baseball, and a cannonball, fall at virtually the same rate. (In a vacuum the handkerchief and the cannonball would fall side by side.) This phenomenon appears to violate Newton's Law of Inertia. For why should all objects travel vertically at the same velocity regardless of their size or mass, if those same objects, when projected horizontally by an equal force, move at velocities that are strictly determined by their mass? It would appear as though the factor of inertia operates only in a horizontal plane.

Newton's solution of this riddle is given in his Law of Gravitation, which states simply that the mysterious force by which a material body attracts another body increases with the mass of the object it attracts. The heavier the object, the stronger the call of gravity. If an object is small, its inertia or tendency to resist motion is small, but the force that gravity exerts upon it is also small. If an object of the same density is big, its inertia is great, but the force that gravity exerts upon it is also great. Hence gravity is always exerted in the precise degree necessary to overcome the inertia of any object. And that is why all objects fall at the same rate, regardless of their inertial mass.

This rather remarkable coincidence—the perfect balance of gravitation and inertia—was accepted on faith, but never understood or explained, for three centuries after Newton. All of modern mechanics and engineering grew out of Newtonian concepts, and the heavens appeared to operate in accordance with his laws. Einstein, however, whose discoveries have all sprung from an inherent distrust of dogma, disliked several of Newton's assumptions. He doubted that the balance of gravitation and inertia was merely an accident of nature. And he rejected the idea of gravitation being a force that can be exerted instantaneously over great distances. The notion that the earth can reach out into space and pull an object toward it with a force miraculously and invariably equal to the inertial resistance of that object seemed to Einstein highly improbable. So out of his objections he evolved a new theory of gravitation which, experience has shown, gives a more accurate picture of nature than Newton's classic law.

objected to + got own theories.

11

IN ACCORDANCE WITH HIS USUAL MODE OF creative thought Einstein set the stage with an imaginary situation. The details have doubtless been envisaged by many another dreamer in restless slumber or in moments of insomniac fancy. He pictured an immensely high building and inside it an elevator that had slipped from its cables and is falling freely. Within the elevator a group of physicists, undisturbed by any suspicion that their ride might end in disaster, are performing experiments. They take objects from their pockets, a fountain pen, a coin, a bunch of keys, and release them from their grasp. Nothing happens. The pen, the coin, the keys appear to the men in the elevator to remain poised in midair—because all of them are falling, along with the elevator and the men, at precisely the same rate in accordance with Newton's Law of Gravitation. Since the men in the elevator are unaware of their predicament, however, they may explain these peculiar happenings by a different assumption. They may believe they have been magically transported outside the gravitational field of the earth and are in fact poised somewhere in empty space. And they have good grounds for such a belief. If one of them jumps from the floor he floats smoothly toward the

78

ceiling with a velocity just proportional to the vigor of his jump. If he pushes his pen or his keys in any direction, they continue to move uniformly in that direction until they hit the wall of the car. Everything apparently obeys Newton's Law of Inertia, and continues in its state of rest or of uniform motion in a straight line. The elevator has somehow become an inertial system, and there is no way for the men inside it to tell whether they are falling in a gravitational field or are simply floating in empty space, free from all external forces.

Einstein now shifts the scene. The physicists are still in the elevator, but this time they really *are* in empty space, far away from the attractive power of any celestial body. A cable is attached to the roof of the elevator; some supernatural force begins reeling in the cable; and the elevator travels "upward" with constant acceleration—i.e., progressively faster and faster. Again the men in the car have no idea where they are, and again they perform experiments to evaluate their situation. This time they notice that their feet press solidly against the floor. If they jump they do not float to the ceiling for the floor comes up beneath them. If they release objects from their hands the objects appear to "fall." If they toss objects in a horizontal direction they do not move uniformly in a straight line but describe a parabolic curve with respect to the floor. And so the scientists, who have no idea that their windowless car actually is climbing through interstellar space, conclude that they are situated in quite ordinary circumstances in a stationary room rigidly attached to the earth and affected in normal measure by the force of gravity. There is really no way for them to

tell whether they are at rest in a gravitational field
or ascending with constant acceleration through
outer space where there is no gravity at all.

The same dilemma would confront them if their
room were attached to the rim of a huge rotating
merry-go-round set in outer space. They would feel
a strange force trying to pull them away from the
center of the merry-go-round, and a sophisticated
outside observer would quickly identify this force
as inertia (or, as it is termed in the case of rotating
objects, centrifugal force). But the men inside the
room, who as usual are unaware of their odd predicament, would once again attribute the force to gravity. For if the interior of their room is empty and
unadorned, there will be nothing to tell them which
is the floor and which is the ceiling except the force
that pulls them toward one of its interior surfaces.
So what a detached observer would call the "outside
wall' of the rotating room becomes the "floor" of
the room for the men inside. A moment's reflection
shows that there is no "up" or "down" in empty
space. What we on earth call "down" is simply the
direction of gravity. To a man on the sun it would
appear that the Australians, Africans, and Argen-
tines are hanging by their heels from the southern
hemisphere. By the same token Admiral Byrd's flight
over the South Pole was a geometrical fiction; actually he flew *under* it—upside down. And so the
men inside the room on the merry-go-round will
find that all their experiments produce exactly the
same results as the ones they performed when their
room was being swept "upward" through space.
Their feet stay firmly on the "floor." Solid objects
"fall." And once again they attribute these phenom-

ena to the force of gravity and believe themselves at rest in a gravitational field.

From these fanciful occurrences Einstein drew a conclusion of great theoretical importance. To physicists it is known as the Principle of Equivalence of Gravitation and Inertia. It simply states that there is no way to distinguish the motion produced by inertial forces (acceleration, recoil, centrifugal force, etc.) from motion produced by gravitational force. The validity of this principle will be evident to any aviator; for in an airplane it is impossible to separate the effects of inertia from those of gravitation. The physical sensation of pulling out of a dive is exactly the same as that produced by executing a steeply banked turn at high speed. In both cases the factor known to flyers as a "G-load" (Gravity load) appears, blood is drawn away from the head, and the body is pulled heavily down into the seat. To the pilot who is flying "blind" and without instruments, the identical nature of these effects can prove a serious and even fatal matter.

In this principle, which is the keystone of General Relativity, Einstein found an answer both to the riddle of gravitation and the problem of "absolute" motion. It showed that there is nothing unique or "absolute" about nonuniform motion after all; for the effects of nonuniform motion which can supposedly reveal the state of motion of a body, even if it exists alone in space, are indistinguishable from the effects of gravitation. Thus in the case of the merry-go-round, what one observer identified as the pull of inertia or centrifugal force and therefore an effect of motion, another observer identified as the familiar tug of gravitation. And any other inertial effect produced by a change of speed or a change of direction can equally well be ascribed to a changing or fluctuating gravitational field. So the basic premise of Relativity holds true; motion, both uniform and nonuniform, can only be judged with respect to some system of reference—absolute motion does not exist.

The sword with which Einstein slew the dragon of absolute motion was gravitation. But what *is* gravitation? The gravitation of Einstein is something entirely different from the gravitation of Newton. It it not a "force." The idea that bodies of matter can "attract" one another is, according to Einstein, an allusion that has grown out of erroneous mechanical concepts of nature. So long as one believes that the universe is a big machine, it is natural to think that its various parts can exert a force on one another. But the deeper science probes toward reality, the more clearly it appears that the universe is not like a machine at all. So Einstein's Law of Gravitation contains nothing about force. It describes the behavior of objects in a gravitational field—the planets, for example—not in terms of "attraction" but simply in terms of the paths they follow. To Einstein, gravitation is simply part of inertia; the movements of the stars and the planets stem from their inherent inertia; and the courses they follow are determined by the metric properties of space—or more properly speaking, the metric properties of the space-time continuum.

Although this sounds very abstract and even paradoxical, it becomes quite clear as soon as one dismisses the notion that bodies of matter can exert a physical force on each other across millions of miles of empty space. This concept of "action-at-a-distance" has troubled scientists since Newton's day. It led to particular difficulty, for example, in understanding electric and magnetic phenomena. Today scientists no longer say that a magnet "attracts" a piece of iron by some kind of mysterious but instantaneous action-at-a-distance. They say rather that the magnet creates a certain physical condition in the space around it, which they term a magnetic field; and that this magnetic field then acts upon the iron and makes it behave in a certain predictable

The field of a bar magnet

fashion. Students in any elementary science course know what a magnetic field looks like, because it can be rendered visible by the simple process of shaking iron filings onto a piece of stiff paper held above a magnet. A magnetic field and an electrical field are physical realities. They have a definite structure, and their structure is described by the field equations of James Clerk Maxwell which pointed the way toward all the discoveries in electrical and radio engineering of the past century. A gravitational field is as much of a physical reality as an electromagnetic field, and its structure is defined by the field equations of Albert Einstein.

Just as Maxwell and Faraday assumed that a magnet creates certain properties in surrounding space, so Einstein concluded that stars, moons, and other celestial objects individually determine the properties of the space around them. And just as the movement of a piece of iron in a magnetic field is guided by the structure of the field, so the path of any body in a gravitational field is determined by the geometry of that field. The distinction between Newton's and Einstein's ideas about gravitation has sometimes been illustrated by picturing a little boy playing marbles in a city lot. The ground is very uneven, ridged with bumps and hollows. An observer in an office ten stories above the street would not be able to see these irregularities in the ground. Noticing that the marbles appear to avoid some sections of the ground and move toward other sections, he might assume that a "force" is operating which repels the marbles from certain spots and attracts them toward others. But another observer on the ground would instantly perceive that the path of the marbles is simply governed by the curvature of the field. In this little fable Newton is the upstairs observer who imagines that a "force" is at work, and Einstein is the observer on the ground, who has no reason to make such an assumption. Einstein's gravitational laws, therefore, merely describe the field properties of the space-time continuum. Specifically, one group of these laws sets forth the relation between the mass of a gravitating body and the structure of the field around it; they are called structure laws. A second group analyzes the paths described by moving bodies in gravitational fields; they are the laws of motion.

It should not be thought that Einstein's theory of gravitation is only a formal mathematical scheme. For it rests on assumptions of deep cosmic significance. And the most remarkable of these assumptions is that the universe is not a rigid and immutable edifice where independent matter is housed in independent space and time; it is on the contrary an amorphous continuum, without any fixed architecture, plastic and variable constantly subject to change and distortion. Wherever there is matter and motion, the continuum is disturbed. Just as a fish swimming in the sea agitates the water around it, so a star, a comet, or a galaxy distorts the geometry of the space-time through which it moves.

When applied to astronomical problems Einstein's gravitational laws yield results that are close to those given by Newton. If the results paralleled each other in every case, scientists might tend to retain the familiar concepts of Newtonian law and write off Einstein's theory as a weird if original fancy. But a number of strange new phenomena have been discovered, and at least one old puzzle solved, solely on the basis of General Relativity. The old puzzle stemmed from the eccentric behavior of the planet Mercury. Instead of revolving in its elliptical orbit with the regularity of the other planets, Mercury deviates from its course each year by a slight but exasperating degree. Astronomers explored every possible factor that might cause this perturbation but found no solution within the framework of Newtonian theory. It was not until Einstein evolved his laws of gravitation that the problem was solved. Of all the planets Mercury lies closest to the sun. It is small and travels with great speed. Under Newtonian law these factors should not in themselves

The rotation of Mercury's elliptical orbit, greatly exaggerated. Actually the ellipse advances only 43 seconds of an arc per century.

account for the deviation; the dynamics of Mercury's movement should be basically the same as those of any other planet. But under Einstein's laws, the intensity of the sun's gravitational field and Mercury's enormous speed make a difference, causing the whole ellipse of Mercury's orbit to execute a slow but inexorable swing around the sun at the rate of one revolution in 3,000,000 years. This calculation is in perfect agreement with actual measurements of the planet's course. Einstein's mathematics are thus more accurate than Newton's in dealing with high velocities and strong gravitational fields.

An achievement of far greater importance, however, than this solution of an old problem was Einstein's prediction of a new cosmic phenomenon of which no scientist had ever dreamed—namely the effect of gravitation on light.

12

THE SEQUENCE OF THOUGHT WHICH LED Einstein to prophesy this effect began with another imaginary situation. As before, the scene opens in an elevator ascending with constant acceleration through empty space, far from any gravitational field. This time some roving interstellar gunman impulsively fires a bullet at the elevator. The bullet hits the side of the car, passes clean through and emerges from the far wall at a point a little below the point at which it penetrated the first wall. The reason for this is evident to the marksman on the outside. He knows that the bullet flew in a straight line, obeying Newton's Law of Inertia; but while it traversed the distance between the two walls of the car, the whole elevator traveled "upward" a certain distance, causing the second bullet hole to appear not opposite the first one but slightly nearer the floor. However the observers inside the elevator, having no idea where in the universe they are, interpret the situation differently. Aware that on earth any missile describes a parabolic curve toward the ground, they simply conclude that they are at rest in a gravitational field and that the bullet which passed through their car was describing a perfectly normal curve with respect to the floor.

A moment later as the car continues upward through space a beam of light is suddenly flashed through an aperture in the side of the car. Since the velocity of light is great the beam traverses the distance between its point of entrance and the opposite wall in a very small fraction of a second. Nevertheless the car travels upward a certain distance in that interval, so the beam strikes the far wall a tiny fraction of an inch below the point at which it entered. If the observers within the car are equipped with sufficiently delicate instruments of measurement they will be able to compute the curvature of the beam. But the question is, how will they explain it? They are still unaware of the motion of their car and believe themselves at rest in a gravitational field. If they cling to Newtonian principles they will be completely baffled because they will insist that light rays always travel in a straight line. But if they are familiar with the Special Theory of Relativity they will remember that energy has mass in accordance with the equation $m = E/c^2$. Since light is a form of energy they will deduce that light has mass and will therefore be affected by a gravitational field. Hence the curvature of the beam.

From these purely theoretical considerations Einstein concluded that light, like any material object, travels in a curve when passing through the gravitational field of a massive body. He suggested that his theory could be put to test by observing the path of starlight in the gravitational field of the sun. Since the stars are invisible by day, there is only one occasion when sun and stars can be seen together in the sky, and that is during an eclipse. Einstein proposed, therefore, that photographs be taken of the stars immediately bordering the darkened face of the sun during an eclipse and compared with photographs of those same stars made at another time. According to his theory the light from the stars surrounding the sun should be bent inward, toward the sun, in traversing the sun's gravitational field; hence the *images* of those stars should appear to observers on earth to be shifted outward from their usual positions in

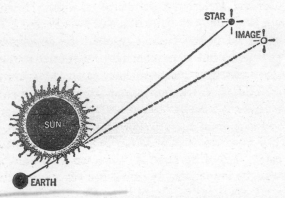

The deflection of starlight in the gravitational field of the sun. Since the light from a star in the neighborhood of the sun's disk is bent inward, toward the sun, as it passes through the sun's gravitational field, the image of the star appears to observers on earth to be shifted outward and away from the sun.

the sky. Einstein calculated the degree of deflection that should be observed and predicted that for the stars closest to the sun the deviation would be about 1.75 seconds of an arc. Since he staked his whole General Theory of Relativity on this test, men of science throughout the world anxiously awaited the findings of expeditions which journeyed to equatorial regions to photograph the eclipse of May 29, 1919. When their pictures were developed and examined, the deflection of the starlight in the gravitational field of the sun was found to average 1.64 seconds—a figure as close to perfect agreement with Einstein's prediction as the accuracy of instruments allowed.

Another prediction made by Einstein on the basis of General Relativity pertained to time. Having shown how the properties of space are affected by a gravitational field, Einstein reached the conclusion by analogous but somewhat more involved reasoning that time intervals also vary with the gravitational field. A clock transported to the sun should run at a slightly slower rhythm than on earth. And a radiating solar atom should emit light of slightly lower frequency than an atom of the same element on earth. The difference in wave length would in this case be immeasurably small. But there are in the universe gravitational fields stronger than the sun's. One of these surrounds the freak star known as the "companion of Sirius"—a white dwarf composed of matter in a state of such fantastic density that one cubic inch of it would weigh a ton on earth. Because of its great mass this extraordinary dwarf, which is only three times larger than the earth, has a gravitational field potent enough to perturb the movements of Sirius, seventy times its size. Its field is also powerful enough to slow down the frequency of its own radiation by a measurable degree, and spectroscopic observations have indeed proved that the frequency of light emitted by Sirius' companion is reduced by the exact amount predicted by Einstein. The shift of wave length in the spectrum of this star is known to astronomers as "the Einstein Effect" and constitutes an additional verification of General Relativity.

13

Up to this point the concepts of General Relativity have dealt with the phenomena of the individual gravitational field. But the universe is filled with incomputable bodies of matter—meteors, moons, comets, nebulae, and billions on billions of stars grouped by the interlocking geometry of their gravitational fields in clusters, clouds, galaxies, and supergalactic systems. One naturally asks, what then is the over-all geometry of the space-time continuum in which they drift? In cruder language, what is the shape and size of the universe? All modern replies to the question have been derived directly or indirectly from the principles of General Relativity.

Prior to Einstein the universe was most commonly pictured as an island of matter afloat in the center of an infinite sea of space. There were several reasons for this concept. The universe, most scientists agreed, had to be infinite; because as soon as they conceded that space might come to an end somewhere, they were faced with the embarrassing question: "And what lies beyond that?" Yet Newtonian law prohibited an infinite universe containing a uniform distribution of matter, for then the total gravitational force of all the masses of matter stretching away to infinity would be infinite. To man's feeble eye, moreover, it appeared that beyond the rim of our Milky Way the lamps of space became sparser and sparser, diffusing gradually in attenuated outposts like lonely lighthouses on the frontiers of the fathomless void. But the island universe presented difficulties too. The amount of matter it held was so small by contrast with an infinity of space that inevitably the dynamic laws governing the movements of the galaxies would cause them to disperse like the droplets of a cloud and the universe would become entirely empty.

To Einstein this picture of dissolution and disappearance seemed eminently unsatisfactory. The basic difficulty, he decided, derived from man's natural but unwarranted assumption that the geometry of the universe must be the same as that revealed by his senses here on earth. We confidently assume, for example, that two parallel beams of light will travel through space forever without meeting, because in the infinite plane of Euclidean geometry parallel lines never meet. We also feel certain that in outer space, as on a tennis court, a straight line is the shortest distance between two points. And yet Euclid never actually *proved* that a straight line is the shortest distance between two points; he simply arbitrarily *defined* a straight line as the shortest distance between two points.

Is it not then possible, Einstein asked, that man is being deceived by his limited perceptions when he pictures the universe in the garb of Euclidean geometry? There was a time when man thought the earth was flat. Now he accepts the fact that the earth is round, and he knows that on the surface of the earth the shortest distance between two such points as

New York and London is not a straight compass course across the Atlantic but a "great circle" that veers northward past Nova Scotia, Newfoundland, and Iceland. So far as the surface of the earth is concerned Euclid's geometry is not valid. A giant triangle, drawn on the earth's surface from two points on the Equator to the North Pole, would not satisfy Euclid's theorem that the sum of the interior angles of a triangle is always equal to two right angles or 180 degrees. It would contain *more* than 180 degrees, as a glance at the globe will quickly show. And if someone should draw a giant circle on the earth's surface he would find that the ratio between its diameter and its circumference is less than the classic value *pi*. These departures from Euclid are due to the curvature of the earth. Although no one doubts today that the earth has a curvature, man did not discover this fact by getting off the earth and looking at it. The curvature of the earth can be computed very comfortably on terra firma by a proper mathematical interpretation of easily observable facts. In the same way, by a synthesis of astronomical fact and deduction, Einstein concluded that the universe is neither infinite nor Euclidean, as most scientists supposed, but something hitherto unimagined.

It has already been shown that Euclidean geometry does not hold true in a gravitational field. Light rays do not travel in straight lines when passing through a gravitational field, for the geometry of the field is such that within it there are no straight lines; the shortest course that the light can describe is a curve or great circle which is rigorously determined by the geometrical structure of the field. Since the structure of a gravitational field is shaped by the mass and velocity of the gravitating body—star, moon, or planet—it follows that the geometrical structure of the universe as a whole must be shaped by the sum of its material content. For each concentration of matter in the universe there is a corresponding distortion of the space-time continuum. Each celestial body, each galaxy creates local irregularities in space-time, like eddies around islands in the sea. The greater the concentration of matter, the greater the resulting curvature of space-time. And the total effect is an over-all curvature of the whole space-time continuum: the combined distortions produced by all the incomputable masses of matter in the universe cause the continuum to bend back on itself in a great closed cosmic curve.

The Einstein universe therefore is non-Euclidean and finite. To earthbound man a light ray may appear to travel in a straight line to infinity, just as to

an earthworm crawling "straight" ahead forever and
ever the earth may seem both flat and infinite. But
man's impression that the universe is Euclidean in
character, like the earthworm's impression of the
earth, is imparted by the limitations of his senses. In
the Einstein universe there are no straight lines, there
are only great circles. Space, though finite is un-
bounded; a mathematician would describe its geometrical character as the four-dimensional analogue
of the surface of a sphere. In the less abstract words
of the late British physicist, Sir James Jeans:

"A soap-bubble with corrugations on its surface is
perhaps the best representation, in terms of simple
and familiar materials, of the new universe revealed
to us by the Theory of Relativity. The universe is
not the interior of the soap-bubble but its surface,
and we must always remember that while the surface of the soap-bubble has only two dimensions, the
universe bubble has four—three dimensions of space
and one of time. And the substance out of which this
bubble is blown, the soap-film, is empty space
welded onto empty time."

Like most of the concepts of modern science, Einstein's finite, spherical universe cannot be visualized
—any more than a photon or an electron can be
visualized. But as in the case of the photon and the
electron its properties can be described mathematically. By taking the best available values of modern
astronomy and applying them to Einstein's field
equations, it is possible to compute the *size* of the universe. In order to determine its radius, however, it is
first necessary to ascertain its curvature. Since, as

Einstein showed, the geometry or curvature of space is determined by its material content, the cosmological problem can be solved only by obtaining a figure for the average density of matter in the universe.

Fortunately this figure is available, for astronomer Edwin Hubble of the Mt. Wilson Observatory conscientiously studied sample areas of the heavens over a period of years and painstakingly computed the average amount of matter contained in them. The conclusion he reached was that in the universe as a whole there is .000000000000000000000000000001 gram of matter per cubic centimeter of space. Applied to Einstein's field equations this figure yields a positive value for the curvature of the universe, which in turn reveals that the radius of the universe is 35 billion light years or 210,000,000,000,000,000,-000,000 miles. Einstein's universe, while not infinite, is nevertheless sufficiently enormous to encompass billions of galaxies, each containing hundreds of millions of flaming stars and incalculable quantities of rarefied gas, cold systems of iron and stone and cosmic dust. A sunbeam, setting out through space at the rate of 186,000 miles a second would, in this universe, describe a great cosmic circle and return to its source after a little more than 200 billion terrestrial years.

AT THE TIME EINSTEIN EVOLVED HIS COS-mology, he was unaware, however, of a strange astronomical phenomenon which was only inter-preted several years later. He had assumed that the motions of the stars and galaxies were random, like the aimless drifting of molecules in a gas. Since there was no evidence of any unity in their wanderings he had ignored them entirely and regarded the universe as static. But astronomers were beginning to notice signs of a systematic movement among the outer galaxies at the extreme limits of telescopic vision. All these outlying galaxies, or "island universes," are, apparently, receding from our solar system and from each other. This organized flight of the distant galax-ies—the remotest of them being about 500 million light years away—is an entirely different affair from the indolent wheeling of the nearer gravitational sys-tems. For such a systematic movement would have an effect on the curvature of the universe as a whole.

The universe is, therefore, not static; it is expand-ing in somewhat the same manner as a soap bubble or a balloon expands. The analogy is not quite exact, however, for if we conceive of the universe as a kind of spotted balloon—the spots representing mat-ter—one would expect the spots to expand too. But this cannot be, because then we would never notice the expansion, just as Alice in Wonderland would have been unaware of her sudden changes in stature if all her surroundings had grown and contracted along with her. Therefore, as cosmologist H. P. Robertson of the California Institute of Technology has pointed out, in visualizing the universe as a spotted balloon, we must think of the spots as inelastic patches sewn upon the surface. Material bodies retain their dimensions while space stretches out between them, like the skin of the balloon between the patches.

This extraordinary phenomenon greatly complicates cosmology. If the spectroscopic analysis that indicates the recession of these outer galaxies is correct (as most astronomers believe it to be) then the velocities at which they are vanishing into limbo are almost beyond belief. Their speed appears to increase with distance. While the nearer galaxies, about one million light years away, are traveling at a mere 100 miles a second, those 250 million light years away are flying off at the fantastic rate of 25,000 miles a second, almost one seventh the velocity of light. Since all of these remote galaxies, without exception, are moving *away* from us and from each other, one must conclude that at some epoch of cosmic time all of them were clustered together in one fiery inchoate mass. And if the geometry of space is shaped by its material content then the universe in this pregalactic phase must have been an uncomfortably cramped and crowded receptacle, characterized by an excessive curvature and packed with matter in a state of inconceivable density. Calculations based on the velocities of the receding galaxies show that they must have separated and started their flight from the "center" of this shrunken universe about five billion years ago.

Several theories have been advanced by astronomers and cosmologists to explain the enigma of the expanding universe. One, put forth by the Belgian cosmologist Abbé Lemaître, proposes that the universe originated from a single stupendous primeval atom which exploded and thus precipitated the expansion which we still perceive. An analogous theory, made public by Dr. George Gamow of George Washington University, reconstructs in detail how the constituent elements might have been forged in the dense flaming core of the universe before it started to expand. In the beginning, says Dr. Gamow, the nucleus of the universe was an inferno of homogeneous primordial vapor seething at unimaginable temperatures such as no longer exist even in the interiors of stars. (The temperature of the sun, which is an average star, ranges from 5500° Centigrade at the surface up to 40,000,000° in the interior.) There were no elements in such heat, no molecules, no atoms—nothing but free neutrons and other sub-atomic particles in a state of chaotic agitation. When the cosmic mass began to expand, however, the temperature began to fall; and when it had dropped to about one billion degrees the neutrons and protons condensed into aggregates; electrons were emitted which attached themselves to nuclei, and atoms were formed. All the elements in the universe were thus created within the space of a few critical moments in the cosmic dawn and their roles fixed for the five billion years of continuing expansion that ensued.

An earlier theory of the expanding universe, put forth some years ago by Dr. R. C. Tolman of the California Institute of Technology, suggests that the cosmic expansion may be simply a temporary condition which will be followed at some future epoch of cosmic time by a period of contraction. The universe in this picture is a pulsating balloon in which cycles of expansion and contraction succeed each other through eternity. These cycles are governed by changes in the amount of matter in the universe; for as Einstein showed, the curvature of the universe is dependent on its content. The difficulty with this theory is that it rests on the assumption that somewhere in the universe matter is being formed. Although it is true that the amount of matter in the universe is perpetually changing, the change appears to be mainly in one direction—toward dissolution. All the phenomena of nature, visible and invisible, within the atom and in outer space, indicate that the substance and energy of the universe are inexorably diffusing like vapor through the insatiable void. The sun is slowly but surely burning out, the stars are dying embers, and everywhere in the cosmos heat is turning to cold, matter is dissolving into radiation, and energy is being dissipated into empty space.

The universe is thus progressing toward an ultimate "heat-death," or as it is technically defined, a condition of "maximum entropy." When the universe reaches this state some billions of years from now all the processes of nature will cease. All space will be at the same temperature. No energy can be used because all of it will be uniformly distributed through the cosmos. There will be no light, no life, no warmth—nothing but perpetual and irrevocable stagnation. Time itself will come to an end. For entropy points the direction of time. Entropy is the measure of randomness. When all system and order in the universe have vanished, when randomness is at its maximum, and entropy cannot be increased, when there no longer is any sequence of cause and effect, in short when the universe has run down, there will be no direction to time—there will be no time. And there is no way of avoiding this destiny. For the fateful principle known as the Second Law of Thermodynamics, which stands today as the principal pillar of classical physics left intact by the march of science, proclaims that the fundamental processes of nature are irreversible. Nature moves just one way.

There are a few contemporary theorists, however, who propose that somehow, somewhere beyond man's meager ken the universe may be rebuilding itself. In the light of Einstein's principle of the equivalence of mass and energy, it is possible to imagine the diffused radiation in space congealing once more into particles of matter—protons, neutrons, and electrons—which may then combine to form larger units, which in turn may be collected by their own gravitational influence into diffuse nebulae, stars, and, ultimately, galactic systems. And thus the life cycle of the universe may be repeated for all eternity. Laboratory experiments have indeed demonstrated that photons of high-energy radiation, such as gamma rays, can, under certain conditions, interact with matter to produce pairs of electrons and positrons. Astronomers have also determined recently that atoms of the lighter elements, drifting in space—hydrogen, helium, oxygen, nitrogen, and carbon—may slowly coalesce into molecules and microscopic particles of dust and gas. And still more recently Dr. Fred L. Whipple of Harvard has described in his "Dust Cloud Hypothesis," published in 1948, how the rarefied cosmic dust that floats in interstellar space in quantities equal in mass to all the visible matter in the universe could in the course of a billion years condense and coagulate into stars. According to Whipple these tiny dust particles, barely one fifty-thousandths of an inch in diameter, are blown together by the delicate pressure of starlight, just as the fine-spun tail of a comet is deflected away from the sun by the impact of solar photons. As the particles cohere, an aggregate is formed, then a cloudlet, and then a cloud. When the cloud attains gigantic proportions (i.e., when its diameter exceeds six trillion miles), its mass and density will be sufficient to set a new sequence of physical processes into operation. Gravity will cause the cloud to contract, and its contraction will cause its internal pressure and temperature to rise. Eventually, in the last white-hot stages of its collapse, it will begin to radiate as a star. Theory shows that our solar system might have evolved, in special circumstances, from such a process—our sun being the star in question and the various planets small cold by-products condensed from subsidiary cloudlets spiraling within the main cloud.

Presupposing the possibility of such events as these, one might arrive ultimately at the concept of a self-perpetuating pulsating universe, renewing its cycles of formation and dissolution, light and darkness, order and disorder, heat and cold, expansion and contraction, through never-ending eons of time. And yet this picture has not been widely accepted because no definitive evidence has been found to support it. Although dust clouds of all dimensions and degrees of density can be seen hanging in the abyss of interstellar space, no one can state from man's brief temporal perspective that they are proto-stars, any more than one can say with assurance that a white cumulus cloud riding the blue atmosphere of our earth on any given day is tomorrow's thunder storm or simply an evanescent wraith of mist that winds have gathered and will presently disperse. But apart from conjecture on the origins of our solar system or the individual stars or any component part of the system of nature in which we stand, there are theoretical as well as empirical difficulties inherent in every suggestion that the universe as a whole may still be abuilding. Nothing in all inanimate nature can be unmistakably identified as a pure creative process. At one time, for example, it was thought that the mysterious cosmic rays which continually bombard the earth from outer space might be by-products of some process of atomic creation. But there is greater support for the opposite view that they are by-products of atomic annihilation. Everything indeed, everything visible in nature or established in theory, suggests that the universe is implacably progressing toward final darkness and decay.

There is an important philosophical corollary to this view. For if the universe is running down and nature's processes are proceeding in just one direction, the inescapable inference is that everything had a *beginning:* somehow and sometime the cosmic processes were started, the stellar fires ignited, and the whole vast pageant of the universe brought into being. Most of the clues, moreover, that have been discovered at the inner and outer frontiers of scientific cognition suggest a definite time of Creation. The unvarying rate at which uranium expends its nuclear energies and the absence of any natural process leading to its formation indicate that all the uranium on earth must have come into existence at one specific time, which, according to the best calculations of geophysicists, was between four and five billion years ago. The tempo at which the wild thermonuclear processes in the interiors of stars transmute matter into radiation enables astronomers to compute with fair assurance the duration of stellar life, and the figure they reach as the likely average age of most stars visible in the firmament today is five billion years. The arithmetic of the geophysicists and astrophysicists is thus in striking agreement with that of the cosmogonists who, basing their calculations on the apparent velocity of the receding galaxies, find that the universe began to expand five billion years ago. And there are other signs in other areas of science that submit the same reckoning. So all the evidence that points to the ultimate annihilation of the universe points just as definitely to an inception fixed in time.

Even if one acquiesces to the idea of an immortal pulsating universe, within which the sun and earth and supergiant red stars are comparative newcomers, the problem of initial origin remains. It merely pushes the time of Creation into the infinite past. For while theorists have adduced mathematically impeccable accounts of the fabrication of galaxies, stars, star dust, atoms, and even of the atom's components, every theory rests ultimately on the a priori assumption that *something* was already in existence —whether free neutrons, energy quanta, or simply the blank inscrutable "world stuff," the cosmic essence, of which the multifarious universe was subsequently wrought.

15

Cosmologists for the most part maintain silence on the question of ultimate origins, leaving that issue to the philosophers and theology. Yet only the purest empiricists among modern scientists turn their backs on the mystery that underlies physical reality. Einstein, whose philosophy of science has sometimes been criticized as materialistic, once said:

"The most beautiful and most profound emotion we can experience is the sensation of the mystical. It is the sower of all true science. He to whom this emotion is a stranger, who can no longer wonder and stand rapt in awe, is as good as dead. To know that what is impenetrable to us really exists, manifesting itself as the highest wisdom and the most radiant beauty which our dull faculties can comprehend only in their most primitive forms—this knowledge, this feeling is at the center of true religiousness."

And on another occasion he declared, "The cosmic religious experience is the strongest and noblest mainspring of scientific research." Most scientists, when referring to the mysteries of the universe, its vast forces, its origins, and its rationality and harmony, tend to avoid using the word God. Yet Einstein, who has been called an atheist, has no such inhibitions. "My religion," he says, "consists of a humble admiration of the illimitable superior spirit who reveals himself in the slight details we are able to perceive with our frail and feeble minds. That deeply emotional conviction of the presence of a superior reasoning power, which is revealed in the incomprehensible universe, forms my idea of God."

So far as science is concerned, there are at the moment two gateways which offer the promise of closer access to physical reality. One is the great new telescope which now, from Palomar Mountain, California, projects man's vision into deeper abysses of space and time than ever were dreamed by astronomers a generation ago. Until recently the extreme range of telescopic perception has essentially terminated at the faint hurrying galaxies 500 million light years away. But the two-hundred-inch reflector of Palomar doubles that range, enabling man to look upon whatever lies beyond. Already it is revealing new homogeneous oceans of space and new myriads of far galaxies whose antique light has swum to earth through a billion years of terrestrial time. But it may reveal other things—variations in the density of matter or visual evidence of a cosmic curvature from which man can accurately compute the dimensions of the universe in which he so insignificantly dwells.

The other gateway to this knowledge may be opened by further development or elaboration of the Unified Field Theory, on which Einstein labored for the last quarter century of his life. Today the outer limits of man's knowledge are defined by Relativity, the inner limits by the Quantum Theory. Relativity has shaped all our concepts of space, time, gravitation, and the realities that are too remote and too vast to be perceived. The Quantum Theory has shaped all our concepts of the atom, the basic units of matter and energy, and the realities that are too elusive and too small to be perceived. Yet these two great scientific systems rest on entirely different and unrelated theoretical foundations. They do not, as it were, speak the same language. The purpose of a Unified Field Theory is to construct a bridge between them. Believing in the harmony and uniformity of nature, Einstein looked for a single edifice of physical laws to encompass both the phenomena of the atom and the phenomena of outer space.

What unexpected new aspects of nature a perfected Unified Field Theory may uncover and how many old mysteries it may resolve it is still too early to predict. But its obvious minimum achievement will be to unite the laws of gravitation and the laws of electromagnetism within one basic superstructure of universal law. In the same way that Relativity reduced gravitational force to a geometrical property of the space-time continuum, a Unified Field Theory will reduce electromagnetic force—the other great universal force—to equivalent status. "The idea that there are two structures of space independent of each other, the metric-gravitational and the electromagnetic," Einstein once observed, "is intolerable to the theoretical spirit." Yet despite all his efforts he could not incorporate electromagnetic field laws into General Relativity. After thirty-three years of exploring endless gambits of mathematical logic he went far toward achieving his purpose. One may ask if he proved that electromagnetic and gravitational force are physically the "same thing." It would be no more accurate to make such a statement than to assert that steam, ice, and water are the "same thing"—though all are manifestations of the same substance. What his Unified Field Theory undertakes is to show that gravitational and electromagnetic force are not independent of each other—that they are in a very real physical sense inseparable. More specifically it attempts to describe gravitational and electromagnetic force in terms of a deeper reality that undergirds both—a basic universal field within which gravitational and electromagnetic fields are merely particular ephemeral forms or conditions of state.

If the fullest implications of a Unified Field Theory are sustained by the tests of the future—if the laws of quantum physics can also be derived from its equations—crucial new insights will doubtless be attained into the composition of matter, the structure of the elementary particles, the mechanics of radiation, and other enigmas of the subatomic world. Yet these will be essentially by-products. For the great philosophical triumph of any Unified Field Theory is implicit in the first word of its title. It will carry to logical fulfillment the long course of science towards the unification of man's concepts of the physical world. Through the centuries the varied currents of discovery, theory, research, and reason have steadily converged, mingled, and flowed onward into ever widening and deepening channels. The first long advance was the reduction of the world's multifarious substances into some 90 natural elements. Then these elements were reduced to a few fundamental particles. Concurrently the various "forces" in the world came to be recognized one by one as varying manifestations of electromagnetic force, and all the different kinds of radiation in the universe—light, heat, X-rays, radio waves, gamma rays—as nothing more than electromagnetic waves of varying wave length and frequency. Ultimately the features of the universe distilled down to a few basic quantities—space, time, matter, energy, and gravitation. But in Special Relativity, Einstein demonstrated the equivalence of matter and energy, and in General Relativity he showed the indivisibility of the space-time continuum. His Unified Field Theory sought to culminate and climax this coalescing process. For from its august perspective the entire universe appears as one elemental field in which each star, each atom, each wandering comet and slow-wheeling galaxy and flying electron is seen to be but a ripple or tumescence in the underlying space-time unity. And so a profound simplicity would supplant the surface complexity of nature. The distinctions between gravitational force and electromagnetic force, matter and energy, electric charge and field, space and time, all fade in the light of their revealed relationships and resolve into configurations of the four-dimensional continuum which Einstein revealed the universe to be. Thus all man's perceptions of the world and all his abstract intuitions of reality would merge finally into one, and the deep underlying unity of the universe would be laid bare.

A complete Unified Field Theory touches the "grand aim of all science," which, as Einstein once defined it, is "to cover the greatest number of empirical facts by logical deduction from the smallest possible number of hypotheses or axioms." The urge to consolidate premises, to unify concepts, to penetrate the variety and particularity of the manifest world to the undifferentiated unity that lies beyond is not only the leaven of science; it is the loftiest passion of the human intellect. The philosopher and mystic, as well as the scientist, have always sought through their various disciplines on introspection to arrive at a knowledge of the ultimate immutable essence that undergirds the mutable illusory world. More than twenty-three hundred years ago Plato declared, "The true lover of knowledge is always striving after *being*. . . . He will not rest at those multitudinous phenomena whose existence is appearance only."

But the irony of man's quest for reality is that as nature is stripped of its disguises, as order emerges from chaos and unity from diversity, as concepts merge and fundamental laws assume increasingly simpler form, the evolving picture becomes ever more remote from experience—far stranger indeed and less recognizable than the bone structure behind a familiar face. For where the geometry of a skull predestines the outlines of the tissue it supports, there is no likeness between the image of a tree transcribed by our senses and that propounded by wave mechanics, or between a glimpse of the starry sky on a summer night and the four-dimensional continuum that has replaced our perceptual Euclidean space.

In trying to distinguish appearance from reality and lay bare the fundamental structure of the universe, science has had to transcend the "rabble of the senses." But its highest edifices, Einstein has pointed out, have been "purchased at the price of emptiness of content." A theoretical concept is emptied of content to the very degree that it is divorced from sensory experience. For the only world man can truly know is the world created for him by his senses. If he expunges all the impressions which they translate and memory stores, nothing is left. That is what the philosopher Hegel meant by his cryptic remark: "Pure Being and Nothing are the same." A state of existence devoid of associations has no meaning. So paradoxically what the scientist and the philosopher call the world of appearance—the world of light and color, of blue skies and green leaves, of sighing wind and murmuring water, the world designed by the physiology of human sense organs—is the world in which finite man is incarcerated by his essential nature. And what the scientist and the philosopher call the world of reality—the colorless, soundless, impalpable cosmos which lies like an iceberg beneath the plane of man's perceptions—is a skeleton structure of symbols.

And the symbols change. While physicists of the last century knew, for example, that the crimson of a rose was a subjective, aesthetic sensation, they believed that "in reality" the quality they termed crimson was a group of oscillations of the luminiferous ether. Today it is conventional to identify crimson in terms of wave length. But it is equally proper to think of it as the value of the energy contents of photons. Such considerations led a famous physicist to remark cynically that on Mondays, Wednesdays, and Fridays one uses the quantum theory, and on Tuesdays, Thursdays, and Saturdays the wave theory. In either case the concepts employed are abstract constructions of theory. And upon examination such concepts as gravitation, electromagnetism, energy, current, momentum, the atom, the neutron, all turn out to be theoretical substructures, inventions, metaphors which man's intellect has contrived to help him picture the true, the objective reality he apprehends beneath the surface of things. So in place of the deceitful and chaotic representations of the senses science has substituted varying systems of symbolic representation. While these systems are distinguished by constantly increasing mathematical accuracy, it would be difficult today to find any scientist who imagines himself, because of his ability to discern previous errors, in a position to enunciate final truths. On the contrary, modern theorists are aware, as Newton was, that they stand on the shoulders of giants and that their particular perspective may appear as distorted to posterity as that of their predecessors seemed to them.

For all the promise of future revelations it is possible that certain terminal boundaries have already been reached in man's struggle to understand the manifold of nature in which he finds himself. In his descent into the microcosm he has encountered indeterminacy, duality, paradox—barriers that seem to admonish him he cannot pry too inquisitively into the heart of things without altering and vitiating the processes he seeks to observe. And in exploring the macrocosm he comes at last to a final featureless unity of space-time, mass-energy, matter-field—an ultimate, undiversified, and eternal ground beyond which there appears to be nowhere to progress. "The prison house," said Plato, "is the world of sight." Every seeming avenue of escape from this prison house that science has surveyed leads only deeper into a misty realm of symbolism and abstraction.

It may be that the extreme and insurmountable limit of scientific knowledge will be reached in the attainment of perfect isomorphic representation—that is, in a final flawless concurrence of theory and natural process, so complete that every observed phenomenon is accounted for and nothing is left out of the picture. In its approach to this goal, science has hitherto achieved its most notable pragmatic and operational triumphs. For while telling nothing of the true "nature" of things, it nevertheless succeeds in defining their relationships and depicting the events in which they are involved. "The event," Alfred North Whitehead declared, "is the unit of things real." By this he meant that however theoretical systems may change and however empty of content their symbols and concepts may be, the essential and enduring facts of science and of life are the happenings, the activities, the events. The implications of this idea can best be illustrated by contemplating a simple physical event such as the meeting of two electrons. Within the frame of modern physics one can depict this event as a collision of two elementary grains of matter or two elementary units of electrical energy, as a concourse of particles or of probability waves, or as a commingling of eddies in a four-dimensional space-time continuum. Theory does not define what the principals in this encounter actually are. Thus in a sense the electrons are not "real" but merely theoretical symbols. On the other hand the meeting itself is "real"—the event is "real." It is as though the true objective world lies forever half-concealed beneath a translucent, plastic dome. Peering through its cloudy surface, deformed and distorted by the ever changing perspectives of theory, man faintly espies certain apparently stable relationships and recurring events. A consistent isomorphic representation of these relationships and events is the maximal possibility of his knowledge. Beyond that point he stares into the void.

In the evolution of scientific thought, one fact has become impressively clear: there is no mystery of the physical world which does not point to a mystery beyond itself. All highroads of the intellect, all byways of theory and conjecture lead ultimately to an abyss that human ingenuity can never span. For man is enchained by the very condition of his being, his finiteness and involvement in nature. The farther he extends his horizons, the more vividly he recognizes the fact that, as the physicist Niels Bohr puts it, "we are both spectators and actors in the great drama of existence." Man is thus his own greatest mystery. He does not understand the vast veiled universe into which he has been cast for the reason that he does not understand himself. He comprehends but little of his organic processes and even less of his unique capacity to perceive the world about him, to reason and to dream. Least of all does he understand his noblest and most mysterious faculty: the ability to transcend himself and perceive himself in the act of perception.

Man's inescapable impasse is that he himself is part of the world he seeks to explore; his body and proud brain are mosaics of the same elemental particles that compose the dark, drifting clouds of interstellar space; he is, in the final analysis, merely an ephemeral conformation of the primordial space-time field. Standing midway between macrocosm and microcosm he finds barriers on every side and can perhaps but marvel, as St. Paul did nineteen hundred years ago, that "the world was created by the word of God so that what is seen was made out of things which do not appear."

Reading List

This list does not include all the sources consulted in the preparation of this book; it does, however, encompass the major sources of material plus some related volumes that might be of interest and value to the reader who wishes to explore further areas of this field.

The Development of Physical Thought by Leonard B. Loeb and Arthur S. Adams. John Wiley & Sons, Inc., 1933. A survey course of modern physics. Comprehensive, beautifully written, and as enjoyable to the lay reader as valuable to the student. Specific discoveries of the last two decades are, of course, not represented; otherwise a superior history of science.

"The Dust Cloud Hypothesis" by Fred L. Whipple, *Scientific American*, May 1948. It should be noted that the new *Scientific American* is no longer a gadget and hobby magazine. Under new management it now presents articles of fundamental scientific importance, brilliantly edited for intelligent laymen.

Einstein, His Life and Times by Philipp Frank. Alfred A. Knopf, 1947. The best biography of Einstein by a former colleague and eminent physicist. Detailed exposition of Einstein's scientific contributions as well as lively biographical and personal details.

The Evolution of Physics by Albert Einstein and Leopold Infeld. Simon and Schuster, 1942. The growth of ideas from early concepts to Relativity and quanta, simply and fascinatingly described. No mathematics.

The Expanding Universe by H. P. Robertson. Reprint from *Science in Progress*, Second Series. A clear, detailed, and interesting discussion of the structure of the universe by a famed cosmologist.

Explaining the Atom by Selig Hecht. The Viking Press, 1947. Unsurpassed as an exposition of the history and the theory of the atom. Written by a famous biophysicist for the layman.

Flights from Chaos by Harlow Shapley. Whittlesey House, 1930. A fascinating survey of the universe and its component parts from atoms to galaxies by Harvard's distinguished astronomer. This book is unfortunately out of print, but should not be.

"Galaxies in Flight" by George Gamow, *Scientific American*, July, 1948. See note under "The Dust Cloud Hypothesis" above.

Meet the Atoms by O. R. Frisch. A. A. Wyn, Inc., 1947. A popular guide to modern physics. Amusingly written by a noted atomic physicist.

Mind and Nature by Hermann Weyl. University of Pennsylvania Press, 1934. The epistemological implications of modern physics set forth by a great theorist and colleague of Dr. Einstein. The philosophical standpoint from which the present volume is written is derived in great measure from this small but remarkable book, comprising five lectures delivered by Dr. Weyl at Swarthmore College in 1933.

Modern Physics by G. E. M. Jauncey. D. Van Nostrand Company, Inc., 1948. Up-to-the-minute text, including sections on nuclear physics, radioactivity, cosmic rays, and the like. Also chapters on astrophysics, Relativity, and the philosophical implications of modern science.

Mr. Tompkins in Wonderland by George Gamow. The Macmillan Company, 1947. Principles of Relativity and Quantum Theory set forth in an ingenious framework of narrative fiction.

The Mysterious Universe by Sir James Jeans. The Macmillan Company, 1932. A classic which has awakened thousands of readers to the relationship between science and philosophy.

The Nature of the Physical World by A. S. Eddington. The Macmillan Company, 1928. Required reading for anyone interested in this field.

One Two Three . . . Infinity by George Gamow. The Viking Press, 1947; The New American Library (Mentor Books), 1953. An eclectic account of facts and theories about the universe in its microscopic and macroscopic manifestations, described by a topflight theoretical physicist who is also the ablest and most entertaining expositor of science writing today.

Physics and Philosophy by Sir James Jeans. The Macmillan Company, 1943. A further discussion of the changing concepts of modern physics and their philosophical implications.

120

Relativity, The Special and General Theory by Albert Einstein. Henry Holt & Co., 1920. Lucid and detailed. Some mathematics, but not too difficult.

Science and the Modern World by Alfred North Whitehead. The Macmillan Company, 1925; The New American Library (Mentor Books), 1948. Another classic, also required reading.

Appendix

IN THEORETICAL PHYSICS THERE ARE OFTEN several avenues of approach to a given concept. The exposition of the principle of the increase of inertial mass on pages 61-63 follows a quickly comprehended pattern analogous to those employed by many college physics texts. Readers with some mathematical equipment may wish to read Dr. Einstein's development of this principle as set forth in his book *Relativity, the Special and General Theory*. Some essential excerpts follow, quoted with permission from Peter Smith, Publisher.

"The most important result of a general character to which the Special Theory of Relativity has led is concerned with the conception of mass. Before the advent of relativity, physics recognized two conservation laws of fundamental importance, namely the law of the conservation of energy and the law of the conservation of mass; these two fundamental laws appeared to be quite independent of each other. By means of the theory of relativity they have been united into one law. . . .

"In accordance with the theory of relativity the kinetic energy of a material point of mass m is no longer given by the well-known expression $m\dfrac{v^2}{2}$

but by the expression $\dfrac{mc^2}{\sqrt{1-\dfrac{v^2}{c^2}}}$

"By means of comparatively simple considerations we are led to draw the following conclusion: A body moving with the velocity v, which absorbs an amount of energy E_o in the form of radiation without suffering an alteration in velocity in the process, has, as a consequence, its energy increased by an amount

$$\frac{E_o}{\sqrt{1-\frac{v^2}{c^2}}}$$

"In consideration of the expression given above for the kinetic energy of the body, the required energy of the body comes out to be

$$\frac{\left(m+\frac{E_o}{c^2}\right)C^2}{\sqrt{1-\frac{v^2}{c^2}}}$$

"Thus the body has the same energy as a body of mass $\left(m+\frac{E_o}{c^2}\right)$ moving with the velocity v. Hence we can say: If a body takes up an amount of energy E_o, then its inertial mass increases by an amount $\frac{E_o}{c^2}$; the inertial mass of a body is not a constant, but varies according to the change in the energy of the body. The inertial mass of a system

123

of bodies can even be regarded as a measure of its energy. The law of the conservation of the mass of a system becomes identical with the law of conservation of energy. . . ."

Index

Victor Suthren is the Curator of the Canadian War Museum in Ottawa. He has a wide experience of sailing and has made many trips in small boats following the routes of the eighteenth-century wars. He lives in Ottawa with his wife and three children. *The Golden Galleon* is the second volume of the Edward Mainwaring books.

VICTOR SUTHREN

The Golden Galleon

GRAFTON BOOKS

A Division of the Collins Publishing Group

LONDON GLASGOW
TORONTO SYDNEY AUCKLAND

Grafton Books
A Division of the Collins Publishing Group
8 Grafton Street, London W1X 3LA

Published by Grafton Books 1990

First published in Great Britain by
Hodder and Stoughton Ltd 1989

ISBN 0-586-20690-6   042490924

Printed and bound in Great Britain by
Collins, Glasgow

Set in Times

1

Thursday, the 6 April, 1741, was a chill, gloomy day of low, drifting cloud and rain showers, carried by a raw easterly wind that rattled shutters and pattered the rain in intermittent drumbeats against the windows of the dock-yard commissioner's house, Portsmouth. It was a day to send the beggars and street-hawkers scuttling for shelter, and coachmen drew their cloaks and oilskins closer round their necks and sank low against the seats of their town chariots, urging their clopping, steaming nags with a touch more venom in their whips than usual.

Lieutenant Edward Mainwaring, Royal Navy, stood with his hands clasped behind his back at the window of the small, stuffy anteroom of the house, where he had been waiting for close to an hour. His sombre brown coat – his one good one – was beginning to dry in the modest heat of the fire crackling fitfully in the grate, but his damp small clothes and the sodden leather of his tight dress pumps redoubled his natural hatred of such formal attire. He sighed and ran his fingers through his wet, matted brown hair. His hat, a plain unlaced tricorne, was thrown on a chair, and he was without a wig, preferring to wear his own undisciplined locks drawn back into a simple, eelskin-bound queue. He was tall, a shade under six feet, with an athletic, slim-hipped body under broad shoulders, and had towered over the swarthy Welsh servant who had wordlessly taken his dripping cloak and shown him into the room. Mainwaring looked out gloomily through the streaked, wet glass, seeing each drop catch the images from without like a hundred miniature prisms. His eyes were blue and clear, under straight dark brows, set in a long and almost aristocratic face which lost that particular distinction through the prizefighter's break in his nose. He had the mahogany complexion of a sea officer, and about his eyes and mouth there were lines that at once spoke of a capacity for warmth and humour, and just as evidently for authority and firm, even harsh action.

He was busying himself with the study of the 'chariot', or coach, which had drawn up a short distance across the dockyard from his window. A black ship of state with its body suspended on C-shaped springs, it was drawn by four muscular bays who stood with barely concealed annoyance in the renewed downpour, stamping in the puddles on the cobbles and shaking the wet from their gleaming flanks in great tack-jangling tremors. Mainwaring wondered if the clot of a coachman nodding asleep under his cloak and dripping tricorne would remember that the beasts would need a hot mash feed and a proper rubdown after they –

'The admiral will see you now, sir,' rumbled the little Welshman, at the door. 'If you'll come this way . . .'

Mainwaring snatched up his hat and followed, cursing as his pumps slipped and skittered on the slick wood of the hallway. His heels echoed hollowly as he passed through the doorway indicated by the servant, whose expressionless, poxcratered features emitted a cloud of gloom. As Mainwaring entered, the man muttered, 'Lieutenant Mainwaring, sir.'

Mainwaring found himself in a surprisingly small room dominated by an oversized fireplace in which a considerable blaze was roaring away. At a narrow board table two gentlemen of apparent seniority raised their eyes to him as he stopped, made as good a leg as possible, and offered a bow.

'Your servant, sir,' said Mainwaring.

Admiral Philip Cavendish, the port admiral, was the smaller of the two men, and his features Mainwaring recognized from previous descriptions. A kindly-looking man dressed in sombre, vicar-like black and conventional full-bottomed wig, his lined, grave face showed a sickly pallor, but the clear, wise eyes were set in a quizzical frown. Cavendish indicated the other man with the barest movement of a thin hand.

'Good day, Mainwaring. Perhaps you've not had the pleasure of being presented round to everyone?'

Mainwaring was about to speak when the second man leaned forward across the buffed tabletop and snorted.

'Damned unlikely he'd have come my way, Philip. I am the Navy Board commissioner here, Mainwaring. Not a sea officer and don't pretend to be.'

'Yes, sir,' said Mainwaring. He was aware that the commissioner at Portsmouth was renowned as a steel-hard man who rarely minced words or bothered to cover the reality that he ran the dockyard with an iron hand, and was, far more than the ailing Cavendish, the true power over the Navy's activities here. Richard Hughes was a florid, bulky man whose pale blue eyes radiated a kind of belligerent challenge Mainwaring had seen before; the truculence that came from admitting no subjective experience other than one's own, which was a complex way of saying Hughes considered most men fools and suffered them poorly, if at all. As senior officers, such men could be disastrous; equally they might be highly effective and to cross them would prove a very unwise move indeed. Mainwaring kept his expression carefully neutral.

Cavendish coughed softly into a handkerchief that materialized out of a cuff and motioned Mainwaring to sit down. The American did so, balancing his hat on his knees. He had no hanger – no longer owning one worth

7

wearing in formal attire – and so was denied the solace of fidgeting with the weapon's hilt and guard.

'Your ship is where, precisely?' asked Hughes, abruptly.

'Ah – alongside, sir. The Gun Wharf. I was directed there by the – '

'Yes, yes. I didn't want you riding to a Spithead hawser where we couldn't get at you. I gather you made an extraordinarily fast passage.'

Mainwaring could not hold back a trace of a smile. *Athena*, a sleek topsail schooner of Bermuda cedar, had been charmed with strong beam and quarter winds from the moment she had cleared Port Royal, Jamaica. She had stormed across the North Atlantic in under three weeks, and the schoonermen were enormously proud of their achievement.

'We were fortunate, sir. Seventeen days all told.'

Cavendish nodded. 'Commendable, Mainwaring.'

Hughes snorted. 'Commendable it may be, but all things must lead to changes. You're to be taken out of *Athena*.'

Mainwaring sat up. The faces of the men he had commanded for almost two years and who had become an enviably efficient team under his leadership – and, in some cases, his friends – flicked before his eyes, and with them the image of the schooner: sleek, beautiful, full of life and graceful speed.

'I – beg your pardon, sir?'

'Not deaf, are you? You're to come out of her at once. *Athena*'s to be commanded by a lieutenant of my staff. I shall use her as a post vessel, among other duties.'

Mainwaring understood at once. The ancient and immutable principle of 'interest' was at work. Hughes, like all officers of position within the naval structure, whether sea officers or otherwise, had their favourites.

8

Relatives, sons of political patrons, it mattered little; without the determination of such men as Hughes to see them well-placed, junior officers like Mainwaring, who were totally without a wealthy or powerful patron's support, had little chance of protecting their commands or positions against such favourites, or even of keeping up with them in the climb to post rank, that almost guarantor of eventually having one's own flag. It would do little good for Mainwaring to protest; more likely, Hughes' reaction would damage Mainwaring's career prospects even further. No one questioned the justice of the system, and indeed many pointed out that it was the best way to bring competent men up in rank, selected for merit by influential superior officers able to assess professional skill when they saw it. That it might be misused to advance incompetents was a risk; but that such 'interest' existed at all meant that friendless or unnoticed officers like Mainwaring would begin an upward climb only by a desperately brave or successful action at sea. And such achievements were by no means easy.

'You needn't look so damned glum, Mainwaring.' Hughes' voice shook Mainwaring out of the downward spiral of his thoughts. 'We don't intend to let you sit on the beach at half-pay. Admiral Vernon has had far too much to say about your role in the taking of Porto Bello for that.' He pulled a vast handkerchief from one coat sleeve and blew vigorously into it.

'We're giving you the *Diana*, twenty guns. A damned fine vessel, I'm told. You're to be rated commander.'

Mainwaring stared at him. 'I – I'm overwhelmed, sir,' he managed, after a moment.

'I should damned well think so. Extraordinary enough for a colonial lieutenant to make commander. Oh, yes, you've been entered into the Royal Navy. But to be given

9

a ship like *Diana* is far too much good fortune. By God, Mainwaring, I hope you appreciate your luck.'

Mainwaring swallowed. 'I do, sir.'

Cavendish raised a thin finger. 'Your record has spoken for itself, Mainwaring. The task in question calls for an officer of independent spirit and initiative. Admiral Vernon', and here Cavendish tapped a manila folder before him, 'feels you have these qualities in abundance. We hope for all our sakes he is correct.'

Mainwaring nodded, the hair at the nape of his neck prickling as he heard the warning.

'What do you know of vessels of her type, Mainwaring? Very little, I would presume?'

'I'm afraid so, sir.'

'Very well,' said Cavendish. 'She's one of the better twenty-gun sloops build on the Establishment of 1719. A sixth-rate, what? Three hundred and eighty tons, perhaps a hundred and fifty or so people. Her batteries are six-pounders.'

'A post captain's command, Mainwaring' sniffed Hughes. 'But Their Lordships understandably are not about to confer that rank upon you.'

'In any event,' went on Cavendish, a flicker of irritation crossing his face, 'she's well-found and able. A lucky ship, I'm told.'

'What of her ship's company, sir?' asked Mainwaring suddenly. It came to him that he wanted in the worst way to bring as many of his Athenas with him as he could. Even if there was no prospect of promotion for *Athena*'s sailing master, the gruff, able Isaiah Hooke, and his midshipman, Stephen Pellowe, it would mean –

'She is without her complement of officers, Mainwaring,' said Hughes, evenly. 'I've an anchor watch of guardship hands in her for the moment. You'll have to see to her manning yourself.'

10

Mainwaring stared at him, deference vanishing in the face of shock. '*No* officers, sir? Or hands? What on earth – ?'

Hughes' face darkened. 'Kindly recall that such dispositions as required by the Service are not your concern, Mainwaring. In point of fact, she was paid off several months ago and was destined to be laid up in ordinary until Their Lordships changed their minds about her, given our need for ships. You're thinking about your Athenas, no doubt.'

'Yes, sir. I was hoping to keep as many as possible with me.'

Cavendish nodded. 'A natural enough intention. You are sensible, I trust, that *Diana* will require two lieutenants, a sailing master, a purser and a surgeon, not to mention a lieutenant for some sea regiment men. And then will come your warrant officers. You'll need true admiralty warrant men for your gunner, boatswain, and carpenter, what? Your schoonermen will offer you little there.' He coughed delicately, like a woman. 'But you may keep the lot of 'em.'

'Thank you, sir,' said Mainwaring, his mind working quickly. 'With respect, sir, I'd like to have Hooke, the master in *Athena*, as sailing master. And Pellowe – a midshipman – should be ready for his board if you'd grant him leave to sit it, sir – as one of the lieutenants.'

'He'll have his chance,' said Hughes. 'Enter him as midshipman and acting second lieutenant, if you wish. The other appointments I shall make. Unless you wish to press more colonial fishermen on me for recognition.'

Mainwaring kept his expression controlled. 'One other, sir. I'd like to rate a man named Jewett as boatswain. He came to me out of *Hampton Court*, at Porto Bello. He'd merit a warrant.'

'Very well. I trust that is all?'

It was evident Mainwaring could ask for nothing more. Hughes would have his own priorities to meet.

'No, sir. I'm obliged, sir.'

Cavendish coughed weakly into his handkerchief again. 'You'll need to see to her commissioning immediately, Mainwaring. Read yourself in when you've a company to hear you. She's riding to two anchors at Spithead with her t'gallant masts sent down. Get a wherry out to her on tomorrow's flood. You may get your Athenas into her directly you go aboard. I shall see that the necessary orders are given to the guardboats.'

Mainwaring raised an eyebrow. His request for his men had been anticipated, and acted upon. It was almost too quick and pat, said his mind. And another part was asking a far more important question.

'When I am ready for sea, sir,' he said, looking at Cavendish, 'what will be my orders?'

It was Hughes who replied. 'You will receive more extensive orders in due course, Mainwaring. For the moment, these instructions will suffice.' He slid a wax-sealed manila envelope across to Mainwaring's side of the table. 'Kindly do not open them until you are in your ship.'

'Aye, aye, sir.'

Hughes and Cavendish exchanged another questioning glance before Hughes returned his eyes to Mainwaring, and for an instant Mainwaring thought he detected a glimmer of warmth in the hard gaze. And some other expression . . .

'Then that is all, Commander. This discussion is over. Good day to you, sir.'

A few moments later, Mainwaring was standing on the front step of the house, shrugging into his cloak as the rain pelted down on him. He looked about him at the grey, rain-drenched dockyard and felt the weight of the manila envelope in his pocket. For every surface reason he should be ecstatic. He had entered the commissioner's house a very junior lieutenant, of American birth and totally without interest, and was leaving it with an appointment as commander of a twenty-gun sixth-rate. He was keeping his treasured ship's company out of *Athena*. And in his pocket burned orders he sensed – he *knew* – would lead him in the path of risk or glory. Why, then, did he feel a nagging tension at the back of his neck? He had recognized in himself the ability to sense, almost in an animal way, the presence of danger. It had helped him survive his youth in the forests and on the iron coasts of New England, and in sea action on the decks of *Athena*. Now it tingled again, alert for some hidden menace. But for the first time in his life he could not feel the source of the danger.

Cramming his tricorne low over his eyes, he clumped off across the wet cobbles. He had to get back to *Athena*, warn her company of what was to transpire, and decide who among them would fill the myriad posts and tasks in a sixth-rate: his own steward; a proper clerk; a commander's coxswain; stewards for the wardroom; Hooke to talk to about the duties as sailing master, and who to rate as master's mate; the list was endless. And then the unknown people to come would be a worry. Hughes and Cavendish would send him a first lieutenant, to be Mainwaring's right-hand man, senior to Pellowe; they would appoint a purser, and God knew what he would be like, hopefully not a tu'penny-pinching scoundrel; and a proper surgeon, who equally hopefully would not be a gin-sodden failure from a shore practice or, worse, an unqualified quack. In addition would come a military man, a lieutenant of one of the four regiments of sea-going infantry Parliament had approved.

Mainwaring stopped to let a wagon clatter by, laden

13

with hogsheads. *Athena* carried no more than twenty hands before the mast, while a sixth-rate required upwards of one hundred and fifty souls in her complement, including twenty marines whom Cavendish and Hughes would worry about. But it would be up to Mainwaring to find the seamen. That meant relying upon the harvesting abilities of the impress service to cull a crop of men 'using the sea', as the limit of their mandate supposedly went – or send his own lieutenant, boatswain and a cudgel-armed clutch of men ashore to do the job themselves.

As he splashed along the High Street towards the Grand Parade he could see the bulk of the square tower ahead through the murk. Already he was drenched to the skin, and shivering, and he swore at himself for forgetting the way. He would have to huddle around *Athena*'s firebox coals when he finally reached the vessel. His mind kept racing over the things he had to do, and there still lurked that old wariness, centring now on the bulk of the manila envelope slapping against his thigh in his coat-tail pocket.

'You have something in store for me, *Diana*,' he muttered to himself, the words drowned in the hiss of the rain. 'Why do I feel so damned certain I shan't like it?' And he squelched on through the icy downpour.

The grey dawn had brought no respite, and as the light grew over the east it revealed the greasy gunmetal waters of the Solent, battered by the driving rain and the easterly that carried it out of the low, hurrying cloud. The little wherry punched and dipped its way along, the dark brown spritsail curling and thumping as the craft rolled, causing Mainwaring to curse and clutch at the narrow thwart where he sat under his cloak, his sea chest jammed against

14

his legs before him amidst a jumble of lines, buckets, grapnels and other gear.

'Pardon, zur,' said the wherryman, a toothless, lank-haired apparition in a stocking cap and old soldier's coat. 'She's 'eavy laden. Harry, yew be easin' o' that sheet, now!' This last to the scruffy boy squatting on the floor-boards by the wherryman's knee.

Mainwaring said nothing, trying to see ahead round the face of the dark, patched canvas. Perhaps half a dozen ships rode at anchor here at Spithead; dark hulks in the rain, indistinguishable unless you recognized an odd look to the cutwater here, a raken mizzenmast there. Most were bigger vessels, third- or second-rates, with sodden, huge ensigns rippling in pallet-knife streaks of colour against the grey and black shades of sea and sky.

'She's there, zur,' offered the wherryman. 'T' seaward a cable or so uv *Windsor Castle*, zur. Ye'll glim 'er jib-boom end presently.'

Mainwaring grunted. His mind was too full, and his temper too foul, to exchange any conversation with the wherryman. He had returned to *Athena* to find the schoonermen already alerted to what was taking place, and surrounding him with anxious faces as he boarded the vessel. There had been little he could tell them, and with some reluctance they had slung their seabags and chests into the two pinnaces that had arrived alongside, sent over by the dockyard officer of the day. Then it had been a last, painful look round *Athena*, the greeting of the two rum-reddened pensioners who were to be her watchmen, and the packing of his own small chest before seeing Hooke off in the last pinnace, tacking off into the drizzle towards the anchorage. He had found an old seaman with a barrow to carry his chest to a small inn at the upper end of Saint Thomas' Street. Next morning he could take the

15

schooner's books to the commissioner's house, as Cavendish had inexplicably requested by a messenger that had come to *Athena*. He had lain huddling miserably under the thin blanket in the garret room, watching the rush dips burn down and gutter out, thinking of the morning and worrying as the rain pattered unceasingly on the shingles a few inches above his head. He had fallen asleep with very few of the details in his mind put into any kind of order, and –

'There she be, zur. Fine on th'la'b'd bow.'

The wherryman's voice pulled Mainwaring back to reality, and he squinted ahead through the rain as the wherry rolled and wallowed. They were moving past the dark rampart shape of a line-of-battle ship, and a smaller vessel had come into view, the mustard and black hull paint brightly visible even through the mist and drizzle. Mainwaring felt an involuntary thrill and ran his eyes over her eagerly, blowing the water from the tip of his nose. *Diana* was riding easily to her hawser, the beautiful line of her sheer a delight to the eye. Mainwaring tried to remember what he knew of her class, the twenty-four gun ships that had been set up by the sundry 'establishments' since 1719. Ship-rigged, with short t'gallant masts, a pole mizzen topmast, and a lateen mizzen yard on the after part of which one of the new type of four-sided 'spanker' sails was brailed up. At their tonnage of slightly less than four hundred tons they were small, agile vessels, incapable of lying in the line of battle but able to do the fast, roving work of the class of ships the French call '*frégates*'. Their gun batteries were all carried on the upper deck, and the lower deck, instead of gunports, had oar or sweep ports. If Mainwaring remembered correctly, they carried eighteen sweeps a side. *Diana* would look more like a Mediterranean galley under that power than a north European warship, he mused.

16

As the wherry drew closer, Mainwaring could see that *Diana*'s boats were riding off her stern. They looked to be an eight-oared pinnace, and a little jolly boat. Not enough, in Mainwaring's mind. He would have to see if he could beg, borrow, or steal another ship's boat.

'She's a pretty thing, zur,' offered the wherryman breathily, his mind on an extra coin or two in payment for cheerfulness.

Mainwaring grunted. 'Yes. Mind you bring me in on the loo'ard side.'

'Aye, zur,' said the wherryman, and subsided.

The wherry bobbed and pitched in towards the ship until it finally loomed high overhead, the mustard-painted hull gleaming wetly, a rain-darkened red ensign curling heavily at her ensign staff. As the wherryman hauled his wind and beat up for *Diana*'s quarter, a face appeared at the mizzen shrouds, the hail carrying faintly across the wind.

'. . . boat, ahoy!'

'*Diana*!' bellowed the wherryman, with all the gusto of a seasoned hand, and Mainwaring made a mental note to add tuppence to his fare for that remembrance of proper etiquette. Aboard the ship there was a sudden scurry of activity. As the wherry drew in, the spritsail suddenly luffing and collapsing in *Diana*'s lee, Mainwaring was staring up at the towering rig, noting the neatly-squared yards, the canvas in the smooth rools of a harbour furl snugged down tight by their gaskets.

In the next moment the wherry was rolling and wallowing under the still, high wall of *Diana*'s side. Mainwaring put a handful of coins into the pleased wherryman's calloused paw, gathered his cloak about him, and leaped awkwardly for the battens that led up the entry port in the ship's rail. His knees banged against the rain-slicked, painted wood, and he hung on in fear of toppling back

17

into the wherry or the chill, leaden sea. But then he found his balance, and he was moving up the side, Hooke peering down at him, a sodden and badly-cocked hat pulled down around his ears. Mainwaring reached the rail and pulled himself to the deck, realizing that he had not the slightest notion of what to expect.

Perhaps eight to ten seamen stood in a rough line, some hatless, most barefoot, in an assortment of cast-off landsmen's clothes, tar-smeared duck frocks, and the odd, skirt-like 'petticoat breeches' that were many a seaman's identifying mark. Mainwaring recognized none of them, which meant they likely were Cavendish's anchor watch. But before them, warm smiles on their faces, were Isaiah Hooke and Stephen Pellowe, the latter's fair hair streaked by the rain across his forehead.

Hooke, who had been Mainwaring's sailing master in the schooner, was thick-shouldered and burly, and his ruddy features were creased in pleasure. He knuckled a forelock at the American.

'Beggin' yer pardon, zur. 'Tweren't time nor people t' greet ye aboard proper.'

Mainwaring grinned at the ursine figure, who was for Mainwaring a friend as well as a trusted officer. 'Time enough for ceremony later, Isaiah. Where are our own lads? I take it these are the watchmen?'

'Aye,' said Hooke, lowering his voice. 'An' a rum lot they are, too. Our lads are below, gettin' squared away.' Hooke shook his head. 'We'll never man her wiv just our Athenas, zur. Need twice as many hands.'

Mainwaring nodded. 'I know. And we'll be using a press to get 'em. You'll have to do your best till then. Stephen?'

'Sir?'

'Congratulations. You are as of this moment acting second lieutenant of this ship. And arrangements will be

18

made to have you sit your Board as soon as possible, I've been promised.'

The young midshipman, whom Mainwaring counted as a friend equally with the grizzled Hooke, gaped at him for a moment, and then beamed in pleasure.

'Second – thank you, sir! I – I don't know what to say.'

'Save your breath for your work. Is Jewett still with us? He's not run?'

Hooke bared tobacco-yellowed teeth. 'Nah, zur. None of th'lads've run. Not from yew.'

Mainwaring noted the compliment, feeling oddly humble. 'Very good. Tell Jewett he's to get his warrant as boatswain. And you'd best think of who among the Athenas you'll want to tell off as mates for him and the other warrant officers. I doubt whether we'll be lucky to press experienced men.'

Hooke nodded, his face dripping with rain. In his oilskins, his shaggy head of thick blond hair, now shot through with grey, still worn 'hauled aft' into a tarred, waist-length queue, the sailing master resembled nothing so much as a sea-going bear, and Mainwaring felt a rush of affection for him. They had been through so much together, and now faced who knew what fresh trials.

'Zur. I've twenty-seven lads, all told. When are we – ?'

'The admiral will send our other officers to us in short order, Isaiah. I wouldn't doubt that before sunset we'll have the first lieutenant, and perhaps a few of the others. There may be an admiral's favourite or two among 'em.' Mainwaring turned to Pellowe. 'Mr Pellowe,' he said, dropping into a formal tone, 'please get my chest swayed aboard directly. And are there any provisions in the ship? Any victual stores?'

'Some, sir. Several casks of salt pork. Some biscuit, oatmeal, and peas.'

'Have you rated a man as cook?'

19

'Winton, for the moment, sir. Not that he likes it.'

'Good. He's too good a hand to leave there, and hopefully the press will help us there. See all hands get a warm meal, even if it's boiled biscuit. I hope to God we get a responsible purser.' As Pellowe made off, he eyed the anchorwatch men still drawn up in the drizzle, watching him suspiciously.

'Look at that lot,' he said under his teeth to Hooke. 'Certain I'm going to try and keep 'em and take away that easy guardship life. Any of 'em worth it?'

Hooke shook his head. 'No, zur. Slack an' slovenly, most of 'em. An' a few ruptures in the bargain. Wiv yer permission I'd take me chances wiv the pressed men.'

'All right. Pick a reliable man and send him in the wherry. He's to report to the officer of the day in the guardship *Jarrow* and have 'em send a boat for 'em.' Mainwaring blew a drop of water from the end of his nose. 'And then we shall have to see about running the bloody press,' he finished, morosely.

Hooke touched his brow. 'Aye, zur,' he said, and clumped off, sending the watchmen scattering with an invective-laced bellow.

Behind Mainwaring there was a squeal of blocks and a thump as Mainwaring's chest came up from the wherry, wrestled on board by two Athenas.

'Gently with that,' called Mainwaring. 'Take it to my cabin, Adams, will you?'

'Aye, aye, sir. And a proper cabin for you it is too, sir, after *Athena*!'

Mainwaring nodded. He looked around *Diana*, seeing the lofty rig, the expanse of deck. Many things were different, after the schooner. *Diana*'s beam of thirty feet made the decks – once holystoned white, but now gritty and stained – seem a vast, boardwalk-like expanse. The long rows of guns, glistening black and ochre in the rain, snug caps of painted canvas lashed over their vents, seemed an enormously powerful battery in comparison with *Athena*'s few four-pounders and swivels. The ship appeared huge, and the resources available to Mainwaring so small. And still the question returned to tighten his neck muscles: why such a well-found and fully-fitted vessel should have been laid up as if 'in ordinary' when she was clearly in a state of commission. Even at first glance, this was no worm-riven wreck, told off as virtually a hulk for prison use, or a bare hull still without spars or masts after launching. *Diana* looked neglected, but she had obviously been a working, fighting ship, until recently. But what had happened to her officers? Her ship's company? Why was Mainwaring greeted only by a sullen clutch of suspicious guardship men, other than his willing but equally baffled Athenas? And why had he been selected to command her, over the heads of dozens of better-placed men and junior post captains who would have leaped at the chance of a small-ship command like *Diana*? The unanswered questions came thick and fast as Mainwaring moved to the after companionway, following his sea chest, and the sense of foreboding and warning swelled within him.

At the foot of the companion he found himself on a spacious deck that, like all the twenty-fours, was more like the orlop of a larger vessel than the first deck below the weatherdeck. It was low-beamed and dark, only a glimmer of light showing from the sweep ports, and whether there was anything stowed in its shadowy length Mainwaring could not tell. Ahead, the two men wrestling his chest along passed by one small door in a partition and opened a second farther aft. Stepping through, Mainwaring found himself in a broad stern cabin more than twice the size of his tiny quarters in *Athena*. A line of stern lights crossed the end of the cabin, and through their slanting glass Mainwaring could see the rain-dappled surface of the anchorage grey and misted, the distant hulks of anchored ships faint, dark shapes. Under the stern lights, similar to *Athena*, a long settee ran, covered in dark leather. A plain desk, with a ladderback chair behind it and two before it, was in the middle of the cabin, below a brass lantern that swung gently from a deckhead hook. To one side there was a box bunk, with drawers below and shelves above, and a reversed compass hung in its gimbal over the bunk. To the other side, a musket and sword rack stood – empty – beside a narrow door through which the captain's private 'seat of ease' on the quarter gallery could be glimpsed in its shadowy cubicle. There was a hook or two about the cabin, and the deck was covered with plain painted canvas.

'That'll do, lads. Thank 'ee,' murmured Mainwaring as the men set down his chest at the foot of the box bunk, touched their brows at him, and left. He threw his dripping tricorne on the settee and hung the cloak on a hook behind the door, which he shut. Then he sat on the bunk, feeling its coarse ticking mattress, wondering how old and vermin-infested the straw within might be, and looked round the cabin.

'Empty as a widow's purse, aren't you?' he said to the ship. 'Stripped bare.' He peered up at the deckhead and the great beams, wondering if an answer might somehow be printed there for the questions bedevilling him.

He rose and went to the desk. It was unlocked, and in each drawer he found nothing save the key to that drawer.

But in the last drawer he found a single folded piece of writing paper. It bore but one sentence, in a neat and scholarly hand.

Do not trust her.

Mainwaring stared at it for a moment. Then, very carefully, he folded it and put it back in the same drawer.

'Well, I'll be damned,' he murmured.

There was a knock at the cabin door.

'Come,' said Mainwaring.

A dark-haired seaman, an earring gleaming in one ear under his locks, looked in.

'Beggin' yer pardon, zur. First lieutenant's come aboard, zur.'

'Has he, by God. Show him down to me. You're Jackson, aren't you?'

The man grinned. 'Aye, zur. Join'd at Port Royal, zur.'

'I remember. Glad you stayed with us.'

The grin widened, white crooked teeth bright in a mahogany complexion.

'Thankee, zur!'

A few moments later the steps of shod feet came to a halt outside the door, and a voice cleared its throat. Again a knock.

Mainwaring was behind the desk. 'Yes?'

Stephen Pellowe looked in, his face expressionless. 'The first lieutenant to see you, sir,' he said.

A figure stepped through the doorway, tall, almost as tall as Mainwaring, but not as broad across the shoulders. Mainwaring had an image of a slim, almost schoolmasterish form: mid-brown hair, dressed simply back in an eelskin queue; a grave, thoughtful face, with tired grey eyes and a cautious set to the thin mouth; a worn but clean suit of dark green clothes, and unlaced tricorne in one long-fingered hand. The other hand reached out, somewhat in surprise, to the one offered by Mainwaring as the American rose from behind the desk.

'James Howe, sir. I – I believe you were aware of my appointment?' The face was not weak, but there was a hesitation in the manner.

23

'I am learning who you are for the first time, Mr Howe. But I was most anxious to have my first lieutenant aboard. It's good that you're here.'

Howe stared at him for an instant, as if Mainwaring's reaction was unexpected. He pulled a packet of papers from his coat-tail pocket, offering it.

'I – thank you, sir. Here are my orders and the letter from the Admiralty. You'll find – '

Mainwaring waved him towards a chair. 'Sit down, Mr Howe. I'm sure your papers are in order. What ship were you in last?' He sank into the chair behind the desk.

'Er – *Active*, sir. Twenty-four. With Sir Chaloner Ogle's squadron. We put into Lisbon to repair storm damage and – and I came home at that time, sir.'

'I see. What were you in her?'

'First lieutenant, sir.'

Mainwaring nodded. He noticed a faint colouring in Howe's face at this last statement. The man was obviously nervous or on edge. Was there something hidden in Howe's past? Had he been sent home for some reason better left unsaid? Or, for the good of *Diana*, would it have to come out?

'You'll be familiar, then, with the needs of a ship such as this one. I should explain immediately that this is the largest thing I've commanded, and I shall be relying on you for a great deal.'

'I – I know a bit of your record, sir. I'm sure you'll find little problem in adjusting to her.' Howe was sounding surer, but the weary, defensive look was still in the grey eyes. It was time to test his knowledge a touch.

'I hope I shall. I have no idea, for example, as to the degree of victualling required for a ship of this size. What can we expect of our purser, when he arrives, to seek in the way of such things?'

It was as if a screen had been lifted from Howe's eyes. They became clear and purposeful.

'Fairly straightforward, sir. A four-hundred-ton sixth-rate carries some one hundred fifty people in her complement. For full victualling she'll need a lot, sir. Likely eight thousand pounds, at least, in salt beef, and a third o' that in salt pork; a good five hundred pounds o' salt cod, and between twenty to twenty-five thousand biscuit. Then there'd be oatmeal, about thirty bushels, and perhaps the same in dried peas; anywhere up to a hundred casks of flour, if the cook can bake worth a damn. There's a good deal more. In spirits, ye'd need six casks o' rum, and ten to fifteen casks o' small beer. Ye'd need fresh fruit and greens if you can find them, and as much livestock as the carpenter can crate and pen on the weatherdeck – '

Mainwaring held up his hands. 'Thank you, Mr Howe. At least we shall not be ignorant of what we need.' He paused. 'Were you aware of any other appointments to this ship? The surgeon, or the purser? Or the lieutenant of marines?'

Howe shook his head. 'No, sir. But if you'd permit, if I can get my chest aboard and struck into my cabin, I'd like to go over the ship immediately, to see who – or what – we have, and what our state is, to let you know, sir. Are some of the hands aboard from your old ship, sir?'

'Yes. About twenty. As is your sailing master, Isaiah Hooke, and your second, Stephen Pellowe. Both fine and capable men.'

'I'll take your word for it, sir.' The guarded expression had come over Howe's eyes again, and Mainwaring sensed there was something to say at this point. A gamble to be thrown.

'Please do. By all means, carry on,' said Mainwaring. 'See me before the First Dog with what you've found of our state.'

'Aye, aye, sir.' Howe rose with Mainwaring.

'And one more thing, Mr Howe. I'm new to this ship, every bit as much as you are. In a sense we are all starting over, starting anew.' He glanced at the manila packet and then directly into the grey eyes. 'I shall read those, of course. But *Diana* is a new beginning, as far as I am concerned. In all respects. Is that clear?'

A light arose in Howe's eyes, and in a moment of unguarded honesty they showed the wariness and wear vanish, to be replaced with a flicker of energy, and hope. And something else. Gratitude?

'Aye, aye, sir,' said Howe, briskly. 'Thank you, sir.' And he strode out through the cabin door, with a different set to the slim shoulders from when he had entered.

Eighteen hours later, *Diana* was a somewhat more crowded and far busier ship than when Mainwaring had first come aboard. Most of the other warrant officers had arrived. A one-eyed gunner named Soper, with a piratical look to him; John Jenkins, the carpenter, all bustle and hung about with tools, balding and bespectacled, the tiny, lead-framed lenses giving him the look of a sunlit mole; and a dignified sailmaker, grey hair neatly queued, wise blue eyes set in a mahogany face, named George Morris. With Jewett already in beaming expectation of his warrant as boatswain, and proudly carrying his rattan, that gave *Diana*, on paper at least, all but the master at arms, armourer, and serjeant – as it was spelled – of marines in the way of the key men on the ship, the warrant officers.

The purser, too, had reported aboard, a small, fussy man rowed out by a tiny skiff of his own hiring. He had literally danced and hovered around Mainwaring's desk, showing the latter the meticulously kept books of his previous ship, and through the fidgety nature of the man – rather like a clerkish rat, he thought – Mainwaring could see a clear intelligence and a seeming mastery of the potential needs of the ship. Mainwaring had made but two requests: that the victualling of the ship be undertaken with speed, and that, to help create a uniform look to the ship's company, blue wool and white duck be favoured in the slops clothing carried for sale to the men. William Thorne was the man's name, and it augured well for the ship that Thorne had in fact already sent ashore for bales of slops clothing after seeing the clean but ragged state of the former Athenas. A purser with a proprietary concern for the ship and her men would be an incalculable boon.

The surgeon, Nesbitt Rowe, had been another matter. A slim and handsome man in a dark Celtic way, and dressed well, he had arrived in a wherry with a mountain of luggage, almost incoherently drunk, and had been helped to *Diana*'s deck along with his chests of belongings, only to trip on an eyebolt and sprawl giggling at Mainwaring's feet. Mainwaring had not been able to read the man's documents, but he knew the signs all too well; the promising shore practice ruined by drink, the application for a surgeon's post to escape debtors or responsibilities of other kinds, the life wasted at sea. Mainwaring listened now to the man's voice, muffled as he roared away obscene ditties in his cabin, and a firm resolve was forming in his mind: Rowe would either carry out his duties, or he would leave the ship. A drunken officer was injurious not only to the ship, but –

There was a knock and Mainwaring looked up from the papers scattered on his desk.

'Yes?'

James Howe's head appeared. 'See you for a moment, sir?'

'By all means. Tired of bloody reading in any event.'

Howe grinned pleasantly and slid into a chair, just as the ship's bell sounded faintly overhead.

27

Mainwaring steepled his fingertips. 'Well, then, Mr Howe. What state are we in?'

'Strong in some parts of ship, weak in others, sir. Jenkins tells me there's not enough wood to build a side chair in the ship. Carpenter's stores need replacement. Jewett appears smart enough; he got down in the lazarettes and the orlop and counts our stock of cordage and line as adequate. It's mostly new. And Old Ezrah – '

'Old Ezrah?' Mainwaring raised his eyebrow.

Howe grinned. 'Ezrah Soper, sir. The gunner. Sailed with him in *Centurion*. He says we've not a cask o' pistol powder, no slow match, no shot of any description, no gun tools. And there's not a musket. Nor any small arm, to speak of. Nothing for an armourer to work on.'

Mainwaring thought. 'No small arms,' he said slowly, after a moment. 'I wonder what that suggests. Not even a cutlass?'

'No. Damned odd, sir, to my mind. It's as if they couldn't decide whether she was to be paid off or looted.'

'Astutely put. Go on.'

'Well, we've a cook, and a mate for him, I'm pleased to report. Lost a leg in *Swiftsure* against the Dons. Somewhat of a snarly fellow, but he set about cleaning the kettles with a will.'

'What's his name?'

'Hard to believe, sir. Boyle.'

'And his mate is called Steam, no doubt.'

With a twinkle in his eye Howe went on. Mainwaring sensed a kind of kinship in humour building between himself and the slim first lieutenant, and he was glad, knowing that a meeting of minds between Howe and himself would have to occur on some level if they were to develop an effective understanding and workable relationship. 'Morris, the sailmaker, says, on the other hand, that we're well stored in canvas. And Hooke tells me we've a full suit o' sails, even to stu'n'sls. Is Hooke as competent as he seems?'

'Every inch.'

'I thought as much, sir.' He coughed lightly. 'Thorne appears to be conscious of his duty, I might add, sir. Thank God. Certainly he's bedevilling me for shore parties and boat's crews to get our victuals and stores aboard.'

'As well he should.'

'But that brings up the most pressing question, sir. If you'll pardon a timely play on words. I've barely enough hands to make a boat's crew, let alone man a sixth-rate.'

'I know, Mr Howe.' Mainwaring stood up. 'For that reason I've sent a letter ashore to the admiral informing him we shall be running a press tonight. Under your command.'

Howe rose as well. His face sobered, and took on a firm expression. Impressment was unfailingly a nasty business.

'Aye, aye, sir,' he said, quietly.

Mainwaring watched him closely. The first lieutenant of a fighting vessel was required to be a steady man, able to give orders for, and carry out, difficult and even distasteful tasks without flinching.

'You'll no doubt find Jewett up to it. I'd suggest you have him pick the likeliest of the Athenas. And don't forget to make certain how far you'll be from the ship, and how'll you reach her, when you take your men. You can use the *Jarrow* to hold 'em, if you wish. Remember that until they're read in we've no real power over 'em, and you've got to keep 'em out of contact with shore people.'

Howe's expression was unchanged. 'I shall, sir. Pity we've no cutlasses. It'll be belaying pins and my heaviest walking stick.'

29

Mainwaring grinned at that, wondering what odd shadow seemed to lie across Howe and his career; what reason brought him to *Diana* with such an air of uncertainty. In the grave but resolute face Mainwaring could see nothing but a determined sea officer intent on carrying out a despised but necessary duty.

'Have you a hanger?' he asked.

Howe flushed, and looked away for a moment. 'N – no, sir. Lost it in my last ship, sir. I – '

'Then you'll wear mine. Once I dig it out of my chest – it's very old and rusty, I'm afraid – I'll have it sent to you.'

Howe looked at him in surprised gratitude.

'Thank you, sir.'

In the next instant from beyond the partitions forward, a strange howl arose like the muffled baying of a hound, startling and eerie, until it resolved itself into the half-coherent first verses of a sailor's ditty.

'What in God's name – ?' began Howe.

Mainwaring sucked a tooth. 'Our surgeon, Mr Rowe. A liability, I'm afraid. Drunk when he came into the ship and liable to remain so, unless he cannot reach drink.'

'What can we do about him, sir?'

'I've been pondering that. Certainly I can't bear much more of that serenade. And you'll be needing him to pass the pressed men.'

'Yes.'

'Then my path is clear. Now mind, James, you'll want to make sure Jewett picks good lads, and sees to the boat. With night, the Penny Street grogshops and swills will have their tables jammed with likely prospects. Mind the law, however. You're not to take any man except those 'using the sea', as the expression goes. Parliament's law of last year makes that all too clear. No greengrocers or parsons, what?'

'Aye, aye, sir.' said Howe, the grin returning. He was in remarkably good humour, considering the distasteful and even hazardous duty he was about to carry out. Was it because Mainwaring was talking to him with an assumption of trust and confidence, and nothing more complex?

Mainwaring went to his cabin door and opened it, to gesture to a seaman who was tightening down the fastenings of new partitions to make a cabin for Howe.

'Williams, isn't it? Good. Get on deck and find Mr Pellowe. Tell him I shall need the surgeon alert and upright by the forenoon watch tomorrow, to pass the pressed men for fit and otherwise. Tell him that I don't care how he does it. Clear?'

The seaman, a thickset, powerful Welshman with a livid gunpowder tattoo in the shape of crossed keys on his cheek, grinned at the American as Rowe's howling song echoed through the thin partitions.

'Aye, sir. Any way at all, it is, sir?'

'Any way at all.'

With the grin widening, the man touched his brow and made off up the companionway.

Mainwaring turned back to Howe, who was looking at him with raised eyebrows.

'Don't look at me as if I've lost my senses, James. Stephen Pellowe, you'll find, is an imaginative and dedicated officer. We must have a competent surgeon. If our warbling drunkard in there can be roused to duty, Stephen will find a way.'

Howe's expression was a mixture of humour and wonder. 'Yes, sir.'

'You'll see the method in my madness soon enough. Now you'd best be off. Mind you get your catch aboard as soon as the morning light will allow. If the officer of the day in *Jarrow*, the guardship, seems to be an uncooperative clot, batten the poor wretches down in your boats

31

and make straight for *Diana*. If he argues that he should be the receiving ship, tell him to speak to me, and row on.'

'Sir.' With a nod Howe was gone.

Mainwaring's eyes turned of their own volition to the narrow drawer of the desk where he had locked away his own packet of orders. The process of completing *Diana* ready for sea was progressing. Now was the time to see what was in store for him and this strange ship. Pulling a small brass key from his waistcoat pocket, he went back to the desk and unlocked the drawer. With a pocket-knife he slit the seal of the fat packet and sat down to read.

. . . and as and when you have determined that His Britannic Majesty's Ship *Diana* is prepared for sea, you shall inform me by letter, and shall upon the earliest favourable wind and tide slip and proceed to sea; shaping your course to the south-westward so as to make the most judicious landfall in the Caribbees as may be possible. Thence you shall steer for Port Royal, at Jamaica, and report your vessel to the senior Sea Officer commanding therein; whereby it has been earlier established in our order to that station that His Britannic Majesty's Ship *Diana* shall sail at the pleasure of the Sea Officer commanding upon a Cruize under your command to the Windward, to intercept and interdict known swift vessels of the Spanish King from reaching Cartagena, or similar vessels of the French King, and shall present Prizes as may be your fortune to take possession of to the Admiralty Court at Port Royal . . .

So there it was. The West Indies again. Heat, exhaustion and Yellow Jack. Green islands in aquamarine water baking under a shot-furnace sun. Deck tar bubbling like tea over a grate and men dying in sweaty convulsions. Rum and mosquitoes.

But it would mean Anne, as well.

Mainwaring rose and stood staring out at the black, rain-misted ships, but seeing instead her face. Anne

32

Brixham, suntanned, with clear sea-green eyes laughing up at him, even white teeth showing in a wide, generous smile, the dark chestnut curls ruffled by a sea wind.

Sweet Anne, he thought. *Damme, girl, I thought ye were lost to me. But now, there's a chance. . .*

Anne Brixham was the half-creole daughter of an English planter on the island of San Andrès. A high-spirited girl well able to command her father's small trading sloop, she and her crew of loyal blacks had been taken by the Spanish to Porto Bello, where her father had been imprisoned. Forced by the Spanish to give her men to the defence of Porto Bello against the English squadron of Admiral Edward Vernon, Anne had been rescued by Mainwaring when he and the Athenas had carried out a land assault as part of Vernon's move against Porto Bello. A passionate love had developed between the couple, with ensuing pain when Mainwaring had been ordered back to England with *Athena*, and Anne had stayed on to try to help re-establish her father in Jamaica. Mainwaring had expected that it would be years, if ever, before he saw her again. Now the image of her smile, the memory of her firm, warm body in his arms returned and he felt a rush of joy which, just as quickly, he checked with will and sober caution.

A bump and thumping resounded along *Diana*'s side, with voices raised in orders and babble on the weather-deck. Then, abruptly, there was a crash outside Mainwaring's cabin door, and he could clearly hear Rowe's bleat of terror.

Williams' voice rose over Rowe's. 'Come along, sir. Gently. There's a good gentleman, look you. Hold him steady, lads!'

In the next minute, an enormous tumult erupted very much as if half a dozen men were wrestling a heifer down

33

a narrow corridor. Rowe's cries and ululations indicated clearly the role he was playing.

Mainwaring waited until the thumping and cursing had died away up the companionway and then went out, clamping his still damp tricorne on his head and wondering what sort of scene would greet his eyes on deck.

When he emerged up the companionway, the sun had briefly broken through the low, scudding cloud. A misting rain still drifted over the ship, making the scene gleam wetly in sharp clarity. At the starboard rail, Howe had eight men gathered, Jewett and his rattan at the head and seeing to the issuing out of cudgels and belaying pins. Howe stood nearby, under one arm a huge plant that to Mainwaring had the look of a very formidable weapon indeed. Howe say him and strode over, touching his hat to Mainwaring and patting the heavy stick affectionately.

'My gangers are ready, sir. Seem a rough enough set of lads. And Jewett, there, would give any press dodger bad dreams. I'll not be needing your hanger, sir, with thanks. It'll get in the way, most likely, and with only eight of us I'll likely have to pitch in as well.'

Mainwaring looked closely at the slim first lieutenant, who was actually hefting the great stick in expectant readiness.

'Commendable determination, James. But pitch in only as a last resort. You'll be little bloody use to me or the ship getting coshed in some needless scuffle. And I shall lose a new friend.'

Howe grinned warmly. 'I shall apply force selectively, sir.'

'Very well. Have you fixed your rendezvous?'

Howe nodded. 'In a way, sir. If you'll pardon me a moment – ' He raised a startlingly clear, strong voice. 'Mr Jewett! Over the side with 'em and get settled in the boat!' He turned back to Mainwaring. 'Sorry, sir. I've decided to trust only ourselves, sir. Not *Jarrow* or the shore people. As we collect 'em we'll get 'em straight back to the ship. I've asked Mr Pellowe to prepare a lock-up for 'em.'

Mainwaring wiped his face with the back of a cuff. 'I'd have done the same. Then all I can say is good luck to you. Bring in some good men, mind.'

Howe nodded, licking his lips. 'Do our best, sir. Seamen usually aren't difficult to spot. And if – '

There was a howl of terror from forward, and both Mainwaring and Howe spun round to see Nesbitt Rowe, dishevelled in waistcoat, breeches and saggy hose, hair wild, lashed to a chair and being hoisted high by a line rove off to a block on the larboard foreyard end by a grinning Williams and his men. A neutral-faced Stephen Pellowe stood by in supervision, hands clasped behind him in the tails of his plain green coat, tricorne pulled low over his eyes. As Mainwaring and Howe gaped, Pellowe nodded gravely to Williams.

'Carry on, Williams. Handsomely, now!'

Shrieking all the while, a clearly sobering Rowe was lowered into the grey, rain-dashed swell, kicking and gasping as the frigid seawater touched his legs. Then, in a quick slack and haul, the surgeon was dipped clean under, to be hoisted out streaming and spluttering.

'My God,' muttered James Howe. 'Can he stand it, sir?'

'I've no wish to be needlessly cruel, James. His colour's good and he has lots of breath in his lungs. I want him at least partially sober.'

'He's – ah – getting there quickly, sir.'

Rowe hit the water again with a gasp, and rose from his second immersion shaking his head like a wet dog, looking furiously up at his tormentors.

'Enough, you damned hounds!' he roared. 'Christ, you'll kill me!'

Mainwaring raised his voice. 'Mr Pellowe!'

'Sir?'

'My compliments to both you and the surgeon. I believe Dr Rowe has had enough. Please be so good as to see that he gets into warm clothing, and has that firkin of hot broth I see Winton holding there. And please ask Dr Rowe to join me in my cabin, would you?'

Pellowe touched the front cock of his hat smartly.

'Aye, aye, sir. Very well, lads. Tail on to that vang and get him inboard. Quickly, now.'

Howe shook his head as he watched the shivering, wild-eyed but obviously very alert surgeon swung inboard, released from his bonds, and led off.

'Bit of a shock to him, I'd think,' he said.

Mainwaring smiled slightly. 'Any man in this ship has felt worse during a watch on deck in foul weather, James. But he is now in a state to allow more civilized discussion.'

'Aye, he'll be sober, at least for now, sir.'

'We can hope. And I can also hope my first lieutenant will put aside his concern for our well-rinsed surgeon and see about netting a ship's company.'

Howe flushed, and then grinned when he saw Mainwaring's expression. 'Aye, aye, sir. On my way.' In a few swift strides he was at the rail and then over. Within minutes the longboat had unhooked and was pulling strongly for shore, Jewett at the helm, his blond rat-tail bright against the new blue cloth of his jacket. Beside him, Howe sat resolutely in the sternsheets, the slim shoulders set squarely to the front. He was shouting orders to one of the hands at the oars, and his voice echoed back, dry and hard, against the noise of wind and sea.

Mainwaring stood with his hands behind his back at the

36

foot of the quarterdeck ladder, glad of the thick wool of his coat in the miserable, drifting rain-mist that had settled in again, blotting out the sun. From where he stood he had a superb view of the anchorage, and already Howe's boat was a small white shape passing close under the hulking black-and-mustard form of a sixty-gunner. So much depended on Howe and his men; almost too much, thought Mainwaring sombrely. How could nine men and one officer capture by force enough men to provide the hundred-odd *Diana* required? How much more sensible it would be to use the French system of quotas, that simply demanded a number of men from each parish, going quietly if not willingly to their naval fate.

There might be another method, thought Mainwaring. Pay the men adequately – the pay had not been raised for Royal Navy seamen in a hundred years, it seemed – and feed them adequately. Stop the savage and useless over-application of the lash. Clothe them, beginning with the officers, in uniform dress. Give them ship's companies, indeed a Service, of which to be proud. To *volunteer* for with pride.

'There'd be no need of cudgels and gangers in English streets then, by God!' he muttered to himself.

Regaining the warmth of his cabin, Mainwaring found a blanket-swathed Nesbitt Rowe shivering in one of the chairs before his desk. Rowe was holding the steaming firkin of broth, and set down at Mainwaring's entrance, attempting to rise.

'Sit down, Doctor, sit down,' said Mainwaring, moving behind the desk to his own chair. 'I trust you've warmed yourself somewhat?'

Rowe, darkly handsome and slim, had the kind of expression and manner which at another time would have lent him an air of confidence and easy trust. But about his cheeks and nose a few broken bloodvessels were showing,

37

the first signs of the eventual bloated ruin Rowe's face would become with drink. His eyes were grey and clear, however, and regarded Mainwaring with an odd mixture of anger, deference, and shame.

'The sea was damned cold, sir.' Rowe's voice had a north country tone to it, softened by education.

'I'm sorry. I had no wish to humiliate you unnecessarily in front of the men. But we need a capable and sober surgeon, Doctor.'

'I would have been fine in the morning – '

'You would have been either more drunken, if that is possible, or dead, Doctor.'

Rowe dropped his gaze and reached for the firkin, his hands trembling as he raised it to his lips and sipped the hot liquid.

'My health is my affair, Captain. With respect.'

'With respect, it is not,' said Mainwaring, his voice like a cold knife. 'For the welfare of this ship and the ship's company I require that each of my officers be capable of carrying out his duties. There is no middle ground. Either you are capable, or you are not. At the moment Mr Pellowe had you dragged on deck, you were of no use to anyone, Doctor.'

'Sir, I protest – !'

'No use, sir!' snapped Mainwaring. 'For the ship, for the men, for me, for yourself! In several hours, James Howe and his men will have risked their lives in acquiring sufficient men to begin manning this ship. Men they will literally have to attack, subdue, and *drag* to us, Doctor! I need those men. And so do you, for without them we have no ability to sail, or fight, and in that event, Doctor, you will have no berth! Do you wish that? Do you in fact wish to be put ashore?'

Rowe stared at him. 'No. I can't – No.'

'Then hear me, Doctor. You are not the first man to

ruin his life with drink and you certainly won't be the last. But I will not sacrifice this ship and these men to your weakness. I need – the *ship* needs you to examine and pass the pressed men. And I'll not have ruptured or diseased misfits filling my messdecks because a drunken sot of a doctor waved 'em by instead of properly examining them! Clear?'

Rowe was silent, staring at Mainwaring with red-rimmed eyes, his cheeks flaming.

Mainwaring met his gaze with a hard and unpitying frown.

'You are not to appear on deck, or in any of the spaces of the ship, or at the gunroom table over which James Howe presides, in a drunken state. If you do so, I will have you bathed over the side in the manner you've just experienced, each time it occurs. Do I make myself quite clear?'

Rowe's expression was a mixture of incredulity and dismay, but now with a deep anger showing as well. Did this presage the awakening of something for which Rowe had desperate need: his pride? It was time to add the final note.

'Doctor Rowe,' said Mainwaring quietly. 'I am aware of your record. You are – or were – a respected and competent physician, with an enviable practice in the City. An unfortunate event' – and at these words Rowe winced visibly – 'caused you to give up that practice and seek a naval surgeon's post. Whatever that event may have been, it clearly is undermining your will to work, or perhaps even to live.'

Rowe glared at him, his face a sudden mask of pitiable agony. 'What in God's name could you know of such – of such – ' His voice broke off in the beginnings of a sob.

'Could I know of such things? Perhaps little. But I know that here you have a new beginning, Doctor, with men who depend upon you. I will put you through that idiotic business with the dunking chair, to my infinite regret, if I must. But I would rather have the help of a man who recognizes his duty and needs no discipline but his own.'

Rowe stood up, his face a mask of conflicting emotions.

'Your pardon, sir. I – am much indisposed, and beg your leave to retire.'

Mainwaring's voice hardened. 'I've had your cabin searched, Doctor. Your bottles have been found and put under lock and key.'

'You've no right – !'

'I am my own law, Doctor, and I shall expect you to obey it. You will be present when the pressed are brought aboard to be passed and entered. Is that clear?'

Rowe's face was stone. 'Perfectly, sir,' he whispered.

'Then you may go.'

Silently Rowe left, closing the door behind him. For long moments, Mainwaring stared at the door. Then, with a sigh, he turned back to the mass of papers on his desk, desperately in need of a clerk.

Another knock sounded on the cabin door.

Damn and blast, now I need a sentry as well! thought Mainwaring. 'Come!' he roared.

The blond hair of Stephen Pellowe looked in.

'I'm sorry, sir. Perhaps another time – ?'

Mainwaring relented at the young man's expression. For all his youth, Pellowe had proved a willing and finally a capable officer in the schooner *Athena*, and there was mutual loyalty and regard. With his open blue eyes and ruddy cheeks, Pellowe was a favourite among the Athenas, and it had doubly pleased Mainwaring that by merit and ability alone the youth had earned Mainwaring's recommendation of the acting lieutenancy. More and more, Pellowe displayed the canny judgement and resourcefulness of a first-rate sea officer. Time would tell if Pellowe's drastic treatment of Rowe would prove equally judicious. Mainwaring has been prepared to support Pellowe in what he did, but had not expected to see his surgeon dangling in a chair at the end of a yard-arm.

'No, Stephen. Come in.'

'You've talked with Rowe, sir? Does he seem – ?'

'Well, he's certainly sober, if that's what you mean. Your rinsing produced that. Must've been a bloody shock.'

'You *did* say sober him, sir.'

'Yes. But perhaps I meant not so literally or dramatically.' Mainwaring's set expression gave way involuntarily to a grin. 'Poor bastard. Looked like a drowned rat.'

'Seemed the best way, sir. Actually, can't take the credit myself, sir. Williams thought of it. Saw it done with gossiping women, on Anglesey. Think they do it in Massachusetts, too, sir.'

'Mmm. A desperate man in heartfelt pain is a different matter from a tongue-wagging fishwife.' He paused, thoughtful. 'Still, you did well. I hope more than I care to think that he'll be ready for Mr Howe and his catch.'

Pellowe nodded. 'I came below to tell you, sir, that I've had part of the orlop partitioned off as a lock-up. Two hands can guard it easily enough.'

'Good. I suppose it's bilge stench and rats in legions everywhere?'

'Not as bad as that, sir. But it's not a place to keep 'em long.'

'Very well,' said Mainwaring. 'I hope that'll not be necessary. I want the pressed men taken on the books and put into slops, if they need 'em, within a few hours of arriving on board. It's a damned depressing business, and I want it over as soon as possible.'

'I meant to tell you, sir. A lugger came alongside from

41

the Gun Wharf just before the turn of the glass. We've a hundred stand of arms being swung aboard, three hundred cutlasses, about two score pikes and tomahawks, and at least a score of pistols. And there's five thousand rounds o' ball cartridge for the muskets, about a thousand for the pistols, and twenty casks of priming powder. Mr Soper's seeing to getting it stowed safely, sir.' He grinned. 'Gives us a few teeth at least, sir.'

Mainwaring nodded. There would still be the matter of shot and powder for the great guns. But now at least *Diana* could begin to defend herself. He rose and paced to the stern lights, looking at the dark curtains of rain swirling across the greasy, gunmetal surface of the Solent.

'I hope we'll need no teeth to bring our reluctant new lads into the ship,' he said, eyes narrowing. 'It's the Dons they've got to be used on. Make *certain*, Stephen, that the magazine is set up properly. And tell Mr Soper that I'll want to see all his magazine and arms locker keys when he's done.'

'I will, sir,' said Pellowe, rising. He paused.

'Well?' said Mainwaring. 'Something else?'

'Er – all the lads who came over with us from *Athena* are saying they're glad they did, sir. They've been made quite a fuss of when they say they were at Porto Bello with you and Vernon. They say they'll follow you anywhere, sir. Thought you'd like to know.'

Mainwaring nodded, feeling touched, and oddly humble.

'I – thank you, Stephen,' he said, after a moment. 'I wonder if we can ever make pressed men feel that kind of – '

There was a flurry of knocking at the cabin door, and a tousled head that Mainwaring recognized as Winton thrust itself in.

42

'Beggin' yer pardon, zur. It ain't 'alf a sight, zur. Yew'd best come on deck an' see!'

A moment later Mainwaring emerged on deck, Pellowe at his heels. As he crammed his hat down over his eyes against the slanting drizzle, Mainwaring stared, following the gazes of the men pointing shoreward who lined *Diana*'s rail.

'Now, what in blazes – ' he began.

Isaiah Hooke arrived at his side, his great seacoat steaming, a broad grin on his face.

'That young Mr Howe's a right hellion, zur. Look at that!'

Mainwaring cuffed the rain out of his face and followed Hooke's point. Then he saw clearly, as the rain parted like a stage curtain, Howe's boat rowing strongly for *Diana*, no more than five hundred yards off. The slim figure of the first lieutenant was standing, waving his hat back and forth over his head, oblivious to the rain. Behind him was an astonishing flotilla of perhaps a dozen other boats: longboats, jolly boats, cutters, and even two ponderous launches; ship's boats, all of them. And they were crammed with men, so full it was a wonder that their oars and sweeps could be manned.

'Isaiah,' said Mainwaring, 'what in the name of all that's holy is *that*?'

'It's Mr Howe, zur!' said Hooke, unnecessarily. 'An' strike me if 'e ain't found some 'ands fer us!'

'What?' Mainwaring spat forcefully over the lee rail. 'Mr Howe put off ashore barely two turns of the glass ago. If this is some kind of silly bloody *skylark* – !'

Then Howe's longboat was thumping alongside, the oar blades flashing in the grey light as they were tossed, and Howe was appearing over the rail, shouldering through the men gathered there to doff his hat before Mainwaring, his face a grin from ear to ear.

'Hands, sir! For the ship!' he said.

Mainwaring stared at him as the little armada pulled in alongside in a tumult of flashing oars, cheers, and dangerously brandished boathooks.

'For God's sake, James, explain all this. I sent you off barely a clock's tick ago as a damned press gang! Now, what – ?'

'They knew we were coming, sir! Everywhere! And damned near *all* the ships of the squadron were running a hot press. The orders have come down for 'em to sail, and the word was out!'

'I'm afraid I still don't see – ' began Mainwaring.

'Sir, any man absolutely determined to dodge was already long gone into the countryside or else under his Poll's bed for the next few days. That left a fair clutch still swilling down their rum and awaiting the inevitable. But then the word got out that *Diana*'s gangers would be on the streets too. So they dodged the big men-o'-war's gangs – the sea regiment men had closed the bloody gates in any event: King William's Gate, King James' Gate, the lot – and figured that if a press would get 'em, they'd pick their ship. And they picked *us*, sir!'

'What?'

'Aye, sir! It's all over Portsmouth, what you did with Vernon! And that we're sailing as a cruiser to chase Don prizes in the Caribbees, and sail home awash with booty and swag! Grand stuff, sir!'

Mainwaring turned to stare at the men who were beginning to pour over the rail. Men with a rough, competent, sailorly appearance for the most part, looking *Diana* over readily and then bellowing for a seabag or chest to be handed up.

'There's almost a hundred of 'em, sir,' laughed Howe. 'And they've *volunteered*!'

'Well, I'll be damned,' exclaimed Mainwaring. '*Booty*

and swag?' He turned on Howe, an odd expression on his face.

'Then you'd best get our ship's company read in, Mr Howe. You'll find the doctor able, I think, to examine 'em. But quickly. We've a very great deal to do,' he said, his voice turning hoarse. 'A very great deal indeed!'

Howe beamed. 'Aye, aye, sir!'

2

Fourteen days later His Britannic Majesty's Ship *Diana* was eight hundred and fifty miles south-west of Ushant, bowling along a course to the south-west across a strong north-westerly wind that had turned the dark blue Atlantic alive with gleaming whitecaps under a cloudless sky. Snugged down on a reach, the ship lay over to leeward with an easy grace under her still, sculpted canvas and forged towards the distant Caribbean in an endless rhythm of lift and plunge into the great swells. Above the roar under her bows and counter rose the thrum of the rigging, a deep *basso* counter to the creak of the ship's timbers, a symphony touched now and then by the counterpoint of a fluttering leech in a headsail or topsail as the helmsman pinched up too tightly for a moment.

Edward Mainwaring emerged up the after companionway and crammed his tricorne down more firmly as the wind struck him, gasping a little as he felt its full force, and squinting at the brilliantly lit scene about him. His coat-tails rumpled and flapped against his breeches as he moved on to the quarterdeck and the weather rail, his legs spread wide for balance, his hands clasped behind his back in an increasingly familiar pose. As he gazed about him, he noted that Pellowe, who was officer of the watch, had moved in deference to the leeward side of the helm. There was much to be thankful about, thought Mainwaring, even beyond the good feeling of the coffee and fresh biscuit still warm in his stomach. The extent of what he felt was extraordinary good fortune continued to amaze him.

The men who had followed Howe aboard *Diana* on that gloomy, rain-soaked day in the Solent had indeed volunteered, much as Howe had explained. A hot press had been afoot in Portsmouth, with the anchored squadron under orders to sail. But word had run through the swills and grogshops that the great ships of the line were meant for blockade duty in the Channel and the Biscay; wet, cold hells in winter. And at the same time the word had spread that *Diana* was sailing independently to cruise against Spaniards in the Caribbean approaches and that spelt prize money to any seaman with sense. Mainwaring's daring reputation had played a major part as well, and for each of the paid-off hands thronging the seaport who wanted nothing more than to dodge the gangers, there had been two or three who had realized that escape was unlikely, impressment almost a certainty, and that the best choice was volunteering into *Diana*.

They had proved useful men in the main, thought Mainwaring. There were a few landsmen swept up in the enthusiasm, a rupture case or two who would have to be kept as simple duty men, or 'waisters', a few drunkards – the mix was remarkably good, given the needs of the Navy. Nesbitt Rowe, pale and trembling but sober, had inspected the new men, and Mainwaring noted with cautious satisfaction that the doctor appeared to have kept off drink for the time being. James Howe had been ecstatic at the volunteer haul; he had found prime hands among them, young and active topmen as well as seasoned hands to make up the fo'c'slemen; a carpenter's and a boatswain's mate, and even a quite literate librarian named Moll, volunteering for inexplicable reasons, and too weak and light, if game, for seamen's work, but who had become a diligent and competent clerk and secretary for Mainwaring. There had even been a runaway manservant, a sad-faced, gentle man named Jenkins, who had volunteered to be Mainwaring's servant, a luxury indeed: the American now stood in a pair of gleamingly brushed boots which had not looked so fine since he got them during the attack on Porto Bello. The list of capable men went on: a seasoned gunner, to act as Ezrah Soper's mate; two cheeky but amiable boys who had become the wardroom stewards; half a dozen other boys, half-wild but developing a healthy respect for Jewett's rattan, who would handle the niplines when raising the anchor and 'monkey' up powder to the guns in action.

Mainwaring grunted with satisfaction as a seaman coming aft to the weather mizzen shrouds knuckled his forelock to him before swinging up over the deadeyes and sheerpole for his climb. The man, in sturdy white duck trousers and a blue, brass-buttoned 'fearnought' jacket, looked smart and warmly clad, thanks to William Thorne's industry in obtaining the white duck canvas and blue wool Mainwaring had demanded – and the quick fingers of the amateur messdeck tailors. The men of *Diana* had a brisk uniform look to them under the tar and salt rime, a vast improvement over the urchin-like appearance of most ship's companies.

A flash of red forward, and a soldier appeared up the forward companionway, staggered to the lee rail with a bucket, and emptied its contents over the side. He was one of twenty sea regiment soldiers, or 'marines' as they were called, who had come to *Diana* in the last days before they had sailed. Clad in brick-red breeches and coats, with grenadier-style mitre caps and striped gaiters to above the knee, they were docile, and steady, their seasickness already the butt of humour from the seamen. The marines were shepherded by a muscular, beet-faced sergeant named Pound. Their officer was the slim and languid Aston Millechamp who kept very much to himself in his tiny cabin, but who Howe revealed was a delightful conversationalist at the gunroom table and already a friend of Stephen Pellowe, whose age he matched. There had been musket drill a day earlier, and the marines' ponderous, methodical priming and loadings, and thunderous volleys at a floating cask target were very smart and impressive; but since *Diana* had got into a seaway the marines had hidden below in the private misery of a soldier in a seaman's world.

Mainwaring braced against the rail as *Diana* lifted and then plunged with a roar and burst of spray into a great long-shouldered swell. All in all, the ship was as well-manned as Mainwaring had had any right to hope. Far better, in fact. Now, if only the men could be brought up to the gunnery standard Mainwaring knew was necessary; they sailed the ship for Hooke well enough, but much drill at the great guns was needed before –

'Morning, sir!' said James Howe, appearing up the ladder from the waist. He touched the front cock of his hat to Mainwaring, beaming at the clear, wind-riven beauty of the scene around them. 'Damme, it makes you wonder why all men aren't seamen, doesn't it, sir?'

Mainwaring smiled. He thought of the ashen-faced marine and his bucket.

'Perhaps not everyone sees it as we do, James. But it is beautiful, aye.'

'Sir. If you'll excuse me – ' He moved to Pellowe, from whom he was taking over the watch as *Diana*'s bell struck eight, the quick double chimes whipped away by the wind almost as the boy sounded them. Mainwaring eavesdropped on Howe and Pellowe without being too obvious about it.

'Good day, Mr Pellowe,' said Howe, formally. 'What is our situation?'

Stephen Pellowe had become somewhat more serious

with his assumption of duties as the ship's second lieutenant, and the relatively enormous distance that now existed
between him and Mainwaring meant that their relationship was a far more formal one. It was unavoidable, if
discipline and the exigencies of the Service were to be
upheld; but it was a distance that Mainwaring regretted,
and which made clear to him in yet another way how the
step out of *Athena* to *Diana* had meant leaving behind
more than the informality of the schooner's routine.

'Good day, sir,' Pellowe was saying, doffing his hat to
Howe. 'Ship's course is sou'west by south. Wind one point
abaft the beam, out o' the nor'west. Jib and foretopmast
stays'l, fore and main tops'ls and t'gallants, fore an' main
stays'ls, and mizzen tops'l. Trys'l on the lateen yard. Jewett
and one of his mates are aloft on the mizzen tops'l yard
reeving a new clewline. The gunner's attaching vent covers
to the starboard battery guns, and the carpenter came up
ten minutes ago and asked permission to lay out partitions
he's making in the waist. I said yes,' He glanced forward.
'The forenoon watchmen are falling in there in the longboat
lee, and Mr Hooke's with 'em, sir.'

Howe nodded. 'Very good. I relieve you, sir. And
you'll find Spink has kept some coffee warm for you.'

Pellowe grinned. 'Thank you, sir.' With a glance at
Mainwaring the youth went off down the ladder.

Forward in the waist, Mainwaring could see Isaiah
Hooke's burly figure as the sailing master talked with the
senior hand of Howe's watch. Overhead, reliefs for the
lookouts in the fore and maintop were already scrambling
up the ratlines, and at the wheel Pellowe's helmsman,
Evans, was being relieved by a blond, muscular hand
whose name, Mainwaring recalled, was Parker.

'Mind your helm, Parker,' said Howe. 'She's got a fair
amount of weather helm. Don't let her pinch up.'

'Aye, aye, sir,' said Parker. The man had a faint but visible knife scar that began at one ear and vanished down under the bright-coloured bandana around his neck.

Mainwaring nodded at Howe as a sign that he was willing to share his windward domain, and the first lieutenant climbed up the slope of the spray-slick deck to join him.

'She's good in a seaway, sir,' said Howe. 'I've never sailed a vessel this quick before. Braced up sharp, she'd tack well, I'd warrant.'

Mainwaring nodded. 'Aye. She's handy enough. Makes me think I'm in a damned schooner, the way she leaps about. You'd think she was French-built.'

'Aye, sir. Though I'm glad she's good English oak. The Froggy ships are too light-built for my taste.'

Mainwaring peered forward where he could see the gunner, Soper, and his mates hunched over one of the six-pounders in the waist.

'I'm concerned, James. About our gunnery. I've watched what you've worked the people up to in sailhandling, and I'm pleased. Your watch and quarter bill seems to have put the right mix of lubbers and prime men aloft and alow. But it's the damned guns that bother me.'

'In what way, sir?'

'James, the one advantage we have over the Dons, or the French for that matter, is not bravery, or even seamanship, by and large. It's our ability to fight our ships. Gun for gun, cutlass for cutlass, we beat 'em because we're simply better than they are at those fighting skills. But being good means being practised, and we've not exercised the great guns anywhere near sufficiently.'

Howe looked away. 'Been difficult to do, sir. Getting the people into the right mix for topmen, fo'c'sle, waisters and afterguard hasn't been – '

'Excuses, now, James?' said Mainwaring, quietly.

Howe flushed. 'No, sir. I – it's my fault, sir. I haven't provided for sufficient gunnery exercise. I – '

'Then please correct that deficiency immediately, James. At the turn of the glass, call the ship to quarters, and exercise the guns' crews. Larboard and starboard batteries both. Movements for a dozen rounds. Then in the afternoon watch call 'em to quarters at two bells and exercise 'em again. But this time with powder and shot. Each gun to fire at least five rounds. Put a cask overside as a target. And Lieutenant Millechamp he's to exercise his marines with cartridge as well.'

'Sir, the marines can hardly stand up – '

Mainwaring looked sharply at Howe. Was he seeing hints of why he so precipitously left his last ship?

'I don't care, James, if they muster on their hands and knees. We shall exercise as a fighting vessel. Is that quite clear?'

Howe's face became set, with no hint of emotion.

'Aye, aye, sir,' he said.

'Very well,' Mainwaring spread his feet as *Diana* thundered over the shoulder of a huge swell. 'James, I cannot stress enough that we must know our capacities before we – '

'Deck! Deck, there!' the foretop lookout's voice rang out, high and thin over the sea noise.

Mainwaring cupped his hands. 'Deck, aye!'

'Sail, sir! To windward, dead abeam! Tops'ls of a ship, sir!'

Mainwaring looked at Howe. 'How is your recognition of rig and hull lines, James?'

'Excellent, sir. I'll take the glass.' Striding to the binnacle box and pulling the long, brass-bodied telescope from its leather sheath, the first lieutenant was off forward, and in a minute was climbing steadily up the foremast ratlines, his coat-skirts billowing round him.

Mainwaring watched him climb, his eyes narrowing. What had he glimpsed in Howe, that had been so quickly hidden? Was it a hard-pressed and overworked man simply angry at himself for not dealing with all his responsibilities? Or was it something else: a reluctance to be ready to fight, to face that necessity? The hint of something Howe could not afford to have. Cowardice? It was not pleasant to contemplate.

Mainwaring paced back to the helm, careful of his footing on the wet, sloping planking.

'Steady as she goes, Parker. Try not to counter that corkscrewing too heavily.'

'Aye, zur. She's light as a feather under th' wheel, zur.'

Mainwaring nodded. 'Then just see you stay as light.'

He looked at the horizon off to the north-west. From deck level, there was nothing he could see. But Howe had reached the foretop, and was hunkering down in the top against the roll of the ship, the telescope trained out towards the invisible stranger. Mainwaring was certain he saw Howe lower the glass and move his lips in a curse.

Mainwaring cupped his hands. 'What is she, Mr Howe?'

It took a moment before Howe replied, cupping his own hands against the sea noise as his precarious perch heeled far off to leeward.

'Spanish warship, sir, a *frégata*!'

Mainwaring swore. A Spanish warship, with *Diana* unprepared, was not the most welcome encounter.

'Very well. Come down, please, Mr Howe!'

A few moments later, Howe, his face flushed from the climb, was back on the quarterdeck, thrusting the great telescope into its sheath.

'Well?' said Mainwaring.

'It's a Don, all right, sir. Allen, there, in the foretop recognized her type as well. A *frégata*. Could be anywhere from twelve to thirty guns or so. Damned formidable ship, sir.'

'Christ, not what we need at this point. What's her course?'

'Sou'east, sir. Likely inbound to Ferrol. She's flying ensigns at her fore and main truck, and as I watched she was shaking out her main t'gallant. I think she's seen us.'

'Sou'east. Then her track will intercept ours. And the bastard's likely faster than us in the bargain.'

'We could turn off the wind and stay ahead of her till nightfall, sir. Likely lose her then.'

Mainwaring looked at Howe and then forward. Everywhere about the ship the men were eyeing the two figures on the quarterdeck, aware already what the strange sail meant. Knowing what was being said.

In that moment Mainwaring made his decision.

'I'd be pleased if you would call the ship to quarters, Mr Howe. Gun action presently, I should think.'

Howe paled, but his expression gave away nothing. 'Aye, aye, sir!' he said, and touched his hat. In the next minute he was bellowing for Jewett to come down.

Mainwaring turned to the rail, squinting over the rolling, ink-and-white prairie of sea for the Spaniard. And now he could see her. A tiny speck of white on the horizon: the gleam of a fore t'gallant in the brilliant sun.

Coming down on us quickly, Mainwaring thought. *Likely overhaul us before sundown even if we had run.* The usual damnably quick Spanish hull design. And under Mainwaring's feet was an untried vessel. And one whose former captain had left a cryptic note warning against trusting the ship. Or had that referred to a woman? There were too many damned unanswered questions.

A flicker of colour in the corner of Mainwaring's eye made him turn to see the youthful sea regiment drummer, his face white as chalk, looking at him with sticks at the ready, the deep unsnared drum huge at his side. The boy could scarcely have been twelve years of age.

'Good steady rhythm now, lad. Beat to quarters, if you please.'

'S – sir,' said the drummer, and raised his sticks. The hollow boom of the tenor drum echoed through the ship, and with it now the squealing of Jewett and his mates on their silvered pipes, barking out the message of the drumming.

'D'ye hear, there? Hands to quarters, hands to quarters! Lively, there, lively!'

If there was concern in Mainwaring's mind about the training of *Diana*'s gun crews – and of Howe's inner uncertainty – without doubt the first lieutenant's dispositions and quarter bill had ensured effective enough reaction to the order to ready the ship for action. The notes of Jewett's pipe and the last thump of the drummer's sticks had barely ceased when the watch below began pouring up the companionways and the ship became a scene of swift, but silent and orderly, work.

The purpose of the watch and quarter bill – endless copies of which poor Moll had penned through many a candlelit night – was to state where each man's post was in any predictable circumstance. Parker, for example, might be listed as the trail tackle man on number three gun, starboard battery, in gun action; armed with a pike and stationed on the fo'c'sle for boarding; stroke oar in the commanding officer's boat's crew, and so on. The lists were nailed up over the mess tables below in *Diana*, so that each man if he could read – or had a messmate who could read – knew what his task was in almost any situation. Now *Diana*'s men were moving to their duties with the silent orderliness characteristic of a British warship.

The most immediate activity was the arrival on deck of

the offwatchmen with the lashed hammocks; these were forced into a U-shape, bend uppermost, and thrust into the twin row of upright irons and netting that circled the upper deck, so forming a kind of musketry shield. Dodging past these men were the ship's boys, wild-eyed with excitement as they scampered the length of the ship with their wooden buckets, scattering sand over the slick, wet planking to afford a better footing in action. A half-dozen men were already half-way up the ratlines, wrestling with a hugh net that would hang suspended above the deck, to provide protection from falling gear. Other men would be bending on chain lifts to the yards, dangerous and difficult work as *Diana* rolled and wallowed in the beam sea.

Mainwaring cupped his hands at Isaiah Hooke, who was standing, hands on hips, at the mainmast bitts, watching the rigging of the net and the chain lifts.

'Mr Hooke! We'll pay off before the wind, and clew up for action! Stand by to wear away!' There was a scramble of men to the braces as Mainwaring turned to Parker, still on the helm, with another man to help him on the wheel's leeward side.

'Coxswain, are you, Parker? I should have known. Very good. Then put your helm up. Let her run down.'

'Helm up, aye, zur!' said Parker, spinning the great wheel.

'Wear ship!' bellowed Mainwaring. 'Have a care, there!'

In ponderous grace, *Diana* swung off the wind, to take the long, rolling swells and wind from astern. Other than her slow hobby-horsing now, she was upright and steady, and the work aloft picked up in pace. Blocks squealed as the yards were braced in swiftly, and then halyards were snaking across the deck in coils as the staysails and t'gallants were taken in.

The gun crews had arrived at each gun, their captains

56

distinguishable by the large priming horns slung over their shoulders. Match tubs thumped down amidships behind the guns, and slow match was soon smouldering in the tub notches over the water within. The deck racks for the gun tools followed, and the tools were laid out: rammer, ladle, worm, sponge, handspikes, portfire, bucket. The seizings on the gun tackles, a precaution for sailing in a seaway, were cut away, and the side and trail tackles and the heavy breeching line set up.

A clump of boots sounded on the companionways, as Millechamp's marines came up in two squads, muskets at the trail. With Pound roaring away at them they fell into two elbow-touching ranks on the quarterdeck behind the helm, looking bulky and awkward in their full-skirted uniforms and buff crossbelting. Above their tight throat-stocks their faces were pale, but they stood swaying to the ship's motion with an evident dignity, and as Pound ordered them through the musket-loading drill they moved with a snap and precision that Mainwaring could not help but admire. He remembered his own retching seasickness, and thought what purgatory it must be for the marines, to lie below in agony without access to the sailor's usual cure, activity and work in the open air.

'Prime and load!' bellowed Pound, his face a sunburnt pink. '*Slap* that cartouche box, Spink! Don't just fondle it!'

Behind the guns, Howe and Pellowe were pacing in the waist, Howe to larboard, Pellowe to starboard, watching that each gun captain readied his piece properly, looking for the kinked fall here, the adrift gun tool there. Howe's great walking stick had materialized in his hands, but Pellowe carried nothing, merely locking his hands behind his back as he paced.

Howe was calling. 'Load with cartridge, sir?'

57

'Aye!' Mainwaring shouted. 'Load and shot your guns. Double-shotted, there!'

'Aye, aye, sir!' came Howe's reply, and then he and Pellowe passed the order. The cries came up on the gun captains' lips, and the men threw their weight with a will on the trail tackle falls, hauling the guns inboard for loading. The squealing trucks rumbled over the gritty decking, and at the sound Mainwaring shivered involuntarily. The tampions were being pulled out now, and the vent covers, while up the companionways the men and boys 'monkeying' up the powder from Soper's felt-curtained magazine were arriving with their leathern buckets. It was all going fairly smoothly; the men, for all their relative newness, showing well the fruits of previous training in other ships – and the efficiency of the men Soper had picked from his gun crews to be gun captains. *Diana* would be ready to engage fifteen minutes after Mainwaring first gave the order. It was twice as long as Mainwaring ultimately wanted, but it was a creditable showing none the less.

But could they fight? he wondered.

Mainwaring turned and looked aft over the transom rail, the enormous red ensign rippling like a scarlet wave over his head. He could see the Spaniard's t'gallants now, clearly indicating he was steering to close on *Diana*.

He tried to calm the sudden fluttering in his stomach by concentrating on the activity of the six-pounder gun crew nearest him. A man was carefully putting the heavy, baglike powder cartridge into the bore, ensuring its seam was down, and then a thick ropestuff wad. Another seaman armed with the rammer pushed this with long, smooth strokes until with an audible thump the bag was home at the breech end. 'Home!' cried the man, and held the rammer in place while the gun captain thrust in his priming wire and slapped the vent. At the blow, the rammer was withdrawn, slowly at first, and then with a quick rush.

The gun captain, a dark-haired man in broad petticoat breeches and little bells hung before his ears on the braided hair of his temples, spat over the rail and barked, 'Shot yer gun! Double shot, mark ye!'

Two black, heavy iron round shot were thrust into the bore, with attendant wads, and on the cry, 'Ram home shot and wad!' the shot were seated home in the gun, the man with the ramrod finishing with two ringing thumps that ensured all were aware of the job done.

'Right, now. Stand to yer side tackles. *Run out!*'

On the gun captain's order, with three men on each side hauling rhythmically on the heavy purchases that linked the cheeks of the gun carriage to ringbolts on either side of the gunport, the ugly little gun squealed forward, its trucks rumbling as its red-painted muzzle snouted out through the open gunport. From forward, rumbling marked the running out of the other guns in the two batteries.

Mainwaring cupped his hands. 'Mr Howe! Mr Pellowe! D'ye hear, there! Prime and cover!'

'Prime and cover, aye, sir!' chorused both officers, in the next breath repeating the order to the gun captains.

Mainwaring watched the near gun's captain carefully. The man pulled the priming wire from the vent and thrust it into his belt. Then he unslung the great powder horn and filled the vent with the fine black powder, also filling the depression round the vent known as the 'pan'. With great care, he stoppered the horn and fixed the vent cover, snugging it down.

Mainwaring looked forward, to see the other captains attaching their vent covers. *Diana* was ready to discharge her murderous broadsides, but the guns' temperamental charges were protected from spray and wind, a problem not faced by gunners working in the shelter of a gun deck. Now *Diana* could manoeuvre, able to tack or wear, until at the right moment the vent covers could be removed.

'Ye know the drill, lads,' Mainwaring could hear the gun captain whispering, 'but when 'is 'onour give us th' word t'fire, why, ye'll think thunder, an' lightnin', an' th' crack o' doom itself 'as struck. But yew'll carry out the drill, smart as paint, wivout a word from old Dick, yew will, an' fire like devils till 'is 'onour tells yew t'stop. An' yew'll do that even if poor Dick here 'as 'is glims doused, won't ee, lads, there's true shipmates. Clear?'

The gun crew nodded. At least two of them were obviously new men, still pale with seasickness, and they looked wide-eyed at the gun captain and each other. Mainwaring pretended not to have heard.

He turned on his heel and scanned astern for the Spaniard. The latter's topgallants were clearly visible now, and part of the topsails; the enemy vessel was no more than three leagues away at most.

'Mr Hooke! Stand by your braces and sheets! We'll harden up to windward on the starboard tack!'

'Starboard tack! Aye, aye, sir!' came Hooke's voice, and the master was bellowing at his sailhandlers as they threw coils off pins, clustering at the fiferails and pinrails.

Mainwaring looked astern, waiting for an approaching 'smooth' in the long rollers bearing down on *Diana* in dark, white-capped beauty. Then it was time.

'Helm to larboard, there, Parker! Bring her up to due west! Braces and sheets, there! Lively, lads, lively!' ordered Mainwaring.

In a long, majestic turn *Diana* swung into the wind, its roar in the rigging suddenly loud and strong as the run ended. The ship rolled heavily as the swells came abeam, and then she was turning on, the blocks squealing as the hands leaned into bracing up the yards and hauling taut the tacklines. Behind Mainwaring, Parker was sure-handed at the wheel, 'meeting' the vessel skilfully so that she settled her jib-boom on the westerly course, and began to punch in spray-rinsed energy on the first board of her tack. Aloft, the canvas was cemented into hard, curving glory, and the scarlet masthead pennant was rippling out like a lance to leeward. The great ensign at the stern snapped and rippled like an unsheeted staysail, and *Diana* leaped and plunged ahead over the swells that now seemed eager to rush down on her. Within minutes, the cloud of spray bursting regularly over the bows and drifting aft over the gleaming, sun-washed deck had soaked each man to the skin, and the gun crews huddled down behind the bulwarks to keep out of the way of the spray and Hooke's sailhandlers, who were scrambling about the slick, pitching decks, making last adjustments at braces or sheets, or shaking free fouled buntlines.

Now Hooke had them hauling taut the lee bowlines of the topsails, which would give the little ship even more windward efficiency. Throwing out a track of hissing, leaping spume three times her length, *Diana* drove to windward and to her adversary.

Mainwaring glanced at Howe and Pellowe, still pacing in spreadlegged readiness behind their batteries, and then up at the Spaniard, who was well up over the horizon now, no more than a league and a half away, and coming on rapidly.

Hooke was at the foot of the waistdeck ladder, cupping his hands to call aft over the sea and wind roar.

'Bearin' down on us quick-like, zur! She means t'fight, right enough. D'ye want a stays'l set, t'give ye a knot or two more?'

Mainwaring shook his head, and spat salt rime from his lips. 'No! We'll stay with fighting canvas, Mr Hooke! No more! She'll be on us too soon to have you wrestling with dousing a stays'l in action. Just stand ready to come about smartly!'

'Aye, aye, zur!'

Mainwaring lurched over to the binnacle box and peered at the sweating Parker. 'Can you handle her, Parker? Need another man?'

'No, zur, thankee. Two of us can 'old 'er, zur, fine as kine.'

'Good. See you don't lose her. No nearer to windward. And stand ready to put the helm down quickly. Ship's head?'

Parker glanced down. 'West, a half south, zur.'

'Steady on due west.'

'Steer due west, zur.' The wheel moved. 'Steady on due west, zur.'

'Very good.'

Mainwaring pulled the great telescope from its sheath and staggered back to the windward rail. He braced himself against the aftermost lanyard of the weather mizzen shrouds and pulled open the glass. Water droplets dappled the field, and with *Diana*'s pitching it was difficult to hold the Spaniard's image. But it was enough to see.

'Christ,' muttered Mainwaring, 'thirty guns, or I'm a newt!' He shut the glass, biting his lower lip in thought. The Spaniard was very obviously a warship of His Most Catholic Majesty's navy, and was flying Spanish ensigns at the fore and main trucks. No canvas had been clewed up yet, and the *frégata* was lifting and plunging in stunning grace as she overhauled the broad rollers, the foam gleaming white in rhythm under the cutwater. Towering over a characteristically gaudy red and gilt hull, so favoured by the Dons, was a ship-rig of gleaming white canvas, all set and sheeted home with admirable skill. When the Spanish were good at sea, they were very good indeed – as Mainwaring had cause to remember – and there was a disturbingly efficient look about this ship as she rushed down on them.

Mainwaring cuffed a spatter of stinging spray from his eyes. The Spaniard was also clearly looking for a fight; she had likely seen *Diana* first, and with the assurance of a larger broadside and an almost certainly better hull speed, had decided to make an engagement of it. *That* was not typical of Spanish thinking; like the French, they had become obsessed with the idea of a 'fleet in being' as the goal to protect, and so in essence gave away the offensive – and the command of the sea – to the English. But this tautly-trimmed *frégata* was bearing down on *Diana* with uncharacteristic determination, and Mainwaring would have to meet that determination head on. And hard. He squinted again at the looming Spaniard, his mind working.

There *was* a way . . .

'Mr Howe! Mr Pellowe!' he was calling, 'I cannot tell you which battery will fire first! But your *after* guns will bear first! Do you follow?'

Howe and Pellowe exchanged surprised glances, and then acknowledged the order.

'Good!' Mainwaring scanned for the burly sailing master. 'Mr Hooke!'

'Zur?'

'We're turning off the wind to run before it, once more! Stand by your braces and sheets! And I'll trouble you to see the fore and main courses when we're afore the wind!'

Hooke stared. '*Courses*, zur? But – !'

'You heard me, Mr Hooke! Stand ready there, now!' He moved to the helm.

'Helm up, Parker! Put her dead before the wind! *Wear ship!*'

Again *Diana* turned away from the wind, and again as she put her stern lights to the wind and swells, the thunder of the sea under her bows and the wind howl died away, the sound of the sea now a hiss under her speeding counter, the blocks overhead rattling as the yards came in and the sheets were paid out.

Mainwaring saw several faces staring at him in confusion. Hooke was bounding up the ladder from the waist, eyes troubled.

'Beggin' pardon, zur. But are ye – are ye *runnin' away* from 'er, zur? If ye wants the courses – '

'Isaiah, get them set and sheeted home. I want her to think we're running away. I want her to reach out to get us, to rush in quickly. *Too* quickly. Follow?'

A light flickered in the shaggy master's eyes. 'Aye, zur!' he said, after a moment. 'Sorry, zur. I thought – ' With a bound the ursine form was in the waist, his growls sending men in to quick work. The fore and main course clewlines and the buntlines were slacked away and the great quadrilaterals dropped with sonorous, rippling thumps, bellying out immediately as the wind caught them. Then the sheets came in, with rhythmic hauling, and under Mainwaring's feet *Diana* noticeably lifted and increased her speed.

Hooke was looking up at the sails, and then at Mainwaring. 'Gives 'er a touch more, zur!' he boomed.

'Aye! She's to think we meant to fight and then lost our nerve, trying to run away.'

The master was up the ladder and at his side again. 'But when 'e overtakes us, zur? What d'ye – ?'

'I want the course clewlines and buntlines with hands on 'em, ready to haul in the moment I call for it, like the very devil. Clear, Isaiah? At the *instant* I call for it!'

'Zur!' said Hooke, and went back to his post.

'Mr Howe, Mr Pellowe!' called Mainwaring. 'I'll ask that you keep your gun crews low behind the bulwarks as this Don comes in on us. No need to lose good men to musketry needlessly!'

He spun and looked at the Spanish ship. With the added canvas, *Diana* was making the creditable appearance of a vessel attempting to run away. But the Spaniard was swifter, and was closer still, her canvas a beautiful, towering cloud of brilliant white above the curtseying hull and the boiling foam at her bows. The *frégata* was no more than a thousand yards off, and closing rapidly. It would not be long . . .

Mainwaring pursed his lips. Was the Don going to close alongside? Or at the last moment would she swing across the *Diana*'s stern, to put a raking fire from stem to stern through the English vessel's stern lights? If the latter, Mainwaring's plan might already have spelled disaster. He had to hope the Spaniard was confident, even cocky, and would range in alongside, broadside to broadside, for a more glorious defeat of a warship of the perfidious English. But if the Don was a cool, methodical fighter, she would go almost certainly for the turn across the stern and the raking fire, and Mainwaring would have offered up his ship and untried crew for nothing save butchery. Five hundred yards. Still no flicker of movement at the Don's rail, suggesting quick sailhandling. Instead, he could see the gleam of sunlight on metal. All along the larboard side. Musket barrels, cutlasses, pikeheads.

The *larboard* side!

Mainwaring sprang to the rail. 'Mr Pellowe! Your guns will fire first! Give orders to your captains to quoin 'em high, and not to fire until they see the first gunport of the Spaniard over their piece! Then fire until I order you to cease. Now get your vent covers off. Clear?'

'Aye, aye, sir!' cried Pellowe, and ran along the line of guns, speaking to his captains. The crews tore at the vent covers.

65

'Mr Howe!' called Mainwaring.

'Sir?'

'Your crews will stay at their guns. If men fall in Mr Pellowe's battery, replace 'em with your lads!'

'Aye, aye, sir!'

Mainwaring had been right. The Spaniard was thundering down on them, committed to pass, broadside to broadside, along *Diana*'s starboard side. They had a chance, he thought. *Now if only these poor half-trained lads can fire quickly enough . . .*

Two hundred yards. The *frégata* was a beautiful ship, rushing through and over the seas at a speed *Diana* could never have matched. Mainwaring stared in fascination at the towering pyramids of canvas, the gleaming red hull, the elaborate figurehead of a bearded religious figure in white and gilt robes, the massed men with their readied muskets, suddenly very visible lining the larboard rail, and the open mouths of the Spaniard's larboard battery guns, grinning red circles in the shadows of the raised gunport lids.

'Musketry, sir!' barked Pellowe, and at the same moment a volley of pink flashes winked from the mass of men on the *frégata*'s foredeck. Several balls hummed in the air near Mainwaring, and struck home sharply about *Diana*'s deck.

'Steady, steady as you go, Parker,' said Mainwaring evenly, trying to control the fluttering in his stomach. 'Not a hair off. And listen for my orders!'

'Aye, zur,' said Parker, eyes riveted on the binnacle box. He and his mate were sweating heavily.

The thin rattle of the musketry sounded again, the ripple of flashes oddly pretty along the Spaniard's rail, and again the balls pinged about *Diana*. One of Pellowe's gun captains cursed and clapped a hand over a welling

66

track gouged in his forearm, and Howe's hat went spinning from his head over the rail into the sea.

'Bloody cheek!' came Howe's cry. 'My best hat, at that!'

Mainwaring glanced quickly at the first lieutenant, as his own heart seemed to pound in his throat. If cowardice was Howe's hidden problem, he was certainly showing very little sign so far.

He spun back. The Spaniard was huge, towering over them, rushing in at dramatic speed, the faces of the men manning her decks clearly visible. They were holding their fire now, waiting for the full broadside perhaps, relishing the certain victory over the hated, pink-faced men of the north. A few moments more . . .

And then the *frégata*'s jib-boom end, lifting and plunging along, was even with *Diana*'s transom rail, and Mainwaring filled his lungs.

'Now, Mr Hooke!' he cried. '*Clew up!*'

With frantic hauling, Hooke and his men collapsed the great courses upward in bulging gathers against their yards, blocks squealing. *Diana* slowed dramatically, dropping her bows, wallowing down.

And the *frégata* forged ahead, the men on her decks staring at *Diana* as they rushed past, frenzied orders ringing out on the Spanish quarterdeck from a group of scarlet, befeathered figures. Mainwaring felt naked and alone as for a split-second he was staring across into the muzzles of muskets being levelled at him not fifty yards away by a packed clutch of men along the *frégata*'s rail. In the next instant he would be smashed back by a hail of musket balls –

'*Fire!*' shrieked Pellowe. And the first six-pounder, aimed high, banged out with an ear-splitting report, the 'huff' jetting head-high from the vent as the portfire arced down, and the gun leaped back against its breeching line.

A tongue of pink flame lanced out towards the Spaniard, billowing, acrid smoke in huge clouds suddenly filling the air between the two ships. And then the next gun fired, and then the next, the concussion deafening and stunning. So rapid was the *frégata*'s run down the deliberately slowed *Diana* that each of Pellowe's guns bore within a clock's tick of one another. The guns thundered out in a ripple of explosions, more akin to a ragged broadside than a gun-by-gun firing, and the towering column of smoke between the ships swirled up and around them both, obscuring the view of the *frégata*'s hull.

Below in the waist, Pellowe was railing at his gunners, the new men wide-eyed and stunned at the noise and power of the guns, their training and the example of the experienced men taking them like puppets through the loading drills. They were working furiously, and still it seemed too slow, as if the two ships in their cloaks of smoke were drifting in suddenly peaceful company together across the sea, the thunder still for moment. God, would they never fire the second round?

And then the aftermost six-pounder, scarcely ten feet from Mainwaring, fired again, a thunderclap that deafened him, the pink flash blinding, followed by the next gun, and the next, echoing the intermittent thunder of the first broadside. Again and again the twenty-foot tongues of flame licked out from *Diana*'s side, the smoke swelling and choking, the deck leaping under Mainwaring's feet as if from a mallet blow each time a gun exploded. The gunners were wild now, working like demons, the battle frenzy of the British seaman in their blood.

At last an answering blast resounded from the hulk drifting past in the dim half-light of the smoke. *The bastard's finally fired*, said a voice in Mainwaring's brain, and a few pink flashes flickered along the *frégata*'s side,

68

the reports like·thunder cracks in an open field. Mainwaring gripped the rail, waiting for the splinter that would kill him, the air full of dark, tumbling bits moving with dreadful slowness past and around him. He felt fragments tug at his sleeve, ping against the deck where he stood, and something whirled past inches from his head with a whooshing noise.

And then, in the next instant, the gunnery stopped as if on order, and the smoke was whipped away from the two ships by the wind. *Diana* still held her course, Parker and his mate gripping the wheel with fierce determination. The sun washed over the deck, and Mainwaring saw the crews hunched at their guns, the sailhandlers at the rails, all frozen for an instant in statuary poses of action and effort. And here, one man lay sprawled in a pool of brilliant scarlet blood, and there, a man had fallen to his knees, hands pressed against his eyes, his mouth open in a soundless shriek as the hands of another man reached out to help him.

'Cease fire!' cried Mainwaring, staring at the Spaniard.

The *frégata* was slewing round abeam to the wind, turning away from *Diana*. Her canvas was rumpling and booming, and everywhere Mainwaring could see lines adrift and streaming out in the wind. The deck was a shambles of heaped dead and struggling wounded over which only a handful of survivors seemed to be moving. The quarterdeck was empty, the wheel smashed, red-clad shapes thrown like bloodied dolls against the rail. The smoke of the *frégata*'s own guns was pouring up her companionways like chimney smoke, and from within the wretched ship Mainwaring heard shrieks, voices raised in terror and anger, an incoherent jabber of shouts and cries.

Hooke was pointing in the waist. 'She's in irons, zur! Lost 'er 'elm, an' driftin'!'

'Stand by to come into the wind, Mr Hooke! Starboard tack!' He spun on the wild-eyed Parker.

'Down helm, Parker! Bring her up to a starboard tack, north by east!'

Parker spun the wheel, and as Hooke and his sailhandlers scrambled for the braces and sheets, *Diana* swooped round into the wind. Within minutes, the feverish hauling at the lines had *Diana* plunging smartly up to windward, arrowing for the stricken *frégata*'s stern.

Mainwaring cupped his hands. 'Mr Howe! Stand to the cutlass tubs! Never mind the small arms! Mr Pellowe! You'll lead your gun crews in boarding from the fo'c'sle!'

'*Board*, sir?' gasped Pellowe. 'I – aye, aye, sir!'

'Mr Hooke!'

'Zur?'

'Grapnels, if you can! Starboard side, and quickly! I mean to board her!'

'*Board*, zur?' gaped the master. 'Christ's guts, zur, ye can't – !'

'*Do it!*'

Diana leaped over a towering swell and smashed down into a cloud of spray. She was closing in on the *frégata*'s quarter rapidly. On the Spanish ship's quarterdeck Mainwaring could see a group of men working over the lines of the smashed helm, likely trying to jury rig a helm. Mainwaring slapped the rail in frustration. It would only work if they could get aboard her before the Spanish recovered from that first horrid shock of *Diana*'s gunnery . . .

Then, suddenly, they were there, the *frégata* hard aboard, the English vessel plunging up alongside, the sea between both ships a hissing cauldron as they lifted and plunged, streaming, like coach horses at full gallop side by side.

'Now, Isaiah!' roared Mainwaring.

Hooke had managed the grapnels, and they flashed in the air. There were howls and shouts from the deck of the *frégata*, and now pistol shots. With a grinding, splintering impact, *Diana* locked in alongside the Spaniard.

'Away, lads! Boarders away!' cried Mainwaring, and leaped for the rail. He reached it, teetered on it for an instant as he stared at the surging, foaming abyss between the two hulls, and then he launched himself across.

Dear Christ, I've no weapon! cried his mind in mid-air. *And the lads! Did the cutlasses reach 'em –*

He banged down hard against the wet, splintery side of the *frégata*, conscious that a gunport was directly beside him, the gun muzzle an obscene, red-lipped mouth swathed in smoke, gaping at him. He clutched for the mizzen channel and missed, and with a choked cry of dismay he toppled sideways, sure he was plummeting into the boiling sea below. Then, with a jar that made him gasp, he banged his ribcage against the muzzle of the run-out gun. He scrabbled at the black, tarry surface of the gun, the pain in his ribs bringing him back to awareness of the tumultuous noise around him. Above the roar and hiss of the sea rose a chorus of screams and curses, musket and pistol blasts, the clash of steel on steel, and the awesome, ear-splitting grinding of the two hulls together, forward where they met and were held by the grapnels. His legs swinging in mid-air, Mainwaring clutched desperately at the slick metal of the gun until with a cry he managed to swing up one leg and hook it over. Sobbing with effort now, he pulled himself on to the gun and wormed along to the darkness of the gunport, still wreathed in the acrid smoke that swirled from it. Sure that half-a-dozen Spaniards were waiting within to fall on him like dogs, he toppled headfirst through the open port. In the darkness he banged down hard on both knees and a shoulder, the smoke stinging his eyes, the chaos and clink of the fighting still loud about him. He rolled to his feet, stumbling over the tangled coils of the gun's tackles, coughing uncontrollably, sure he was inches away from men who would gut him in the next instant, and he cursed himself for coming unarmed, his hands empty.

But the snarl of anger, the killing blow, did not follow. He looked up, eyes adjusting to the gloom, the smoke lessening slightly. In the flickering light of the candlelit 'glims' over each gun he could see no movement on the gundeck. Bodies, wreckage, heaped cordage were everywhere. But no living movement

They're on deck, said his mind. *Where I should be!*

He looked quickly round, and out of the corner of his eye saw two simple, sturdy-looking cutlasses set in a rack above the gunport. He wrenched one free, hefted it, and lunged towards the companionway just ahead.

Overhead the sound was deafening; a steady roar of harsh curses, shrieks, musket blasts, of bodies thumping heavily to the deck. His heart pounding like a drum in his throat, Mainwaring was at the companionway and then up it, two steps at a bound.

He plunged out into the smoke-swirled, brilliant daylight, to have a split-second's glimpse of men's shapes everywhere locked in fearful, frantic struggle before a figure bodied into him, thrusting him hard on to the gritty decking, the cutlass hilt banging down with a ring. The planking under his nose was streaked with a dark spray of fresh blood. Instinctively, Mainwaring threw himself into a roll to one side as the bayonet of a musket speared down with a thump where his spine had been.

Above him, a Spanish seaman in striped trousers and wide-ripped red shirt, his hair dark and tangled about a thin face twisted in fury, was struggling to tug the bayonet from the planking. Mainwaring's foot lashed out, and the musket spun out of the man's hands. With amazing speed a dirk appeared in the Spaniard's hand, and he dived headlong at Mainwaring. Rolling again, Mainwaring felt the man thump down with a curse where he had been. The American spun to his knees and swung a vicious backhand with the cutlass as the Spaniard rose. With a sickening thud the blow caught the man's thin throat, and as a cloud of scarlet burst over Mainwaring's blade the man rolled away, screaming in a horrid, liquid way.

Nausea rising in him like a wave, Mainwaring fought to his feet, wishing the terrible tumult about him would end. And then he found himself staring at another figure; aristocratic and slim, in blood-spattered velvet, dark hair tightly queued, dark eyes burning in hatred and fury at Mainwaring above thin white lips. As Mainwaring paused for a split-second, the Spanish officer lunged, and his slim blade sliced through the heavy material of Mainwaring's sleeve. The American twisted his arm away, and the cloth ripped the sword from the Spaniard's hand. The man stared, aghast, the hatred in his features suddenly turned to dismay, and then Mainwaring's fisted free hand came back in a powerful roundhouse punch to the man's temple. With a grunt he staggered sideways, and then toppled headfirst down the open companionway.

His nausea had subsided, and instead Mainwaring seemed to be flooded by some wild, exultant joy. Roaring at the top of his lungs, he threw himself at a bunch of Spaniards who were thrusting half-pikes at him, hacking with furious strength at the shafts with the cutlass, feeling the weapon leap in his hand, hearing the clang and thump as it struck steel and wood. And then the blade struck home against flesh, and a Spaniard was falling away with shrieks, clutching at the cloven ruin of his face. The pikemen vanished, and Mainwaring was suddenly before a huge, swarthy man in dirty petticoat breeches and a ragged white jacket smeared with blood. He was throwing

73

aside the body of a dead Diana, the blade and guard of his heavy cutlass scarlet and dripping.

'Try me, then, you bastard!' snarled Mainwaring, and swung a backhand cut at the man's thick neck. But the Spaniard parried it expertly, a gap-toothed smile opening in the porcine, small-eyed face, and then cut at Mainwaring's head with a whistling blow. The parry rang like a chime, and Mainwaring's arm stung with the force of the blow. But the fighting mania still had hold of him, and with two hands he flailed away in furious energy at the hulking Spaniard, forcing him back through the struggling men on either side to the mainmast foot, seeing the piggish face change in expression from triumph to thick-witted dismay, banging and hacking at him with blow after ringing blow until the fat man, with an odd high cry, lunged at Mainwaring, the cutlass point arrowing between the American's anvil blows for his chest. But Mainwaring was ready for it. He crouched like a cat, feeling the blade slide over his shoulder, and then put all the weight of his body into a counter thrust into the Spaniard's belly. The blade thumped home to the hilt, and the fat face goggled, the man dropping his cutlass, hands clutching at Mainwaring's. Suddenly gagging, the nausea quenching the fighting lust, Mainwaring pulled the bloody blade free with a jerk. The Spaniard sank into a sitting posture, his hands fell away, and he was dead, the fat face still gaping in goggle-eyed horror. The sickness too much to contain, Mainwaring stumbled back a pace or two, and vomited over the rail.

He was still there a moment later, trembling and shaking, staring down at the hissing foam between the two ships, when he realized that the fighting sounds had stopped. And now a hand was on his shoulder, and he was turning to see Isaiah Hooke, his face blackened, seacoat spattered with blood, looking at him in gruff concern.

'Cap'n. Are ye – ?'

'I'm fine, Mr Hooke. Just lost my bloody breakfast, that's all. What – ?'

The master's expression changed to one of wonderment. 'Ye c'n see fer y'self, zur. Don't know how, but we did it, zur. We've taken 'er. She's ours, b'God!'

Mainwaring looked round. The Spaniards were clustered in the waist, dirty and dishevelled, hands held high as the Dianas thrust them together. Weapons were thrown down everywhere, and bodies strewn about the deck, with here and there a few wounded struggling to rise. The *frégata* rolled under them, and Mainwaring knew he had to issue a number of orders quickly and decisively. The trembling in his knees and the queasiness in his stomach would have to be ignored.

'Mr Howe!' he bellowed, looking for the first lieutenant. This would be the test. Had Howe stayed with the fight, or had he run below to –

'Here, sir!' Howe appeared up the waistdeck ladder of the *frégata*. His face was streaked with blood from a diagonal cutlass slash across his forehead. In one hand he carried a light Spanish officer's fusil, its short bayonet bloody.

'Near run thing, sir,' he said, his expression steady. 'Are you all right?'

'Glad you're safe, James,' said Mainwaring. He paused as two of Millechamp's marines clumped past, one without his mitre cap, pushing Spaniards ahead of them with their muskets. 'We must get the situation in hand if we're not to lose both ships in this damned wind and swell. Please set a party guarding the Dons and send Pellowe below to clear the lower decks. Tell him to be as careful as he can; some of the bastards may still have ideas of fighting. Find a place to chain 'em down. If you have to, handspike round a gun to point at 'em and post a hand with a slow match at it.'

'Aye, aye, sir,' said Howe, and moved off, calling for Pellowe. Mainwaring was relieved to see the latter appear from behind the foremast, the cutlass in his hand scarlet from tip to guard. He was hatless, but appeared unhurt.

Mainwaring turned back to Hooke. 'Isaiah, pick a prize crew for this gaudy barge. I want her able to sail and seakeep. But you'll have to get those grapnels off before we grind the wales to sawdust. We'll heave to and ply back and forth with the boats.' He paused, reluctant to ask the next question. 'How many men did we lose?'

'Two, zur. Lads what join'd at Spithead. An' three wounded.'

'Thank Christ. Very well, carry on. But detail off some people to get the wounded lads over to Doctor Rowe as quickly as you can.'

'Zur.' And he was gone, the bellow for Jewett already on his lips.

Mainwaring sank back against the rail, amazement and disbelief flooding through him. The deck was littered with Spanish dead and wounded. And *Diana* had lost but two men killed? It was near incredible.

He saw Millechamp in the waist, surrounded by a little knot of his marines.

'Lieutenant Millechamp! Any losses?'

'One man cut in the leg, sir. Nothing serious.'

Again the phenomenal luck. And with a new ship and an untried crew . . .

'Glad to hear it. Please see Mr Howe at once. He's gone below, and you must guard our prisoners. Herd them to wherever Mr Howe wants 'em.'

Millechamp gave him an elegant little sword salute. 'Directly, sir.'

Mainwaring moved to the inboard rail, lurching a little with the ship's motion. Parker was still there with his mate at *Diana*'s helm, keeping the ship from grinding too heavily against the *frégata*. In this wind and sea it must have been a damned difficult job. And with musket shot whistling about your ears . . .

'Captain, sir?'

Mainwaring turned. It was Pellowe, at the top of the after companionway, hatless still, and with the bloodied cutlass still in his hand.

'Mr Howe's respects, sir, and could you join him in the Don's great cabin.'

Mainwaring went below, reaching the same broad gun-deck into which he had tumbled through the gunport, but now crowded with Dianas and Millechamp's marines, herding the wretched Spanish down to whatever orlop hell Howe had selected. The American turned and passed behind the companion, finding himself between cabin doors, a larger and more ornate one standing ajar ahead of him. He stepped through, pausing a moment as the ship rolled under him, and saw that he was in an infinitely grander version of his own great cabin. The furniture was heavy and dark with leaded-glass wine and book cabinets and even an intricately carved weapons rack. Paintings of austere Spanish nobles filled the available space, and in one corner an elaborate canopied box bunk hung. Across it lay the body of the man Mainwaring had flung down the companionway.

'It's the captain, sir,' said Howe. He was behind the vast desk before the stern lights. 'His neck's broken. Was it you who – ?'

'Quite, Mr Howe. Now what have you there?'

Howe had been going through the drawers of the dark, beautifully finished desk. Now he was examining several documents he had taken from a large manila folio that bore the Spanish crown's ribbon and seal.

'It's this, sir,' said Howe. His face was still streaked by blood from the cut on his forehead. 'I read a little Spanish, sir, and I think I've found something.'

Mainwaring came round the table, laying his cutlass down on its polished wood.

'It's a special despatch of some kind, sir. Goes on at great length about who will command the Terra Firma fleet next summer. But then it alerts the Viceroy at Lima that a special change will be made to the routing of part of the Plate fleet. It appears they're worried about Commodore Anson's squadron, sir.'

Mainwaring frowned. 'Sensible enough. If Anson gets *Centurion* and the others round the Horn into the South Sea they'll raise the very devil with the Spanish settlements along the coast.'

'Yes, sir. But it seems to say that they're aware he's trying to pick off the Manila Galleon as well. Or at least, they think he might try.'

Mainwaring thought for a moment, trying to get the organization of the Spanish shipments of wealth clear in his mind. The Terra Firma fleet would cross to New Spain from Europe and work its way along the South American Caribbean coast – the 'Spanish Main' – until it put into Cartagena. Meanwhile, the South Seas fleet would sail northward from Callao, Peru, with gold and Potosí silver and Christ knew what else looted from the Americas. It would put into Paita, and Guayaquil, and then finally Panama. Mule-teams carried the wealth to Porto Bello and then to Cartagena, where it was loaded into the now-empty holds of the Terra Firma vessels before they sailed for Havana, to await the New Spain fleet from Vera Cruz.

This fleet was already enriched by even more treasures, this time from the Orient. They were carried to Mexico across the vast Pacific in remarkable, endless passages by the heavy-laden galleons of the Manila fleet, sailing from Manila in the Philippines to Acapulco, from where the cargoes were carried overland to the ships at San Juan de Ulva, or Vera Cruz. The legendary richness of the Manila shipments had bred tales known by every sailor, until the 'Manila Galleon' was a watchword for every brigand's dreams of unimaginable wealth.

'Again, reasonable enough,' said Mainwaring. 'What little I've heard of Commodore Anson suggests he'd try if he knew where to look.'

'I think that's the point of this despatch, sir. I can't make out some of the words' – and here Howe squinted at the florid penmanship – 'but I think this letter is to alert the Viceroy that, by orders sent last year to Manila, the Manila fleet's changing its track and destination.'

Mainwaring's eyebrows rose. 'In what way?'

'Again, I'm not sure, sir. But I think there's only to be *one* Manila vessel this year, and will be for the next few years. This year it's a single vessel, bigger and more heavily armed than most. And they've had her sail in the North Pacific winter, sir – that is, now – instead of more to the spring.'

'And where've they directed her?'

Howe squinted. 'Panama, I think it says, sir. One of the *Islas de las Perlas* – the Pearl Islands – just offshore. She's to wait there until it's safe to offload under the guns of the town itself.'

'What? You mean she'll be at anchor in some hidden cove for a few months, waiting?'

'Apparently so, sir. They can't warehouse anything at Porto Bello since Admiral Vernon's attack. So they'll hold it at Panama until it's safe to carry over.'

'Well, sink me,' breathed Mainwaring, pondering the

79

meaning of that despatch. It meant that an enormous, fat-bellied Spanish galleon, groaning with silks, spices, ivory, gold and silver, and God knew what else, would lie at anchor in some quiet island cover in the Gulf of Panama. Waiting there for weeks under the heat of the sun, waiting for the bag-sailed, carelessly-run ships of the grandly named South Seas fleet to straggle in from Guayaquil. Weeks in which crews would become lazy, or diseased; in which defences might be less watchful than they should. In a port not far from a shore reachable by a well-cut trail, the famous *camino real*, from the already-weakened Caribbean shore of Panama . . .

'James,' said Mainwaring carefully, 'when there is time I'll want to know everything that our late adversary was carrying in these pouches. For the moment you'd best address yourself to the problems of making Jamaica with two ships and a clutch of Don prisoners.'

'But, sir, this – '

'I know, James. And we will discuss it over wine and dinner in my cabin tonight, if you'll join me. You answered some questions I had worried over very well today.'

'You mean, was I a coward, sir?' Howe flushed. 'I – I ran from action in Ogle's squadron, sir. That was – why I was sent back. And lost my hanger. It was something I just could not explain. I had to prove something to myself today. And – and to you.'

'I suspected as much, but you've put that to rest, as I expected you would.' Mainwaring took the heavy, parchment-like despatch from Howe and looked at it steadily.

'And now we have another intriguing question. Or shall we say, a proposal. To put to an admiral at Port Royal Harbour, whom I hope will have the bloody imagination to agree to it.' He grinned at Howe. 'You may find,

James, that this cruise proves more worth while than you expected.'

Howe returned the grin. 'It has already, sir.' Then he paused. 'There's another note attached to this letter, sir. I forgot to mention.'

'Oh?'

Howe squinted at a sheet he picked up from the desk. 'It says here that an officer has been specially sent over from Havana to take command of the galleon's cargo and ensure that the bullion, or whatever, is carried safely across the isthmus. He also has authority to sail her to Acapulco if Anson somehow twigs to her presence off Panama. Odd thing, though.'

'What's that?'

'The fellow in charge, sir. Says here he's a Frenchman.'

Mainwaring's neck tingled. The old warning alarm.

'Is his name there?' he said, evenly.

'Yes. Ri – Rigaud de la – '

'The Chevalier Rigaud de la Roche-Bourbon,' said Mainwaring grimly. 'Well, I'll be damned!' He moved to the stern windows and stared out.

'You *know* him, sir?' asked Howe.

'In a manner of speaking. A year and a half ago I took a Spanish *guardacostas* he was commanding. And we'd had an unpleasant set of dealings before.'

He turned back to Howe. 'And that, as well, I will relate to you over dinner tonight, James. Now let's see to making port with these ships, shall we?'

3

'But, surely, sir – !' protested Mainwaring.

Vice-Admiral Edward Vernon raised an arresting hand as he sat behind his broad desk in the great cabin of His Britannic Majesty's ship *Burford*, at anchor in the shimmering heat of Port Royal Harbour, Jamaica.

'Mainwaring, I simply cannot agree to such a harebrained proposal. I need every vessel and every man for this attempt at Cartagena. We were damned lucky at Porto Bello, and later at Chagrès, to get away with what we did. I have a deuced unpleasant feeling about Cartagena and really do *not* wish to consider wild schemes such as you describe!'

Edward Mainwaring sat back in his chair, feeling the sweat trickle unpleasantly down the small of his back. Through the broad windows of *Burford*'s stern lights, he could see the milky expanse of Kingston Bay, with the anchored hulks of the West Indies Squadron, behind which the dark green ramparts of Jamaica rose into a cloudless, searingly hot sky.

Vernon, the voluble and likeable man who had led his squadron and Mainwaring's schooner, *Athena*, in a successful assault on the Spanish city of Porto Bello, looked at the young American with a not unkindly expression.

'You've done bloody well, you know. First cruise out here to me with a new ship and untried hands, and you bag a prize before you even arrive. You'll get a pound or two of prize money out of her, I'd warrant, as well – '

'That's not the point, sir. With respect,' Mainwaring interrupted. In his earlier relations with the active and controversial admiral, Mainwaring had been allowed an extraordinary frankness. Now he used that freedom to voice his disappointment fully. 'You said yourself, sir, that the way to bring the Dons to the treaty table is not to try to hold their land possessions, but to strike at their trade, in particular their bullion shipments from the Americas. Now if this bloody great galleon is going to be riding to anchor off Panama for a matter of months, and we could get at her – even just to sink or burn her where she lies – wouldn't that constitute just the sort of tactical move you – ?'

'Mainwaring, look here. What you've been proposing would mean I should lose an entire ship's company and a capable officer who would die of Yellow Jack trying to hack their way across Darien. Meantime I must contend with this abominable fellow, Wentworth, the land commander for our glorious venture, who appears determined to block my *every* move; my squadron's ship's companies are going down in droves to the damned fever; I receive despatches with every ship sent out from those hounds in the Admiralty urging me to repeat the Porto Bello business on a grander scale; Charles Knowles is muttering in my ear that I have *none* of the tools I should have to reduce Cartagena's fortifications – the list is endless. Can you really think that I would agree to your buccaneering off into the South Sea after one bloody ship that might not even be there, in the event? At any rate, Mainwaring, what you suggest is what Anson is meant to be doing.'

Mainwaring looked away through the stern lights. Across the still shapes of the anchored men-of-war, the bird shapes of bagsailed native workboats were moving in slow, heat-shimmered beauty. When he looked back at Vernon he could see the sweat dappling the admiral's forehead under the full-bottomed wig. In his full suit of scarlet, Vernon must have been intolerably hot, for Mainwaring was finding his own threadbare brown dress coat an oven in the humid, stifling air of the cabin.

'I – understand, sir. It seemed a good idea at the time.'

'And so it might be, at some other time. Sir Harry Morgan did what you propose, you know.'

'Sir?'

'Marched from Porto Bello to Panama, and sacked the place. That'd be in 1671, I think.'

'If he managed, sir, why couldn't – ?'

'Damn your persistence, Mainwaring. Morgan went up the Chagrès River and then marched over the mule-team road to the other coast. Damned thing is partly paved in cobblestones, I'm told. The *camino real*, what? But he did that without the Spanish having any real warning, or managing to stop him. Were you to try it, you'd run into packs of Dons armed to the teeth, waiting behind each tree. We did rather alert them to us at Porto Bello and thereafter, you know.' He sniffed. 'You'd have to cut your way through the damned jungle, instead. And you wouldn't get out of *that* alive. No, no, it's really quite out of the question.'

'But, sir – '

Vernon's expression became firm. 'I have made up my mind, Mainwaring. The answer is no. And I really do not wish to explain myself any further. Is that clear?'

Mainwaring could see that the limits had been reached. 'Yes, sir. I appreciate your indulgence.'

'Not at all. You've no lack of imagination, Mainwaring. I simply can't afford to listen to it at the moment.' He looked at a dossier on his desk and smiled. 'I do, however, have orders for you which may prove somewhat of a compensation.'

'Yes, sir?' Mainwaring sat up.

'I am still some weeks away from sailing for Cartagena.

84

And at that time I shall need your *Diana*. But I have another obligation to fulfil in the meantime. You will, I presume, recall the San Andrès planter, Richard Brixham, and his daughter?'

Mainwaring's heart gave a bound. *Anne!*

'Yes, sir. Of course.'

There was an amused light, not unkindly, in Vernon's eye.

'They lost their trading sloop at Porto Bello, as you know, what? And the Dons will not allow them to resettle on San Andrès. I was able to intercede directly by letter with the Viceroy at Lima on their behalf, and to my great surprise actually received a reply. The Dons've let them return to San Andrès for any of their movable property as may remain, including slaves. I saw to it that they had a small lugger to make the voyage, and on the event of their return they intend to try a plantation of cane on the North Shore, near Port Antonio or perhaps Montego Bay. I shall help them all I can, of course. There is, however, a problem.'

'What's that, sir?' asked Mainwaring, every nerve end alert.

'They're headstrong people, Mainwaring. Although I believe I need not point that out to you. They apparently ran a shellfish fishery on one of the San Blas islands, part way round the coast from Porto Bello to the Gulf of Urabá. Mondego Island, that is. They've determined that they want the boats, or at least the people from there, and indicated to me that they would sail there from San Andrès before returning here.' He leaned forward across the broad desk. 'Even with the most generous allowances of time for foul winds or some other incident, they are weeks late in returning here from the San Blas. I am quite concerned that something may have happened to them.'

Mainwaring felt a chill run up his spine, in strong contrast to the stifling heat.

'Which is why, Mainwaring, I am ordering you to sail at once for the coast of Darien, and the San Blas. You are to locate the Brixhams on Mondego, and ensure their safe return here. Or you must discover, if you can, what other fate they may have suffered. But you must complete this task in time to sail with us for Cartagena. At the very least, I will require you to join me and the principal squadron there. *Diana* must be there for the assault. That gives you very little time, perhaps six weeks at the most, what?'

'Aye, aye, sir,' said Mainwaring firmly. Sensing that the interview was at an end, he rose to go.

'One thing more, Mainwaring,' said Vernon. 'I realize and sympathize with your personal feelings for Miss Brixham. She's a spirited and splendid young woman. But I would be acting in any case to assist the Brixhams. Subjects of His Britannic Majesty are entitled to no less, wherever in the world they may be.'

'Indeed, sir. I'm – grateful you're sending me, none the less.'

Vernon smiled, and then a look of concern crossed his face.

'See that you return, young Mainwaring. I've far too great a need for ships like yours – damn my eyes, for imaginative young scoundrels like you who display initiative! – to want to lose you on a reef to some damned Don *guardacostas*. D'ye hear? You're to come back. Die and I shall be immensely displeased with you.'

Mainwaring nodded, meeting the steady, open gaze of Edward Vernon, and feeling the warmth there.

'I shall, sir. Thank you.'

And within eighteen hours *Diana* had cleared Port

Royal Harbour, and was steering south-south-west across a moonlit sea towards the dark, distant coast of Darien.

His Most Catholic Majesty's *guardacostas Esperanza*, a graceful, ship-rigged small warship, was snugged down on a broad reach, sailing with easy grace through the dark Caribbean, the phosphorescence glowing like blue-green smoke under her bows as she rhythmically lifted and then buried her cutwater in the easy swells. The *Esperanza* was in reality a small *frégata*, and had carried the limited armament of a coastal patrol vessel for the first years of her life. But now, with the war against the English, she bristled with new guns, her below-deck spaces occupied by the arms racks of the added men in her complement, and the partitions of the clutch of officers who, more than anything else in the minds of her crew, obstructed the sailing of the little ship, rather than assisting it.

The commander of the *Esperanza*, a thin, worried-looking man named Ortiz, leaned on the waistdeck rail and stared forward, where half the men of the watch lay sleeping in clumps about the deck. He was worried about the state of the ship's rigging, worried about the lookouts and whether they were slumped in sleep like their ship-mates below. And he worried about the task that the extraordinary gentleman he had been ordered to carry – and obey – from Cartagena was planning. It sounded far too great a risk. Indeed, it sounded *unnecessary*, which to Ortiz was a key concept in life. For him, success meant doing just enough to get *Esperanza* from one port to another without laborious effort and risk, enough to keep disaster at bay without undue expenditure of effort. But now –

'Señor Ortiz!' came a snarl out of the darkness of the after companionway. 'I trust we are on the course I requested of you? For if not, we – '

87

'*Ay, sí!* Of course we are, señor! This ship is one of the finest vessels in all the New World,' Ortiz said, drawing himself up into what he felt was the dignity and bearing of an *hidalgo*, 'and you may be sure her gallant crew – '

'Her gallant crew,' said the dark figure, in lightly-accented Spanish, 'are a drunken, foul pack of layabouts, who disgrace you and this stinking, ill-run barge of yours, Ortiz. Please clarify our course to me, if you will.' The figure rose out of the companionway darkness, slim and elegant in a laced hat and velvet coat which Ortiz knew was a deep burgundy in daylight.

'*Sí*, señor!' Ortiz turned to the binnacle box before the helm, where a fat seaman with a yard-long queue clutched the wheel.

'West, sou'west, señor. As it has been for the last three hours.'

'Your lookouts are awake?'

'But of course, señor. They are Spanish seamen. They know their duty and perform it.'

'I hope for your worthless soul you are right. When we reach Mondego Island I am to be informed immediately. You do understand what immediately means?'

'*Claro*. Of course I understand,' said Ortiz, offended. 'But you have not explained, señor, what it is you – '

The Chevalier Rigaud de la Roche-Bourbon moved lightly to the quarterdeck of *Esperanza* with a quick, cat-like manner that sent a chill up Ortiz' spine. In an instant the tall figure was before him, the glittering black eyes fixed on Ortiz with malevolent intelligence.

'Perhaps it has not been made sufficiently clear to you, Ortiz, that you, and this vessel are at my disposal to do with as I wish in the interest of both our royal houses. I feel no requirement to tell you anything beyond what you are supposed to do. Is that clear?'

Ortiz felt his nerves steady somewhat as a reply came to his lips.

'You have said that, señor. *Muchas veces*. But surely now you would be willing to tell me so that I and the brave lads of *Esperanza* can aid you more loyally in your duty, *sí*?'

'You would do your duty or die on a gibbet, Ortiz,' said Roche-Bourbon, levelly. 'Don't try to milk me.'

'*Con permiso, señor*, I – I have a right to ask,' said Ortiz, his heart pounding.

For a moment the Frenchman was silent, and Ortiz cringed physically, expecting a scathing torrent of anger.

'Very well, Ortiz. You show the first bit of courage I've seen in you,' said Roche-Bourbon in a cold tone. 'You are aware of the usual track of the *armada del sur*?'

'*Sí*, señor. North to Panama from Guayaquil, so that the treasure of His Majesty can be carried to Porto Bello and thence to Cartagena.'

'Correct. And the Manila fleet?'

'To Acapulco, señor. Then across to San Juan and Havana. It all goes home to Spain by Havana, in convoy.'

'Yes. However, this year, Ortiz, we have an extraordinary problem. His Majesty learned that the English have sent a squadron into the South Sea, under a man named Anson. They mean to take the Manila fleet.'

'Truly, señor? *Es malo!*' gaped Ortiz. 'How – ?'

'We do not intend to give them a fleet to chase, Ortiz. Only one ship has come from Manila. The *Nuestra Señora de Granada*.'

Ortiz' eyes widened. '*Madre*, I know her! She is immense! A floating fortress!'

'Precisely why she was chosen. In her will be the Manila shipments. And she has sailed already, if all has gone well, and should be at anchor off one of the Pearl Islands off Panama.'

'*Panama?* I do not understand, señor. Why – ?'

'The Englishman, Anson, will not look for her there. The guns of the town will serve as protection if she must move under them. And there I shall take possession of the bullion from her.'

'You, señor?' Ortiz' awe was growing.

'By the authority of His Excellency the Viceroy, I am to take as many of the Panama garrison as I require and see that the shipment is mule-teamed across to Porto Bello. And since we cannot wait there for the Terra Firma fleet, *you*, Ortiz, will be waiting. With *Esperanza*.'

'*Madre de dios!*' murmured Ortiz.

'You will await my arrival at Porto Bello, and avoid any English cruisers. And when we arrive, we shall fill *Esperanza*'s hold with more riches than you can conceive of in your poor world, Ortiz, and sail for Havana. There we shall put the cargo of *Nuestra Señora de Granada* safely into the holds of the galleons bound for Spain.'

Ortiz stared at the hawk-faced Frenchman with a rush of conflicting emotions. His heart sank as he thought of the vast responsibility. The penalty if he failed. The consequences of being found out by the English –

'Ortiz, you fool, you have nothing to do but keep your head! Be there in Porto Bello when I return, and should we make Havana you'll be a richer man than you could possibly have imagined! I'll see to that. But *fail* me – ' Roche-Bourbon did not finish.

'*Sí.* I shall not fail you, señor. *Yo lo creo!*' He stared forward with frightened eyes, to where a thin light of early dawn might soon reveal the outlying islets of the San Blas chain, off the northern Darien coast.

'But, señor, why do we sail this course? Would it not be best to steer for Porto Bello or Chagrès, so that you might – ?'

Roche-Bourbon's eyes glittered like moonlit steel in the

dark. 'My instructions, Ortiz, come directly from the Viceroy at Lima. And he informed me in passing that a certain English planter and his daughter are on Mondego, planning to take their people and possessions back to Jamaica.'

'*Sí*? So, señor? I don't – '

'The girl, you ignorant fool, is a hot little creole who is valued highly by a colonial English officer with whom,' and here Roche-Bourbon's cheek twitched, 'I have a score to settle. That officer is a favourite of the English admiral most potentially an obstacle to us, Admiral Edward Vernon at Jamaica.' He licked thin lips. 'I daresay this fellow, Mainwaring, may again be part of Vernon's squadron, which is what I am banking upon.'

Ortiz shook his head, still baffled. 'But what – ?'

'By the blood of Christ, Ortiz, you are a thick-witted toad! I intend to put into Mondego and find that woman and her father. And if we are fortunate enough to take her, then she shall accompany me as my guest on this little adventure. A guest that may prove valuable as a kind of insurance should the damned *rosbifs* get too close.'

Ortiz bared yellowed teeth. 'Ah. A hostage, señor!'

'Exactly. Except in one sense. To this one Englishman, she is meant as bait, *hein*? He alone I want to lure to me, even as I want to keep the others at bay lest I cut her throat. For the one, she will draw him to me out of his fear that I shall do just that.'

'But why do you wish to draw this one, señor? Will he not put at risk everything?'

'No, Ortiz,' said Roche-Bourbon, a queer little smile on his face. 'For when he comes, this Edward Mainwaring, I shall be ready with a trap. And I will kill him with it, even as you and I spirit the Manila bullion to Havana under the noses of the other English!'

91

Fear rose in Ortiz at the awesome intensity of purpose which radiated from Roche-Bourbon. Intensity, and a frightening hatred.

'And the woman? When we succeed?'

'Have you not slit the throat of a woman, Ortiz? The soft skin parts like butter before a knife. A most pleasurable experience you will be sure to enjoy, as much as I,' purred Roche-Bourbon.

'*Espero que sí*,' murmured Ortiz. 'I – hope so, señor . . .' And he felt a sick fear in his vitals as he stared at the glittering, unblinking eyes of Rigaud de la Roche-Bourbon.

His Britannic Majesty's Ship *Diana* was some fifty leagues due north of the *Esperanza*, steering south-south-west by south towards the same island group of the San Blas. It was the turn of the watch at midnight, and as *Diana* tracked under plain sail over a sea shimmering silver in the light of a glowing, enormous moon, Stephen Pellowe took over from James Howe, the ship's bell ringing out eight bells, the watchmen mustering in sleepy duty in the lee of the longboat, the men below turning in their hammocks and thankful for four more hours of sleep.

In his cabin, Edward Mainwaring glanced at the gymballed compass that was suspended upside down over his box bunk and then sat back in his chair, rubbing tired eyes. Before him on the desk a chart of the Caribbean was spread out, and sheets of foolscap covered with mathematical figuring. Mainwaring's quadrant lay to one side, and atop the chart, its pages held down by the barrel of a heavy Sea Service flintlock pistol, was a copy of the 1633 edition of Andrew Wakely's *The Mariner's Compass Rectified*. In its archaic explanations Mainwaring had been wandering for some hours, trying to get clear in his mind the process for finding longitude through a preposterously complex series of figurings based on a lunar observation. Like most sea officers, his navigational training had been a hit-and-miss affair based on the old principles of 'lead, latitude and lookout', with longitude, the distance east or west from a given point, remaining a mystery awaiting the production of a reliable sea-going clock – or solvable only through the anguish of an almost impossible mathematical problem.

There was a knock at the door, and the marine sentry looked in. 'Lieutenant 'owe, zur.'

Howe grinned in sympathy as he came in. 'Still at it, sir?'

Mainwaring sighed. 'Still and yet. Bloody business has me stumped. We're either due south of Jamaica exactly where we should be or else about to spill our guts all over the north shore of Guadeloupe. Damned if I know which.'

'An idea, however?'

'Well, it's largely feeling sure where we are by gut reaction, more than anything else. I think we're – here. Better if I had some navigational justification for it. Come in and sit down.'

Howe sank with a sigh of relief on to the broad settee under the stern lights. Like Mainwaring, he was in a simple rig of loose canvas trousers and linen, uncuffed coat with docked tails.

'What's our state?' asked Mainwaring.

'Thirty leagues out o' Port Royal and on course for the San Blas. Or Guadeloupe. Courses, tops'ls and heads'ls. Stephen's got the watch. Millechamp's marines are still groaning about in their mess after that drunken escapade ashore. Did I tell you that when I got down there they had the innkeeper frightened out of his wits, had drunk everything wet in the place and assaulted the Town Watch, and had half a dozen stark naked women dancing

93

on the tabletops to the lad's drum? The little sod was grinning like an ape. Took Pound the better half of an hour to get 'em down to the boats. They're paying for it, now.'

'*Diana* continues to build her reputation. And?'

'Well, I've had Stephen double the lookouts, as per the night sailing orders. Little else to remark on.'

'And the weather? It can be damned unpredictable, you know, James.'

'Yes, sir. At the moment the sky's clear, and there's a moon still. Wind's steady at about ten knots or so, out of the east. Likely it'll veer towards dawn, and we'll have to brace up sharp for a reach.'

'Good. Madeira?'

'Thank you, sir. I'll get it. One for you?'

'Please.' As Howe went to the small rack and filled two glasses from the decanter, Mainwaring peered back at his chart.

Howe set down a glass at Mainwaring's elbow and sank into a chair.

'Where the deuce *is* Mondego Island anyway, sir? I don't think I've ever heard of it.'

Mainwaring poked a finger at the chart, near the upward bulge of the Darien coast.

'Here. Easternmost of the San Blas group. About six leagues off the mainland. A pilot in *Burford* told me it has a good anchorage in a bay on the eastern side, sheltered by a smaller island.'

'And these people ran a fishery there? The Brixhams, I mean.'

The Madeira burned in Mainwaring's throat, and he coughed. 'Shellfish. Likely traded to the mainland as well. All completely illegal, according to the Dons.'

'I – ah – gather you admire this Miss Brixham, sir. And the former Athenas can't say enough good about her.

Was she – ?' He did not finish, aware suddenly that he was overstepping the bounds of his relationship with Mainwaring.

The American was silent. He saw before him the broad, sunny smile, the twinkling, sea-green eyes, the dark brown curls tossed by the wind. And he was hearing again her voice, laughing with him over the sea roar or murmuring in the sweet dark of a lovers' bed . . .

'You put it mildly, James. If I can ever pry her off these damned Caribbean rocks I hope to marry her.'

Howe raised his glass. 'Well, then. Here's to our success, sir. And to your future with Miss Brixham, if you'll permit.'

'Amen to that,' agreed Mainwaring, and tossed off the glass.

Howe was eyeing the chart again. 'What is it you intend to do, sir? At dinner you were only getting into it when that gear parted and we had to go on deck.'

Mainwaring nodded. 'The first and foremost task, James, is to see to Anne and her father. That goes without saying. But that damned galleon keeps bothering me. And all the more so, now I know that Roche-Bourbon is involved.'

'You defeated him at sea, didn't you, sir?'

'Yes. Took his ship and decked him with a punch, although in retrospect I should've run the bugger through. The Navy bought in his ship, but he was released on his parole to Cartagena about a month after I took him.' He paused. 'Presumably the bloody Dons must want to see that bullion safe to Spain very badly indeed to have him involved. He appears to be sent round as a sort of wringer of tough necks.'

Howe looked at him. 'You mentioned that Admiral Vernon turned down the idea of going after the galleon, didn't you, sir? At least, I thought – '

Mainwaring laughed. 'Of course, James. And Vernon's orders are ignored at your peril unless you can prove that you had a better idea. But it would be a remarkable tweak of the Dons' noses to – '

The noise was unlike anything Mainwaring had ever heard. It seemed to begin as a dull, resonant thundering almost below the limits of hearing, and then built within seconds up through the more audible levels of sound until it was at once a deep, shaking rumble and a banshee scream of ear-splitting intensity that reached into the brain and body with the hardness of a knife cut.

Mainwaring looked up at Howe, whose face, suddenly pale, was staring back at him with equally wide-eyed astonishment. The American leaped up and spun to look out through the stern lights.

'Good Christ!' he burst out.

Where an instant ago there had been a serene sea rolling in moonlit peace under a clear starlit sky, now a vast, boiling wall of spray and mist was bearing down on *Diana* blotting out the horizon, gleaming strangely in the bone-white moonlight that played over its tumbling surface as it rolled closer, resembling nothing so much as a huge wave.

'*Pampero!* White squall!' barked Mainwaring, a distant memory of a youthful voyage to the Yucatan flooding back. 'On deck, James!'

The two men burst out of the cabin and made for the companionway, the horrid screaming so loud now that it almost blotted out thought. But before they reached the ladder, *Diana* cracked and groaned as if twisted by a giant hand, and heeled suddenly under their feet. Mainwaring and Howe fell together in a tumble away from the companionway, to slam hard against the thin partitions of Ezrah Soper's tiny cabin. Even as they gasped with the impact, a cloud of spray and seawater burst down the companionway, smashing the lantern that hung at the companionway foot, and then punching into the two sprawling men with the force of a horse kick. Mainwaring found himself spinning and rolling in darkness, a rushing torrent of seawater carrying him across the deck until with a rib-jarring impact, he fetched up against the rounded surface of a lashing-wrapped cask, that he knew was located forward of the companionway on the larboard side. Coughing and gasping, the salt stinging in his nose and throat, he felt *Diana*'s horrifying cant to one side pause, and began scrabbling like a crab up the deck groping through the rushing torrents of water for the companion's ladder foot. In the next instant he had it, and with the strength of his arms pulled himself up to it. His head rose above water, and as he gulped at the air he realized he had been underwater for several moments. Sodden, he clawed up the ladder, feeling *Diana* righting under him. Somewhere above he could hear the terrible crack and snap of collapsing rigging.

Then he was emerging on to the deck, into a scene of chaos and tumult. The moon still shone perversely over all with a cold, blue light. The wind still tore at the ship, the sea to either side white and swirling, torn wavetops leaping up to be whipped away in smoking clouds of spume. *Diana*'s decks were full of struggling, cursing men, Pellowe's and Howe's voices ringing out over their efforts. How the devil had Howe managed to get on deck? Axes rang out, and knife blades flashed in the moonlight as men hacked at a mass of wreckage and tangle that covered the ship's waistdeck. *Diana* was upright, and it occurred to Mainwaring that the loss of the gear aloft had freed the pressure on the ship, likely saving it. Mainwaring and whoever else had been trapped below would have died like trapped rats as *Diana* filled and went down.

Hooke was suddenly before him, clad only in torn canvas breeches.

'Fore t'gallant mast, maintop and t'gallant masts all given way, zur!' he cried over the wind. 'The fore t'gallant's gone over the side! Shall we – ?'

'Cut away the maintop and t'gallant shrouds and get 'em over the side! But leave a cable or two, so it streams like a sea anchor! We'll recover 'em later!'

'Aye, zur!' barked Hooke, and was off, bellowing at the feverishly working knots of men. The moon was blotted out again, and suddenly a deluge of warm rain engulfed them, the wind dropping, the water dancing on the decks until the men sloshed shin-deep as they hacked and cut at the mess.

Mainwaring spotted Howe helping the men struggling to pass lashings over the wheels. There was no heavy swell, and aloft not a single sail sheeted home. *Diana* would be safe enough lying a-hull in the abating wind while her men struggled with the chaos caused by the sudden squall.

The moon broke out once more, the wind dying now almost completely, the rain ceasing. In a few moments *Diana* lay rocking on the surface of the sea under a starlit sky.

Thank God it lasted but a moment, thought Mainwaring. *If that wind had held . . .*

'Mr Pellowe!' Mainwaring shouted. 'Where are you, sir!'

'Here, sir!' cried the youth. He had been sawing with a seaman's knife at a fouled staysail halliard.

'Your watchman! Did we lose anyone over the side?'

'No, sir! First thing I made certain of, soon as we righted. But Winton's down under that mess on the foredeck! He was under the fore t'gallant mast when it came down!'

'Get him out. Quickly as you can. Mr Howe?'

'Sir?'

'I'll want a report on what damage we may have suffered below as well. Get a party down there to look at it and to see if anyone was hurt.'

'Aye, aye, sir!' Howe made for the companionway, calling half a dozen men to follow him.

Forward, there was a series of obscenity-laced orders from Hooke, and a pack of men, the red coats of marines here and there among them, put a shoulder-to-shoulder effort to the tangled mass of spar and cordage that lay in a heap athwart the waist. Mainwaring ran forward and added his strength against what appeared to be the main t'gallant mast cap.

'Now, lads! One to six, *heave!*' rasped Hooke, and with oaths and curses the men strained at the mass, until it slid with a splintery crash and creak of cordage over the rail and into the sea. Almost immediately *Diana* began to slew around, the trailing mass acting as a sea anchor.

Already, several men were scrabbling through the remaining rubble on the deck to reach Winton, whose legs Mainwaring could see sprawled out from behind one of the waist six-pounders.

'How is he, Mr Hooke?' he called as the master reached Winton.

'All right, zur!' came the welcome call. 'Gun saved 'im! Bit of a knock on th' 'ead, is all!'

'Thank Christ!' Mainwaring was fond of the cheerful, blasphemous Winton, who had been with them through so much in *Athena*, and now this new vessel. He looked up. The sky was startlingly clear, devoid of so much of *Diana*'s usually towering rig.

'See that the doctor has a look at him, Mr Hooke! Then I'll want to know our condition as soon as you can report!'

He turned to see James Howe appearing up the after

99

companionway, a lantern swinging in one hand, its light warm and yellow against the moonlight.

'No damage to speak of, sir. A few partitions adrift, and personal gear knocked about a bit in the cabin area aft. No one hurt, thank Christ. A few of the lads were tossed out of their 'micks, and a marine cut his hand on a bayonet. If she hadn't righted when she did, however – ' Howe did not finish.

'Right. We were damned lucky.'

'What was it, sir? I don't think I've ever seen a line squall like that before. It was like a bloody explosion!'

'Rare enough thing,' said Mainwaring. 'Usually happens closer to the South American shore. Wind explosion is a good way to describe it. They call it a *pampero* on the Main. Never seen one of the damned things before this.'

Hooke came bustling up the waistdeck ladder, as axe blows and hammering sounded behind him.

'How bad is it, Isaiah?' said Mainwaring, quietly.

'Not good, zur.' Hooke lanced a jet of tobacco juice over the side. 'We've lost the foretop an' foret'gallant masts, and th'main t'gallant. Jib-boom carried away, but the sprit is still sound. Gammoning came adrift, is all. Other things gone as well: fore pin rails, both sides. Knightheads broke off, sheer wiv th'deck. An' there's worse.'

'Out with it.'

'The foremast, zur. She's split from th' crosstrees to 'er wedges, zur.'

Mainwaring's lips were a tight line. 'You're certain of that?'

'Aye, zur. There's nought but a dockyard'd put us t'rights now, zur.'

Mainwaring turned and moved to the rail. He stood for a moment, his hands gripping the wood as he stared off into the night. Images flickered before his eyes: Anne

Brixham, the face of Edward Vernon, an image of a great galleon at anchor on the Panama coast, the knife-edged features of Rigaud de la Roche-Bourbon. And again Anne. If he turned now to take *Diana* limping back to Port Royal –

Abruptly he turned, Howe and Hooke were looking at him expectantly.

'The longboat, Mr Hooke. Was it damaged?'

'Er – no, zur. All that gear fell for'rard of it. Still snugged down on th' gallows, as ye c'n see.'

'Very well. If the mainyard'll hold the strain, sway it over the side. Rig it for sailing, double lugsails. I'll want a lot of gear in her, so come and see me when you've got her hooked on alongside.'

Howe was staring at him. 'With respect, sir. What is it you're thinking of? Surely not – '

Mainwaring's gaze was level. 'This ship is wounded badly, Mr Howe. Admiral Vernon needs every vessel at his disposal, and if *Diana* is to be of service to him, she must put about for Port Royal and work back under a jury rig. Can she *do* that, Mr Hooke?'

'Think so, zur. It'd be a dog's breakfast o' canvas. Make no more'n two or three knots, an' it's mostly a close reach. But she'd do it.'

'Very well. You'll be taking her back, James. And she'll be under your command as long – '

'But, sir – !' burst out Howe.

'Allow me to finish. She will be under your command – to which effect I shall write Admiral Vernon – and I would hope that the dockyard could effect repairs in time for you to sail against Cartagena.'

Howe was aghast. 'But what the devil – what are *you* going to be doing, sir!' he blurted out, forgetting himself. 'Surely you're not going to risk taking a damned *longboat* – !'

'That is precisely what I intend, James. I have a duty to determine what has happened to the Brixhams as well as to ensure *Diana* sails with the squadron for Cartagena. I shall sail to Mondego Island with the longboat. If I am fortunate, the Brixhams and their lugger will be there and I will return with it to Jamaica.'

'It's suicide, sir,' said Howe, visibly shaken.

'It is what is necessary, James,' said Mainwaring. 'Surely I can rely on you to command *Diana* back?'

The first lieutenant flushed visibly even in the moonlight. 'Of course you can, sir. It's just – '

'There is no other option, James. My mind is made up.' Mainwaring turned to Hooke. 'How competent is Jewett to be master's mate?'

'E's a prime lad, zur. Knows th' ways o' this ship as well as me, near enough. An' the lads'll do what 'ee says.'

'Can he jury rig her?'

'As well as I could, zur. But I'll work out th' rig wiv 'em, afore – '

'Good. James, I'm rating Jewett as master's mate. Stephen will be your acting first lieutenant. Isaiah, you'll be coming with me in the longboat. Christ knows what kinds of ships or rigs we'll run into. Pick six of your steadiest hands – ones who can handle a musket, mind – as soon as you've squared things with Jewett. And get to work on putting the longboat overside. I want to be underway in her by dawn.'

'Aye, zur!' said Hooke, his eyes alight with purpose. The shaggy master knuckled his forelock and went off down the waistdeck ladder, bellowing for Jewett.

Howe moved closer to Mainwaring. 'Sir, are you quite sure you want to do this? It's a hell of a risk. And if the Brixhams aren't there – '

'We shall be on a hostile coast where we shall have to make the most of opportunities if we are to survive. I am aware of that, James. But Vernon must have you and *Diana* just as I must find out the fate of the Brixhams.'

'Is there anything I can do to increase the odds for you, sir?'

'James, you've shown beyond a question of a doubt that you can be relied upon. The main task is to get *Diana* back to the dockyard. And I'll include in my report to Vernon a request that if the Cartagena venture no longer needs *Diana*, you be permitted a sweep along the Darien coast. Should we not return, make an inshore passage from Urabá to the San Blas, will you? If we're there, somehow we'll get out to you or signal you. Three fires in a line, that kind of thing.'

Howe's face was grim. 'You'll have that, sir. Even if I have to steal the bloody ship from under old Grog's nose!'

Mainwaring smiled. 'Now get Hooke down alongside with the boat as soon as you can. There's a great deal to be done in a short time.'

Five and a half hours later a blood-red sun, huge and bloated, rose above the pale, quiet sea, sending a warm peach-toned light over *Diana* as she lay hove to. The ship's decks were clearer now, the wreckage overside rafted into a manageable mess against the larboard side. The lateen mizzen, gathered up in two reef points, was sheeted home hard to keep the bows of the wounded vessel to the wind, while in the waist, on the foredeck, and in the strangely stunted rigging, the sweating work parties were forging ahead with a will, and Hooke reported that *Diana* would likely be able to set working canvas by nightfall at the latest.

On the starboard side, the longboat lay waiting, her two lugsails brailed up against their masts, the tiller lashed inboard so that a launching heave on the boatrope would swing the craft clear. A party of six men, under Hooke's watchful eye, were lowering into the small craft a remarkable collection of gear and equipment which Mainwaring had listed in detail. There was a box of carpenter's and boat's tools; spare cordage and canvas; two grapnel anchors and their lines; eight muskets wrapped in oiled cloth, with slings and bayonets, a chest for cartridge boxes, and half a dozen cutlasses. A small cask of beer, another of water, and a third of rum were struck in under the sternsheets, and several bags of biscuit, along with a single small cask of salt pork. Eight long sweeps lay fore-and-aft down the middle of the thwarts, along with a boathook and two forked bearing-out poles. And now, being carefully set on the floorboards forward of the tiller, was an oiled leather-bound chest in which Mainwaring had put a copy of the Darien chart, his notebook, a small telescope, and a neatly-boxed boat compass along with writing materials – and a powder horn and ball pouch for his pair of flintlock pistols, which would have to be stowed away from the compass.

Edward Mainwaring stood at the rail above the long-boat, a critical eye on the work. He wore the same loose canvas trousers and short linen jacket, with a shirt ripped open almost to the waist, but on his head was an old uncocked hat, crammed down over a bright bandana that was knotted, Spanish fashion, at the back of his head above his queue. He had salt-rimed buckled shoes with no hose, and, at the small of his back, a sheathknife was thrust into the broad waistbelt that held up the frayed trousers.

Mainwaring looked over the men Hooke had selected, nodding with approval. In addition to Hooke there was Williams, he of the inventive ducking chair, who was wrestling Mainwaring's chest into place in the boat; another Welshman, Evans, a swarthy, capable man with powerful arms who had been with Mainwaring at the

Porto Bello attack; Winton, none the worse for wear, with a light bandage round his blond head and ecstatic at being selected; Sawyer, a quick, fair-haired Yankee from Martha's Vineyard whose simian antics in *Diana*'s rigging made Mainwaring's stomach turn, and who had been in *Athena* as well; Tindall, a taciturn Somerset man, who had been Soper's gunner's mate; and Slade, a former Athena, small and quick like Sawyer and his close friend, but a Cockney with a wry sense of humour. All told, they were good choices, and Mainwaring found himself hoping that he was not taking them to some obscure death in a fruitless expedition.

'Second thoughts, sir?' said Howe, materializing at his elbow.

'No time for that, James. Now we must sail on the allotted course. Here is the magazine key, and the small arms locker key. Moll is a morose little fellow, but he'll keep the ship's books straight. Thorne seems to have a set of personal ethics unmatched since Christ, so I doubt you'll have problems with him. You might keep an eye on Rowe; he's been the soul of abstention, but with all this tumult – '

'I shall, sir. Millechamp says good luck, and he's sorry he can't go too, sir. He's below. Suffers from the stone from time to time.'

Mainwaring frowned. 'That's a pity. He fought well taking that *frégata*.' He reached out and shook Howe's hand. 'Take care of them all, James. And yourself. I should like some day to have back my fine ship and my even finer first lieutenant.'

Howe flushed. 'Thank you, sir. For God's sake be cautious yourself.'

'I shall.' Mainwaring looked for Hooke. 'Mr Hooke! Into the boat, when you've got that stowed away. Each man have his own seabag?'

'Aye, zur! Only yours to go in.'

'Very well. 'Ware in the boat, there. Take this, Evans!' Mainwaring picked up a small canvas bag and tossed it over the rail. The Welshman caught it deftly, thrusting it aft under the sternsheets, beside Mainwaring's chest.

'Right, Isaiah. Over you go,' said Mainwaring. As the sailing master climbed down the battens Mainwaring noticed that the men had stopped working about the ship and had clustered into the waist. As Howe nodded they gave three short barking cheers.

Mainwaring's face reddened, for a moment lost for words.

'We're all with you, sir,' said Howe. 'The ship, the lads – all of us. You'd better make it back, sir.'

'I see I have no choice,' said Mainwaring hoarsely. He gripped Howe's hand again. 'For God's sake be careful yourself.'

'I shall, sir.'

Mainwaring turned and went quickly down the battens to the boat. He clambered aft into the sternsheets where Hooke was waiting.

'Clear, lads! Williams, unhook. Sawyer, let go that aft line. Stand by your brails and sheets.' He looked up. 'Ready, Mr Howe!'

Howe moved along the rail, cupping his hands to shout forward.

'Man the boatrope, there. Take up the line and take the strain. All right, roundly, lads! Run away with it!'

The boatrope was a long manila line tied to the longboat's bows and leading to a fairlead, an opening just forward of the foremast channel, and then aft on deck. As a dozen men tailed on to the line and ran aft with it, the longboat shot along *Diana*'s side, the lashed tiller causing it to swing away from the ship's side as it was pulled forward.

'Slip the boatrope!' called Mainwaring. He slipped the eye of the tiller lashing off the tiller and gripped it, steadying the longboat's rush. Forward, as the boat lifted and plunged across the wavelets, Winton freed the boatrope by pulling away the towing bollard from where it had lain fore and aft across two thwarts, the boatrope eye looped over it and passing under the foremost thwart before leading through a chock in the boat's bows. Freed, the eye splashed over the side as the men on *Diana*'s deck hauled in rapidly on the line, and the longboat coasted away.

'Shake out the main. Shake out the fore. Sheets, there, Slade and Sawyer.' The brails were eased, the sheets pulling the lugsails out to their full spread, and Mainwaring turned the boat off the wind. Their course lay to the southward, across *Diana*'s bows and off towards the distant San Blas. As the little craft dipped around, Sawyer and Slade, grinning at each other like monkeys, eased the sheets of the large, four-sided sails until the longboat was lifting along on a smart broad reach ahead of the building morning trade wind. They boiled rapidly past *Diana* as she sat, seemingly motionless, on the sea. Hands were raised in farewell, and then in minutes the ship, looking strangely truncated without its lost masting, was falling astern.

Mainwaring gave the tiller to Hooke and dug the boat compass out of the chest. He set the compass on the seat beside him, squinted at his chart, and made a few mental calculations.

'South by east lies our landfall, Mr Hooke. That's if my navigation skills are worth a damn.'

'How far off, sir?' asked Sawyer, coiling the main sheet.

'Fifty leagues, perhaps. Two days' sail if the wind holds.' He raised his voice. 'Settle yourselves as best as you can, lads. We've a fair time at sea until we land.'

'"Make and Mend", is it, sir?' said Winton.

'Aye, Winton,' said Mainwaring with a grin. 'Just see what you mend is that head.'

'No fear, sir. Tough as a round shot it is, sir.'

'Good. Tindall, I hear you're a good man at the galley firepit. You're cook, so to speak, as of now. Break out some biscuit all around. Mind you're sparing of the water, lads. One cup each. It's got to last.'

'Aye, aye, zur,' said Tindall, cheerfully. Like the others, he was pleased and excited at being selected for the boat. That they might be heading into almost certain disaster mattered little; the seamen followed a hard and unforgiving trade, with no guarantees and little to look forward to beyond rupture, death to sea from disease or injury, or at best a penniless old age ashore, begging for bread in an uncaring society. The leadership of a man like Mainwaring was tonic to them, for he took them in harm's way surely enough, but also in the way of prizes or booty, or of the simple and sheer joy of fighting. So Tindall and the others settled into the running of the longboat and the discomfort of the voyage with unaffected glee, eager to see what time and chance would bring them, showing an unfeigned enthusiasm that would have surprised a more cautious landsman.

'They're all good lads, zur,' said Hooke quietly beside Mainwaring, as if hearing his thoughts.

'Aye, Isaiah.' Mainwaring looked aft at *Diana*, already a dark, distant shape on the horizon, silhouetted against the rising sun that cast an amber glow over the sails of the hurrying longboat. 'They are. I hope to God we're not about to throw away their lives.'

Hooke spat the eternal tobacco stream into the wake and wiped his mouth with the back of his free hand.

'Hell, zur, ain't one of 'em wouldn't jump through

108

hellfire if yew was t'give th' word. Ye c'n ask any price of 'em, zur.'

Mainwaring smiled without mirth. 'All you've done is make damned certain I'll worry about them even more, Isaiah. But thank you.' He squinted down at the compass rocking in its box, and then forward at the distant, empty horizon where the San Blas islands lay.

'Christ grant I don't have to ask them to pay too much!' he said, under his breath.

The night sky was lit with the flickering glow of the flames leaping up from the low buildings which stood just up from the simple jetty on Mondego Island's small sheltered cove. The light was bilious orange, and it lightened or darkened as the great clouds of smoke from the fire swirled round and over the scene. The figures of men with blazing torches in hand were dancing around the edges of a few buildings, not yet aflame, pressing their torches against the wood and heaped furniture piled against the buildings. Farther down the beach, the first of a line of overturned small fishing boats, like beached whales, was beginning to smoke and flicker with the fire built beneath its gunwales.

There were other figures as well, groups of men with torches who stood in hunched activity over forms spread-eagled on the ground in the darkness and shrieking as the torches arced down and the flames were pressed against bare flesh, against eyes, against heads that became brief, incandescent torches as mouths screamed in horrid pain, the cries echoing and re-echoing around the little cove over the curses and cackling laughter of the torch-bearers. And other men were moving in the strange orange light of flame and shadow, staggering with bottles in one hand and long, flintlock pistols in the other. The pistols fired in sharp, pink-flashed reports into the air, or into the struggling, agonized bodies of staked-out men and women already screaming with the agony of their burned flesh, who jerked and then lay still as the balls thumped into them.

The screaming and the whooshing roar of the great fires rang across the still anchorage and over the deck of His Most Catholic Majesty's Ship *Esperanza*, where Rigaud de la Roche-Bourbon, still in the elegance of a velvet coat and egret-feathered tricorne, toyed with the hilt of his hanger and eyed with lazy satisfaction the hellish scene ashore. Then he turned to the shaking, sobbing little figure in the torn gown who was pinioned between two sweaty, leering seamen, their eyes on the heaving, half-revealed breasts over which the nightmarish light flickered in curve and shadow.

'Surely, my dear Miss Brixham,' said Roche-Bourbon in barely-accented English, 'you will admit that my men are enthusiastic as well as thorough?'

Her head snapped back to look at Roche-Bourbon, the dark curls shaking, the beautiful green eyes full at once of sorrow and fury behind their tears.

'You – filthy – animal!' Anne Brixham sobbed. 'There was no need – no reason for *this*! In God's name, have you no pity? No heart?'

Roche-Bourbon's lips curled with the barest of sneers. 'Pity? For the enemies of my king? Enemies who worship a bastard religion and spit at Holy Mother Church? Enemies who loot and plunder the possessions of our cousins, the Spanish, with equal ruthlessness? Surely you know how foolish you sound, my dear.'

'My father,' she cried, her eyes were staring at him in fury. 'What have you done with my father?'

'The old fool? He fired at us from the jetty, and one of

my musketmen dropped him. He fell into the water and I presume is a meal for the sharks, *hein*?'

The girl sank between her captors, pain overcoming the anger. 'Oh, no,' she whispered. 'Oh, no. Father . . .'

A terrible shriek echoed over the water, and Roche-Bourbon looked up to see the figure of a girl, her clothing shredded after the prolonged attention from a group of men who had held her down and mounted her in succession, being thrown bodily into the flame-filled doorway of a burning building.

'How admirably thorough indeed,' murmured Roche-Bourbon. Then he turned back to his half-conscious captive.

'You needn't be concerned for your own welfare, my dear,' he said. 'I intend that you shall accompany me on a journey of some pleasure. A journey which shall serve the dual purpose of performing a duty I have for His Most Catholic Majesty's interests – and for the settling of an old account.'

Anne looked up at the firelit, hawkish face, not comprehending. 'Wh – why? Why not kill me now? Kill me, you disgusting – '

'Tut, tut,' Roche-Bourbon said, raising an admonishing finger. 'Insults will not ensure warm and cordial relations between us, my dear, and will only serve to encourage me to release you to the fervent attentions of men like these. That might prove too much to bear.'

Anne Brixham's chin lifted, the beautiful eyes still defiant.

'You will do that in any event, if I know your kind,' she said. 'So be damned to you.'

Roche-Bourbon smiled thinly. 'I admire your spirit, Miss Brixham.' He moved to her, raising her chin with one hand and then staring with glittering eyes down at her breasts until she turned her face away in a shudder of loathing and disgust.

'But I assure you, you will be quite safe,' said the Frenchman. 'At least until he comes for you.'

'He?' The girl stared.

'Your admirer. The fishpot colonial who has such pretensions of being a gentleman.'

'*Edward?*' Anne whispered. 'He's not – what do you know – ?'

'*Et voilà!* Interest awakes! Why, he has indeed returned to the Caribbean, my dear. And I have ensured he knows of your whereabouts. He will follow you, like the fool he is – and as I have planned.'

'What – what are you going to do?'

Roche-Bourbon's eyes turned to black steel. 'He will pursue us, while I carry out my other duties, my dear. And in the process I shall lay a very thorough trap for your Yankee lover.'

'Oh, dear God. Please – '

'Pray indeed to whatever you think of as God. For both you and your Edward Mainwaring, it will be only a matter of time. I will enjoy killing him. And then of course,' he smiled, 'there will be so many interesting things to do with you before I have the final pleasure of slitting your throat.'

And he touched her cheek gently with one bejewelled hand.

'So *many* interesting things!'

4

The longboat was running before the strong north-easterly trade, its loose-footed lugsails set out wing and wing with bearing out poles. The swells had risen with the lengthening day, and now, as noon approached, they were great sweeping mountains that loomed up, lifting the stern of the hurrying longboat, and then boiling past to rush on ahead, the longboat's bows rising as it sank back into the trough. The sea was a glittering blue-green, with white-caps kissed up here and there by the wind, and overhead in the crystalline sky small puffy clouds of pure white swept westward, as if pacing the boat.

For Edward Mainwaring, the morning's sailing had been a delight. The craft was in no real danger, and it had been an exhilarating and cleansing reward to rush over the sea after a cramped and uncomfortable night in which the boat had jerked to a confused, steep sea and fitful wind under the foresail alone.

When dusk had fallen, *Diana* was long since out of sight over the horizon, limping away to the northward, and Hooke had been growling at the longboat men until a watch and work routine had been established, and each man had found a place to wedge himself amongst the gear and stores which filled the craft. Mainwaring headed one watch, with Winton, Evans and Williams, while Hooke had the other three. It was the turn of Hooke's watch to 'go below', and the burly master was curled up in a bulky heap under a corner of a tarpaulin on the far side of the sternsheets. He was snoring loudly.

Mainwaring gripped the helm firmly, carefully keeping

the boat's transom to the advancing swells, looking over his shoulder as the dark peaks toppled up behind him, watching for the breaking crest that would poop the longboat, only to have the craft lift over them and feel them sweep ahead. On occasion the crests broke as the longboat rode on the forward face, and Mainwaring found himself steering the craft as it rushed along amidst a tumbling line of brilliant white surf, carried on the crest of the swell in an exhilarating surge until the crest hurtled past and the longboat slowed and wallowed. He was enjoying the muscular effort of the steering, and reflected how his attachment to the vast, endlessly variable world of wave, cloud and sky sustained him when the weight of command and responsibility threatened to turn him away from the sea.

Mainwaring scanned the figures forward on the boat. Evans was hunched on a thwart by the mainmast foot, his black locks tossed by the wind, putting a back splice in the end of the mainyard's halyard. Williams, who had been relieved by Mainwaring at the tiller an hour earlier, was now hunkering down as lookout just ahead of the foremast, squinting against the glare as he slowly scanned the horizon. Winton was on the floorboards between another set of thwarts, a bandana knotted around his head giving him a piratical air, and grimacing in concentration as he used a palm and needle to repair a rent in the spare mainsail. Slade and Sawyer were both huddled shapes, one under a blanket, the other under the free end of Hooke's tarpaulin, and a pair of jutting bare feet from behind the water and small beer casks marked where Tindall had burrowed in for some rest. The roar of the sea, the wind and sun, and the motion of the boat had induced a heavy-lidded drowsiness that made every chance for sleep precious.

The American looked down at the boat compass and

then ahead. If his reckoning had been correct, the mountains of Panama would soon appear, a thin grey uneven line above the haze of the horizon. And before that coastline, the scattered archipelago known as the San Blas would be stretched out. Mondego was the easternmost of that group, but how close Mainwaring's rough reckoning had brought them he had no way of knowing. One of the reasons for bringing Winton was his experience in coasting the San Blas group while serving in a Charles Town trader. Vernon had given Mainwaring a fairly clear picture of Mondego's appearance, and had even given him a chart of the island drawn and explained carefully in a neat round hand by Anne Brixham. He was far more worried than he had expected by the whole process, and the old sense of wariness, of lurking danger, was tingling at the back of his neck.

Dear Anne. Dear girl, said his mind. *If any harm has come to you . . .*

Beside him, Isaiah Hooke grunted and stirred, then sat up. He rubbed at the stubble on his cheek and squinted round with small, red-rimmed eyes.

'Christ's guts. Ye sleep as if shot in a damned boat.'

'You look a bit more rested, Mr Hooke,' said Mainwaring. 'Never heard the like of you thrashing about under that tarpaulin last night, however.'

'It's just that a lad needs a 'mick t' sleep properlike, zur, is all. Why, these 'ere thwarts be no gennulman's berth.'

Mainwaring grinned at the master as the longboat surfed on a large swell for several roaring moments. 'You're quite right. Good thing we're not gentlemen.'

Hooke bared gap teeth in reply. 'Whereabouts be we, d'ye reckon, sur?'

'Four, perhaps five leagues out from the San Blas. That's if my reckoning's worth a damn. And we hadn't swung this compass, so I've no idea on the variation of the whoreson thing.'

'Ye know the look o'Mondego, zur?'

'More or less. The admiral gave me a sketch done by Miss Brixham. And Winton's coasted it, although what he may have seen – or remember – is unknown.'

At Anne's name Hooke had brightened. 'Miss Anne. She's a lady, true as gunmetal, that 'un, zur.' He squinted at Mainwaring. 'Beggin yer pardon, zur, but it's clear ye're carryin' all sail on account she might be on a lee shore, so t' speak, zur. All the lads are worried too, zur. Why, she was full o' life, an' could hand, reef or steer better'n a clutch o' landsmen.'

Mainwaring nodded. 'You're right. I'm too bloody worried, to be frank. Thought all night about her and her father. Wondering what may have happened to them. It's not that far a sea passage, and there was little they needed to do. Even if foul weather put 'em harbour-bound for a week . . .' He did not finish.

'Hell, zur. They might've passed us in th' night. Or be standin' in t' Port Royal, smart as paint, right now.' The master paused. 'Ye think summat's happened, aye?'

Mainwaring bit a lip. 'I've that damned feeling of warning I get, Isaiah. And I don't like it. If we – '

Ahead in the boat Williams had abruptly sat upright, and then scrambled up on a thwart, clutching the foremast for support. He pointed, calling back over his shoulder.

'Land, sir!' he cried over the sea hiss. 'High line o' mountains in the haze there, look you! The Darien coast, sir!'

'Winton, what d'ye think? Take a look and see if you recognize anything,' said Mainwaring.

Winton pushed aside the sailmaking and groped his way with sure bare feet over the thwarts and gear, to clamber up beside Williams.

'Keep low, yew two,' growled Hooke. 'Else ye'll over-set us.'

Winton shaded his eyes with one hand. 'Dunno, sir. I can't – Aye, there she be.'

'"She", Winton?'

'Them mountains, sir. Know their cut, right enough. They be mostly inland o' th' Darien coast, eastw'd from Porto Bello to th' gulf o' San Blas. Them islands lie off this coast, sir. That double one, there, the Dons call some long name, but I recall we called it Suzy Wallace.'

'*Suzy Wallace?* Why?'

Winton grinned at Williams and then back at Mainwaring.

'Why, hell, sir, after the maid behind th' bar at the old Rose and Crown. She had a right beautiful pair o' – '

'Right you are, Winton,' grinned Mainwaring. 'I understand. Where does Mondego lie from here?'

Winton was peering ahead, shading his eyes with one hand again. He muttered to Williams as the latter pointed suddenly at something bearing off the bows on the distant shore.

'Speak up, man!' called Mainwaring.

Winton looked back. 'Sorry, sir. Mondego lies about – there, sir. 'Bout three points t'larboard. About where that smoke is risin'.

'*Smoke?*' Mainwaring exchanged a quick glance with Hooke. 'Take the tiller, Isaiah. Where's the glass?'

''Erc, zur.' Pulling the long telescope out of a bag under the near thwart, Hooke handed it to Mainwaring, then gripped the tiller. ''Ere, yew two. Down in th' boat!' he called to the two standing men. 'Cap'n's comin' for'ad.'

Mainwaring clambered on the thwarts until he could stand with his back braced against the foremast. At his feet, Williams and Winton were pointing as Mainwaring unlimbered and opened the long telescope.

'Just there, sir,' said Winton. 'In line with that sort o' cleft, like, sir.'

Mainwaring hefted the glass. It was difficult to keep the narrow field steady as the boat lurched under him. But finally he knew what he was looking at: a low, dark island shape, with higher ground at its right-hand end, a lower, flattish profile on the left.

And from its centre, two thick, black columns of smoke pillaring up until the wind pushed them away into a long black smudge off to the west and south.

'My God,' whispered Mainwaring.

'Is it Miss Anne's, sir?' asked Winton.

Mainwaring's lips were pressed into a hard line as he lowered the glass.

'If that's Mondego, Winton, it may be. It may be.' He paused, fighting back the sudden burst of wild anxiety. He handed the long telescope to Winton and climbed down.

'Both of you stand lookout, now. Winton, use the glass to sweep to either side of the island and tell me if you see so much as a bedsheet hoisted on a canoe. If there's a ship about I must know. And if you see anything move on the island as we approach – *anything* – I want to be told.'

'Aye, aye, sir,' said Winton. 'We'd be about two leagues off, now, sir. Would've seen the coast sooner, like, 'ceptin' for th' haze.'

'That's fine. But watch like hawks from this moment on.'

Mainwaring clambered back to Hooke at the tiller.

'Mondego, zur?' said the master.

'Aye. And with fires on it. Large ones, like burning buildings.'

Hooke's eyes went hard, and he spat forcefully over the gunwale into the sea. The plug of tobacco shifted to the other cheek.

118

'Whoreson Dons 'ave been afoot, likely. Damme, sir, d'ye think Miss Anne – ?'

'I don't wish to think of the possibility. But I think you'd best stir up Sawyer and Slade and have 'em ready the muskets. We're between five and six miles off and at this rate o'knots we'll fetch in there before nightfall. I'll take the helm. And break some biscuit out for everyone, will you?'

'Aye, zur,' said Hooke. Then he paused. 'If we find the Dons have – ?' He stopped.

Mainwaring's face was a grim mask. 'Someone will pay, Isaiah. Someone will pay.'

Through the next hours the wind held steady out of the north-west, and the longboat made rapid progress across the sea towards the Darien coast. A stern, relentless mood had settled over the men at the implications of the distant smoke struck home. Sawyer and Slade set about readying the muskets with a will, their usual good-natured banter silenced. They had fought together in *Athena* and understood what Anne Brixham had meant to Mainwaring. Now they sprung ramrods, aligned and tightened flints and applied oiled cloths with a hard set to their mouths, and very little talk.

Over the long afternoon the boat bore in, and gradually the land took shape. The pale grey line of the mountains resolved into a land mass of dark green, and in the foreground a cluster of low, wooded islets came into view. The ominous columns of smoke, thinner now but still visible, were rising from the humped shape of one at the far left of the group, which evidently was Mondego. Williams and Winton swept the horizon carefully, hardly pausing to gnaw at the biscuit Tindall tossed to them, or swallow Mainwaring's issue of a tot of rum after the biscuit. The men worked or waited in silence, deep in

119

their own thoughts, listening only to the rhythmic roar of the sea under the boat's bows and counter, and the creak of its masts.

For Mainwaring it was a time of reflection, and of worry. He feared that Anne and her father had been the target of some foul Spanish plundering or, worse, a visit from the heathenish pirates who were still present in the Caribbean, although in nowhere near their former numbers. The Brixhams might, after all, have carried off their most valuable possessions in their lugger, and burnt the rest to thwart the Spanish. But somehow that sort of destructiveness seemed alien to the Brixhams. Whatever that smoke was, Mainwaring felt certain it boded no good.

The narrow escape *Diana* had suffered at the hands of the *pampero* had started a complex chain of thought in Mainwaring's head. There was nothing extraordinary about a ship being caught by a sudden squall and taking heavy damage. Doubtless, such phenomena destroyed vessels regularly, thus accounting for at least a portion of those which simply vanished. But Mainwaring had begun to wonder if *Diana* had been luckier than he realized in surviving the *pampero*; his mind turned back to the odd, cryptic note which he had found in the locked desk drawer. Was the 'her' which was not to be trusted a woman, or the ship itself? Again, in an unbidden and impulsive thought rather than a reasoned one, he found himself wondering if he had left Howe in command of a vessel with some hidden flaw that might surface at a critical point, and betray Howe and his men at the very moment when they needed –

'Sail, sir!' called back Winton.

Mainwaring sat up. 'Where away?'

'Larboard bow, fine, sir. Just make out her upper canvas. She's in th' lee o' Mondego, looks like, sir.'

'The lee?'

'Aye, sir. Like as if he's standin' in t' th' mainland.'

'Can you make out her rig?' said Mainwaring.

Winton was hefting the great glass.

'Full-rigged ship, is all, sir. I c'n see a mizzen tops'l. But them's are Spanish colours at 'er maintruck.'

'Dear Christ,' breathed Mainwaring. He looked at Hooke, who was wiping down a cutlass. 'The Dons have been there, Isaiah.'

Hooke spat into the sea, fingering the edge of his blade. 'Aye, zur. They c'n be whoreson cruel, is all I'm thinkin'.'

'That is exactly what I'd rather not think about,' said Mainwaring grimly. He pressed against the tiller bar as the longboat lifted and then surfed for a few moments down the hissing face of a swell, then raised his voice. 'Winton! Can ye see the island itself?'

Winton lowered the glass. 'Aye, sir!' he called back. 'Them fires is mostly out. Looks like a channel on th' left. Like as if there was an island off the east tip, an' a cove betwixt 'em.'

With his free hand Mainwaring rummaged in the small chest and brought out Anne Brixham's carefully-drawn little chart.

'Aye. That'd be Gannet Isle. The anchorage is inside, between Gannet and the main island. Stand by the sheets, there, Slade and Sawyer! We're turning to larboard!' He waited until the sheets were free to ease, and then put the tiller gently over.

'Bearing dead ahead now, sir!' came Winton's cry.

'Very good.' Mainwaring looked for a mark on the distant mountain line and finding one, a sharper notch, steadied the longboat's bows on it.

Three hours more brought the longboat to within a league of the island, and its features were clear now. The swells and wind remained steady on the boat's quarter, and it lifted and dipped as it foamed and rushed along, the stained canvas of the lugsails tugging at their lacing. Each time the stern lifted under an overtaking swell, Mainwaring scoured the shore and hill line that he could glimpse for any sign of life.

'Nothin' t' see, zur,' said Hooke, as if to echo his thoughts.

'Aye. Take the tiller, Isaiah. I want to look at this chart again. There may be something I've missed.'

Mainwaring spread the drawing on his knees, trying to relate it to the low, humped islet towards which they rushed. In plan, it was a long oval, with a cut in its eastern end that formed the anchorage; that cove was protected by a smaller island, Gannet. The plantation was shown as a tiny cluster of buildings on the cove, just above the beach, with a single small jetty. Low hills were penned in by Anne behind the buildings, with a central gully leading off to swampland and a marshy west shore. There were narrow beaches on the north and south side.

'There, sir!' called Williams. 'There's th' channel into th' cove. Ye c'n see Gannet Isle clear-like.'

Mainwaring looked up. They were, perhaps, a thousand yards from the channel into the cove. On this heading they would sail straight in, Gannet Isle to their left, the bulk of Mondego to their right.

'Keep an eye for shoaling water, there!' called Mainwaring to Winton and Williams. Then he nodded at Jonas Slade, who was curled on a thwart cradling the bulk of a Brown Bess musket.

'Slade! Sit for'rard, there, between the fore and the main. Prime and load, and watch our starboard side! Sawyer, do the same for the larboard. Evans and Tindall, stand by the sheets, and be ready to move quickly if we have to come about and beat out!'

'Aye, aye, zur!' There was a sudden clumping and flurry of movement, and the men's eyes came alight.

Mainwaring saw Sawyer sighting along his musket and grinning at Slade.

'Now which of you two is the better shot, Sawyer?' he asked.

The Vineyarder, his blond hair stringing out like lank straw from under his stocking cap, winked at Mainwaring as he clutched his cartridge box and began to slither forward over the thwarts.

'Hell, sir, ol' Jonas couldn't hit his mark nohow with that firelock. He ain't big enough.'

'Jacko, yew stow that Yankee bilge, quick-like!' said the offended little Briton. 'I could lie down an' die, now, an' still 'ave enough air in m' sails t' outshoot *yew*, ye damned Jonathan!' Slade huffed in exaggerated offence.

'Oh, hell, now, ain't that jest the most foolish thing yew ever did say, yew horse-arsed little – !'

'Enough, the both of you!' cried Mainwaring. 'I thought you were messmates.'

Slade winked in turn at Mainwaring. '*Me?* Wiv th' loikes o' *him*?' he gaped in horror. 'Why, true as paint, I'd as sooner sleep wiv a Portsmouth rat than divvy a plum duff wiv' im! Now, lookee, zur, what d' ye think of a wooden head fool who – !'

Slade stopped when he saw the dark look that Hooke and Mainwaring had fixed at him.

'Aye, aye, zur,' he said contritely. 'Starb'd battery I be, zur.' He scrambled forward, dragging a cartridge box and musket with him. Sawyer grinned at him as the Briton arrived beside him, and offered a plug of tobacco; Slade took a portion with immense initial dignity, and then burst out in a cackle of laughter which Sawyer echoed.

Mainwaring shook his head, and looked at Hooke, glad of the moment's diversion from the worry and tension.

'Those two never change, do they?' he grinned. 'Like peas in a pod.'

Hooke nodded, his blue eyes tiny points of amusement. 'Aye, zur. But they've tied a long splice. Closer mates yew'd never meet.'

Winton was pointing. 'Channel ahead, zur! Low breakers to either side! 'Tain't wider'n a frigate c'd get through!'

'Take the tiller, Isaiah!' Mainwaring stood, balancing against the roll of the boat. Mondego Island was suddenly close ahead, the humped hills covered with palmetto that shook and waved in the wind, the beach below them a gleaming narrow line of white against which the swells thumped in mist-shrouded power, the narrow channel dark and smooth between the main island and the small, scrub-covered rock that was Gannet Isle. It was there they must steer.

'Stand ready with those sheets, lads. The wind will likely turn about a bit as we go in.'

The little craft swept in, the loud surf thudding on the long beach off to the right, the mist drifting over the dune grass and lit with sudden rainbows that glimmered and vanished in the declining sun. To the left, the edge of Gannet Isle was more rocky, the break of the surf less solid, a tumbling wash up green-slimed rock faces. But now the longboat was shooting through the gap, the land suddenly rushing past, and they were scudding into a large cove of calm, startlingly pale green water over a white sand bottom.

'Christ, look thar!' exclaimed Hooke.

The wind eased suddenly as they came into the lee of the point, the lugsails going limp and slack, their sagging sheets dragging in the water until they were hauled in. The longboat was footing in towards a curved, short beach, the dark oval shadow of the boat moving below them on the rippled sand thirty feet below.

'Steer for the beach, Isaiah,' said Mainwaring, in an even voice. 'Slade, Sawyer, go to full cock and stay alert. Williams, stand by the bow line.'

The double click of the musket locks sounded over the rippling water under the longboat bows. From ashore a single bird called, echoing and raucous in the dark tree line. The surf still boomed distantly behind them, and now the full heat of the air was obvious. Ahead, a jetty ran out from the beach, as Anne's drawing had shown. But it had been set afire, and only a line of blackened pilings held a few remaining planks. Farther up the beach stood the skeletal ruins of three buildings, little more than blackened heaps of rubbish, smouldering with wisps of smoke swirling round the ashes before dispersing among the rows of singed and blackened palms that marked the edge of the trees.

But a scene of horror lay before those ruins, in the sprawled and twisted human remains scattered between the buildings and the beach. The bodies of men and women, light and dark skinned, stripped naked and placed in grotesque or obscene positions, the bloody mutilations glisteningly evident even at this distance. Overhead, half a dozen vultures, their wings like black hands against the hot sky, circled patiently lower. On the blistering sand of the beach, dark rivulets of blood had left lacy tracks towards the sea edge.

The longboat drifted in silence as the men stared, their mouths dry as the comprehension of what they were seeing sank in.

'Lord Jesus,' Winton finally croaked. 'The Dons are bastards. But *this* . . .'

Mainwaring found himself shaking with a violence that threatened to overwhelm him until through sheer force of will, he stopped the tremors, pushing away the disgust and nausea, controlling his mind and voice.

'Stand to, lads,' he shouted firmly. 'Evans, Williams, brail in the fore and main. Slade, keep your eye keen. You as well, Sawyer. Winton, you and Tindall each get a sweep out. Lively, now!'

In shaken silence the men gathered in the sails, the canvas crumpling against their yards as the brails were hauled. Winton and Tindall wrestled two long sweeps out from the clutter in the boat and set them in their thole pins with a thump.

'Right, then. Give way together,' said Mainwaring.

The boat crept in over the pale green shimmer. With a few strokes of the long, heavy sweeps the stem of the craft was suddenly grinding against sand, and they were aground in the shallows of the beach.

'Slade, Sawyer, out and watch to either side! The rest, out and push.'

Winton and Tindall boated their sweeps with a clump, and the men went over the side wordlessly. With Hooke beside him, Mainwaring threw his legs over the gunwale and splashed into six inches of tepid water. Together they grasped the gunwale and thrust the boat firmly on to the beach.

'Muskets, Slade. How many?' said Mainwaring.

'Weren't able t' get but two readied properlike, sir. Bad flints an' all,' said the little man. His face was pale, and his fingers were white where they gripped his musket.

'Can't be helped, then. Just see you two keep a sharp eye open.'

In silence, the men moved up the beach until they were level with Slade and Sawyer, and stood staring round them grimly at the horror.

Hooke's eyes had become points of steel.

'Lookee thar, zur,' he said hoarsely. 'Why, that weren't but a child!'

Mainwaring could not follow Hooke's extended finger.

A mist had closed over his eyes, and within him, under the disgust and anger, with a cold knot of fear.

Dear God, said his mind. *Where was she?*

He had to move. Action was needed.

'All right, lads. Break out the cutlasses from the boat. Isaiah, take Tindall, Slade and Evans and look over that warehouse, or whatever, by the tree line. Williams, Sawyer and Winton, with me. We'll look at the houses. And all of you, bark it out if you find someone alive.'

'Aye, zur,' said Hooke, and shifted his tobacco plug to the other cheek. 'Come on, lads.'

With his party at his heels, the weight of a cutlass heavy in his hand, Mainwaring moved cautiously up the beach, his throat dry. He looked quickly at the pathetic figures as they passed them, seeing the Spaniards' cruelty and deliberate brutality, a deep anger boiling within him. With each huddled form he desperately hoped he would not see her features frozen in pain and death.

'Must be nigh on twenty dead 'ere, sir,' whispered Winton at his elbow.

Mainwaring nodded, looking now at the smoking ruin of the warehouse. The wood and wattle structure, with palm-leaf thatch roof, must have gone up like a torch. In the black, twisted debris of the interior Mainwaring could make out the forms of several more bodies, huddled where they had died in each other's arms.

'Dear God,' muttered Mainwaring through his teeth, 'let's get on with this before I swear to kill every damned Don I come across. Winton, circle round to the left, there, and – '

The musket's blast was a solid, ear-punching thump, the pink flash bright at the edge of Mainwaring's vision. As he spun, the puff of smoke had burst out from the undergrowth under the palm tree line, and a ball had hummed by, inches from his ear.

127

'Down!' barked Mainwaring, and dived headlong into the shelter of a toppled, charcoaled timber from the warehouse roof. His shoulder hit the sand hard, and grit flew into his face, stinging in his eyes. He rolled once, twice, to one side, then whipped off his tricorne and risked a look over the log.

Ftoom!

The musket blasted again, a scant twenty seconds after the first round. Beside Mainwaring's ear there was a sharp *thwock*, and splinters of the timber sprang away, one lancing a cut in Mainwaring's cheek.

'Damn!' Mainwaring ducked, cuffing at the cut, looking for Winton and the others. He hefted the cutlass, cursing it, wishing for a pistol or musket. He saw Winton now, curled behind a barrel, his pale features grimacing as he tried to peer around his pitiful shelter, looking for the hidden musketman.

'Don't move, Winton!' hissed Mainwaring. 'He'll get you if you move! Stay there! Williams, Sawyer! Where in hell are – ?'

'Here, sir!' came Williams' hoarse whisper. 'In behind the log wall o' th' shed!'

Mainwaring twisted round on his back to look, and spotted both men squatting in the shadows of the ruined warehouse, behind a section of remaining log wall. The American could see Sawyer wiping furiously at the lock of his musket with his shirt-tail, while Williams was peering out through chinks in the logs, trying to see the hidden marksman.

'Sawyer!' Mainwaring hissed. 'Can ye fire?'

Sawyer's eyes were white in the gloom of the ruined building. He nodded. 'Aye, sir! Damned priming spilled out when I tumbled in here, is all!'

'All right. He's just to the left of the double palm,

there, with the cut marks on the trunks. Be ready when I draw his aim!'

'Christ, sir, he'll put a ball in ye – !'

'*Do it!*' Mainwaring waited until he saw Sawyer ease the muzzle of the long flintlock over the logs, draw back the piece to full cock, and sight carefully along it.

Then he took a deep breath, and lifted his head and shoulders above the shelter of the timber. The flash of the musket, and its thump, were matched by the almost simultaneous blast of Sawyer's musket, deafening in Mainwaring's ears. In the same instant, he had heard a thin cry from the tree line, and felt the sleeve of his linen coat twitch. He looked down and saw a thumb-sized hole in the cloth of the upper arm. Acrid smoke from Sawyer's musket was swirling round him, and his mouth felt dry.

'Got him, sir!' hooted Sawyer. And then he and Williams were up and over the logs, and sprinting for the tree line.

Mainwaring stood up, a weakness in his legs, as Hooke and the others came sprinting through the sand from the far side of the building.

'Yew all right, zur?' puffed Hooke. 'Hell, it sounded loike yew'd sprung a Don ambush!'

Mainwaring picked up his hat and slapped it against his leg, feeling the grit in his teeth.

'Just one, Isaiah. But a damned good shot, by God!'

Sawyer and Williams were standing at the tree line looking down at something in the undergrowth.

'Still alive, sir!' called Sawyer. 'Shall we do 'im?'

'No! There's been enough throats cut!' Mainwaring strode through the sand, Hooke and the others behind him, until he was looking down at the man who had very nearly killed him.

'Jesus. A mere lad,' said Hooke. The other men gathered round, staring down at a slim Spanish youth in his mid-teens, with dark curly hair held down by a stocking cap. He was barefoot, and wore ragged, striped breeches torn open at the knee, and a stained white shirt. Blood soaked the side of the shirt and streaked across the thin brown chest, where a crude pewter crucifix on a thong lay. He was breathing in quick, shallow rhythm, his eyes tightly shut in pain.

'Looks like yer ball hit 'im in the chest, Jacko,' said Williams.

'Aye, He'll not last long,' said the Vineyarder, and spat.

''Vast, there. Belay that talk,' said Hooke. He turned to Mainwaring. 'Mayhap we could bind 'im up, zur. There might be summat he c'd tell us about – '

'Sure as – you're a damned Protestant rat – I'll tell ye nothin', ye – great hairy poltroon – !'

Mainwaring and the others stared. It had been the Spaniard who had spoken, and whose eyes, an unexpected and startling pale blue, were glaring up at them in reckless enmity.

'Well, I'm buggered!' gasped Slade, at Hooke's elbow. 'A Paddy!'

Mainwaring squatted beside the man. 'Mr Hooke, find some water, from the boat if you must. Sawyer, I'll have your shirt-tail, if you please. Quickly, now.' He reached out and ripped away the shirt from the thin chest, exposing a bloody furrow that oozed blood.

'A graze across the ribs. That'll heal soon enough. Who are you?'

The Irishman smiled, showing even white teeth. 'A darlin' lad – down on his luck. And,' he grimaced, 'not likely to say anyt'ing to the loikes of you, sorr. With respect.'

Mainwaring could not resist a smile at the youth's brave front. But a certain trembling in the latter's hands gave away more than the pain of the wound.

'Well, then, your name at least?'

'Fergus Shanahan. And – if yez t'ink oi'll tell yez anyt'ing else, sorr, ye may go – straight to hell, where isn't it likely His Nibs is already waitin' for yez.'

Hooke handed Mainwaring a wooden canteen.

'Bloody bog Irish!' he snorted. 'Full o' gunpowder an' poison, and spoutin' poetry while they slits yer throat!'

Mainwaring took Sawyer's ripped shirt-tail and used a moistened corner to clean the wound. It was not a serious one, and the impact of the ball had merely knocked the youth's wind from his lungs. With a few deft strokes Mainwaring wrapped the strip of cloth around the thin chest and under the back, knotting it in the front.

'Now,' he said, 'sit up and see if you can breathe.'

The Irishman sat up, grimacing slightly. He flicked a quick, appraising look at Mainwaring and the others.

'It'll do fine, sorr. I take it ye be captain?'

'Aye, I be captain, Shanahan. Of his Britannic Majesty's Ship *Diana*.'

'Sweet Mother Mary!' breathed Shanahan. 'The Navy. Poor Fergus in the clutches of the godless English Navy, no less!'

'Ere, just yew watch 'oo yew calls godless!' spoke up Slade, who was leaning on his musket to one side. 'No Papist 'as the right t'call down any – '

'Ease your oar, there, Slade,' said Mainwaring. He turned back to the little Irishman. 'What were you doing with the Dons, Shanahan? Were you a party to all *this*?' And he gestured at the corpses.

The Irishman flushed and looked down. 'Dear God,' he said, 'no, no. I was not a part of – of that. I couldn't have. It was merciless cruel, and an abomination to God. I wouldn't do it. Couldn't.'

'But you were in that ship?'

Shanahan looked at the corpses in hard bitterness.

131

'Signed on with the Spanisher in Bocca Chica, sorr. Not out of any love for the garlicky bastards, but t' get off the beach. A sailor has t' sail, yer honour. I'd been in a Dutchman, before, what went aground on Aruba. And a Spanisher 'twere all I c'd sign on, more's the pity.'

'What ship, then?'

'The *Esperanza*, sorr.'

Mainwaring looked at Hooke. 'Could've been the ship we saw sailing towards the mainland,' he said.

Shanahan nodded, fingering his wound. 'That's be her. Lifted her hook and sailed this morning. The *Esperanza*, she is, with a terrible cruel man of a captain. Terrible, that Frenchman!'

Mainwaring's arm shot out in lightning speed, bunching the front of Shanahan's shirt in his fist.

'A *Frenchman*? Who, by God! Tell me his name!'

Shanahan paled at the expression on Mainwaring's face, and shrank back.

'Rock – Rock something, sorr! I can't – !'

'Roche-Bourbon?' said Mainwaring.

'Yes! That was him, sorr. A vicious fellow. Took a real delight in killin', he did.'

Mainwaring relaxed his grip and stood up, his hands on his hips. He nodded at Hooke.

'That bastard. And he did *this*!' Mainwaring's eyes burned as he looked round the beach.

Beside him, the Irishman rose cautiously to his feet. He was not tall, and winced at the pain of his wound. He hung his head as he spoke.

'It's a terrible t'ing he did, sorr. And I were no part of it. I t'ought he was doin' a bit o' piratin', like, roustin' out a fish station. But when we got ashore and he began the killin', I took to th' bush, Sweet Mary be my witness. I couldn't stand it. The screams was somet'ing pitiful. It – I – ' The man stopped, unable to go on.

'You're not too bloodthirsty, are ye, Shanahan?' said Mainwaring gently. 'Why did you shoot at us, then?'

Shanahan shrugged. 'T'ought ye was Spanishers comin' back t' get me. For killin' that Frenchman's mate, sorr.'

'What? You *killed* one of them?'

'Yes, sorr. He was about t' rape a poor wee girl, couldn't be more than twelve years old. I put a ball into him an' let her escape for the trees. Poor creature, I don't know if she made it.'

A thought came into Mainwaring's head, and he looked at Hooke, seeing that the same idea had occurred there. A glance round the faces of the others showed him they shared the same feeling.

'Shanahan, you're no cut-throat Don. And we've a need for good men. Ye can sign the Articles with us, if ye've a mind,' he said. 'Better with us than the Spaniards.'

The Irishman look up sharply at Mainwaring, and then at the other faces. Where a few moments ago there had been hostility and suspicion, there was welcome and recognition. He flashed an even, bright smile that must have been a memory in some village girl's thoughts somewhere.

'You're a gentleman and a Christian, sorr,' he said. 'And bein' as I have no ship, I'd be pleased.'

'Done, then,' said Mainwaring. 'And ye can pick up your musket. It'll stay yours.'

Shanahan beamed.

Mainwaring pursed his lips. There was one question he must ask.

'Shanahan, this fishery was owned by some English planters. An older, tall man named Brixham, and his daughter. Do you have any idea what might have happened to them?'

Shanahan leaned on the long musket.

'Aye, sorr. The old gentleman ran down on the jetty as

133

soon's we came to anchor in the cove, and took to shootin' at us. The Frenchman had some o' the Dons fire at him, and he fell into the shallows.'

'Slade!' barked Mainwaring. 'You and Sawyer get down to the remains of the jetty. See if you can find anything of the old man. Quickly!'

'Aye, zur!' knuckled Slade, and the two men sprinted off across the sand, their bare feet kicking up a fine dust.

'Go on, Shanahan,' said Mainwaring.

'Oi remember the girl too, sorr. Pretty thing, she was, with a sort o' queenly air, a lad might say. Dark hair, and proud; and didn't she fight like the furies until the Frenchman's bully boys took her.'

The next question came through gritted teeth. 'What did they do to her, Shanahan? Did Roche-Bourbon – ?'

'No, he did not, sorr. An' seein' as how he was visitin' the very tortures o'hell on the other poor divvils, it were remarkable, says I, t' see how careful, like, he treated her. I saw her bein' taken down th' after companionway in *Esperanza* gentle as you please. 'Ceptin', o' course, th' tongue lashin' she was giving the Frenchman. Ye'd think she'd been a sailor, t'hear it!'

A kind of bitter-sweet pain gripped Mainwaring's chest, and he had almost literally to shake away the overwhelming rush of anxiety and care that came over him. He bit his lip and stared out at the low, sand-dune hills, behind which the Spanish ship had vanished in haze virtually moments ago, carrying Anne with her.

'All right, Shanahan. I'm glad you were there to see what happened,' he said evenly. 'And glad you had no stomach for what went on here.' He paused. 'Would you have any idea where Roche-Bourbon is headed? We know a little of what he's about. But can you help?'

Shanahan furrowed his brow as Hooke and the others leaned closer, listening intently.

'Why he put in here, no one knew, sorr. The ship's orders were clear. We wuz sailin' for Porto Bello – and didn't you and your lads do half a job on the forts there, by Saint Patrick! – and were meant to leave the ship at anchor, sure, whilst we took the *camino real* over to th' Panama shore and brought back most of a cargo o' bullion and whatnot from some great whoreson Spanish hulk as was there, hidin' from the English squadron the Spanishers have heard is in the South Sea.'

Mainwaring nodded. 'Aye. The damned Manila Galleon. Likely called the *Nuestra Señora* of something.'

Shanahan was startled. 'Aye, sorr! That was her! The *Nuestra Señora de Granada!* We wuz promised a divvy that'd make us kings, if we'd offload th' galleon an' muleteam as much of it as we could back to Porto Bello and the *Esperanza*.'

Mainwaring spat into the sand to clear his throat. 'Mark that, lads,' he said. 'Just as we thought. They're using the old South Sea fleet route to dodge the galleon's haul past Anson and get it back to Spain!'

Hooke scratched at his stubble chin. Like them all, he was dripping with perspiration in the close, windless air of the island lee.

'That's a temptin' target, zur. Ain't it too bad we don't have our *Diana*, and c'd wait off Porto Bello an' take the *Esperanza* when she put out, booty an' all!'

There was a growl of assent from the other men.

Mainwaring's mind was racing. 'But we don't have *Diana*, Mr Hooke. We've eight men – nine – and a longboat. And in the meantime that bastard Roche-Bourbon's got Miss Brixham in his grip.'

Hooke knew the look in Mainwaring's eye. And his own twinkled as he spoke next.

'What'd ye intend to do, zur?'

135

'*Do?* Damme, I think it's pretty clear, lads. We're going after the bastard. I want Miss Brixham back alive.'

Hooke squinted at him. 'How d'ye mean, zur? Surely ye can't mean a landin' on th' coast an' marchin' overland t' bloody Panama – !' Then he saw Mainwaring's mouth lift in a small smile.

'Christ on a crutch, ye *do* mean that, zur!'

Mainwaring's eyes burned with purpose. 'Look here, Mr Hooke. The Frenchman's going to anchor his ship in Porto Bello harbour. No defences, now, to speak of, and likely only a few Dons in the town, half-frightened out of their wits. And he's going to march over the road to the Panama coast. It's twenty-five leagues or so, true enough, but by God, Sir Harry Morgan did it! So can we!'

Hooke scratched his thatch. 'But why, zur? With respect. Can't we just wait along th' shore until the Frog comes back over th' mountains wiv th' swag, and jump 'em afore they can lift their hook?'

'Because, Mr Hooke, we've a chance to do more. We've a chance to take *all* the cargo of that galleon, instead of whatever portion comes across on Roche-Bourbon's pack train. We've a chance to take a damned galleon itself!'

'Wiv *nine* men? Beggin' yer pardon, zur, but – !'

'Who can say what we can do, Mr Hooke! At the least, we can burn the damned thing, and that'll singe a few Dons' tail feathers!'

Hooke and the others looked at one another, a reckless light dawning in their eyes.

'And we might save Miss Brixham's life, into the bargain,' said Mainwaring quietly. 'It's worth a gamble, lads!'

Hooke's rough-hewn features set in a firm mould. 'Aye, zur! By God, that it would. What d'ye say, lads? Are ye for Panama and a whoreson galleon full o'gold?'

There was a bark of assent from the men, and Shanahan's voice was one of them. The Irishman stepped forward a pace when the voices quieted.

'If ye'll pardon the liberty, sorr, I can suggest a way t' get a leg up on the Dons, so to speak.'

'Tell us,' said the American.

Shanahan crouched and quickly drew a crude map in the light sand wih his finger.

'Look here, sorr. The Frenchman'll anchor in Porto Bello – here – and take horses or *burros* over the trail to the Panama coast. But with your longboat, we c'd outflank 'im, so t' speak.'

'Indeed? How so?'

'The Chagrès River, sorr! It begins at the sea at Chagrès, westward along the coast a bit from Porto Bello. Your ships attacked there, too. The river runs inland from there and then cuts easterly along the central valley and crosses the pack-team trail almost halfway across the way to Panama, at Venta de Cruces. If we wuz t' row up the river t' there – it's passable that far, I knows – we c'd arrive on the Panama coast from therc four, maybe five days sooner!'

'Wouldn't the Dons be watching the river?' said Mainwaring.

'Only at Chagrès itself, sorr, and then there'd be nothin' till we got to the ford at Venta de Cruces. An' there's little there but some God-forsaken huts, a customhouse for the *duaneros*, a stable for relief mules – where we c'd get mounts for ourselves, one way or t' other – and mayhap ten leagues left to march to the Panama coast!'

Mainwaring looked at the crude map, and then at Hooke. 'What d'ye think, Isaiah?' he said quietly. 'Think we could do it?'

Hooke spat again. 'It'd be a whoreson risky business, zur. But I'd rather row than march wiv all them snakes an' whatnot nippin' at me 'eels. By God, I'd wager we could do 'er!'

Mainwaring nodded, resolution crystallizing within

him. 'Right, then. We'll do what we must here, and then ready the longboat for the run to the mouth of the Chagrès.' He looked round the dismal scene at the pitiful shapes and the black-winged vultures circling patiently overhead, their feathers tinged golden now by the setting sun. 'See what you can do about burying these poor wretches, Mr Hooke. Then we'll spend the night, and sail at dawn.'

He paused, about to say more, when Slade and Sawyer came puffing around the corner of one fire-blackened ruined building.

Slade halted before Mainwaring and dropped the butt of his musket to the sand.

'Nuffin', zur,' he panted. 'Nought. No sign o' th' old gentleman, 'ceptin' a pair o' shoes on th' beach edge beside th' burnt jetty pilings.'

'Aye, sir,' said Sawyer. 'Ain't no sign. Reckon a shark might' a come in from th' lagoon an' et' im'.'

Mainwaring swore silently. Poor Anne.

'Very well. Thank you both,' he said. 'Mr Hooke, let's get the burial party going. I'll lend a hand if you find enough tools. But quickly, now. When that first dawn light breaks, I want us to be at sea.'

He looked westward, towards the setting sun and distant Porto Bello.

'At first light!' he breathed.

His Most Catholic Majesty's ship *Esperanza* had cleared Drake's Isle and was standing in for the harbour mouth of Porto Bello. The sun had set in a riot of colour to the west, and in the dark of the harbour only a few feeble points of light marked the anchorage before the squalid little town and the ruins of the fort of San Geronimo.

The wind had faded, until now it was only a fitful, hot cat's-paw touching at the ship, and the men moved to the pinrails and taffrail in surly slowness, clewing up the slack canvas and cursing the sodden heat that drifted out over the ship from the land like some odorous mist. Porto Bello, after Vernon's destructive attack, was even more a pestilential, fever-ridden hellhole, and the crew of the *Esperanza* cursed, too, the steely-willed Frenchman who had driven them here, unmoved as they were by the promises of rich payment for carrying the bullion over from the Panama shore. They were cynical, all too aware that by far the greater part of any reward for the thankless task in which some of them would die would go to the officers, the *hidalgos*, the *duaneros* – in short, to almost anyone but themselves.

Below, in the gloom of the tiny cabin which had belonged to the unfortunate Ortiz – now dead in the undergrowth of Mondego Island with Fergus Shanahan's musket ball through his heart – Anne Brixham knelt on the coarse ticking mattress of the box bunk, working rapidly as she listened for approaching feet. She was still in the torn, grimy gown, and her face was smudged with soot and dirt, across which tears had made courses. But now she was working with furious speed. She had ripped a narrow strip from the hem of her gown, and two similar lengths from the rough wool of the bunk's coverlet. Now her fingers were working rapidly as she began to braid the three strips together into a strong cord that, when finished, would measure about half her height.

Suddenly the passageway outside the cabin door echoed to the thump and scuffle of feet, and Roche-Bourbon's voice sounded in a snarl over the words of another man and a softer, pleading voice. Anne thrust her half-finished rope under the coverlet edge and shrank back against the bulkhead, her heart pounding in her throat.

The door was opened with a kick, and Anne stared as another girl, with nothing but her tousled long black hair to cover her nakedness, was thrown roughly into the room, where she fell painfully hard to the decking and lay cowering, sobbing silently. A squat Spanish seaman in a filthy shirt and tattered breeches threw a bundle of clothing at the girl, knuckled his forelock to the tall figure of Roche-Bourbon behind him, and left, a toothless grin on his face.

The Frenchman stepped into the cabin, his immaculate boots gleaming in the yellow light of the lantern that hung outside, at the foot of the companionway. He was still in his velvet elegance, despite the heat, and toyed with a slim cane as his dark, glittering eyes centred on Anne.

'No doubt you've been lonely, my dear,' he said pleasantly. 'I've brought you a companion. And some things to wear. You must be quite bored with that gown by now.'

Anne pressed her back against the hard planking of the ship's side, feeling the revulsion at this man rising in her like nausea.

'Who is she?' she whispered, looking at the wretched figure on the deck. 'What have you done to her?'

'A slave. A Mosquito Coast woman, *hein*? She speaks a kind of English. I thought she was a *cimarron*, until Ortiz revealed he bought her in Cartagena. Had no idea she was on board. Poor Ortiz. When that treacherous Irishman did for him, she belonged to no one. These tedious Spanish were amusing themselves with her in the fo'c'sle when I decided you might care to have a lady in waiting, so to speak.'

Anne looked down at the huddled form of the shaking, weeping girl. Even in the gloom she could see the red welts and cuts across the girl's slim back and felt a cold contempt surfacing through her revulsion and fear.

'Is there no limit to what you will do? To what you will

tolerate? What kind of King's officer can you claim to be, to behave as you do!'

Roche-Bourbon laughed lightly. 'Ever hopeful for a gleam of decency in me, aren't you, *ma petite*? I fear it is a waste of effort. And do not think I wished to rescue that wretch from the hands of those swine. The louts were about to knife one another over her, and one must have the full attention of one's crew.'

'Then what do you intend for her? The same with which you have threatened me?' Anne asked, determined not to show Roche-Bourbon an inch of weakness.

'We face a rather tedious journey by mule across the *camino real* to the South Sea. You can look after each other, and spare me the necessity. I've provided clothing, and you might consider getting this wretch into some of it, and select a suitable riding costume for yourself. You really cannot enjoy our travels dressed like *that*, you know.' His eyes dropped to her breasts. 'Your charms become far too evident, for one thing.'

Anne's cheeks flamed, but she bit back the quick retort. She looked down at the girl, who had raised a dazed, tear-streaked face in a kind of beseeching terror. The girl was clearly one of the beautiful products of black slave inter-marriage with Arawaks, or Mosquito Indians: high cheekbones, dark-lashed eyes, olive skin. A thin trickle of blood ran from one corner of her mouth. On impulse, Anne held out her arms to her, and the trembling girl crept up on to the bunk and huddled against her like a child.

'How touching and comforting,' sneered Roche-Bourbon.

With her head pressed against the girl's dark hair, Anne Brixham fixed Roche-Bourbon with a cold look.

'I wonder, Chevalier, what viper was your mother,' she found herself saying. 'She must have despised you from

141

the moment she spawned you. But then at first *sight* of you she must have turned away in disgust!'

The Frenchman's face went pale and stone-like, and the savagery in the dark eyes chilled Anne to the heart.

'You cause me to repeat myself,' he hissed. 'It serves my purpose at the present to leave you unmolested. But if you try my patience too greatly, I warn you, what will pass for your existence would be exceedingly unpleasant. I suggest you remember that.'

Anne's gaze did not waver. 'Certainly. And I shall remember, while you bully women, that you are less successful against men. And one in particular.'

For a terrifying instant Anne thought Roche-Bourbon would spring at her, like some great velvet cat. But the flash of violence left the black eyes, and the coldly reasoned venom returned.

'*Formidable!* A woman of such spirit. I really do admire you. But now, you see, you have given me more than one wound to savour. And eventually repay.' He looked at the naked girl huddled against Anne. 'This one will be a diversion. A few moments of sport to lay her cut open like a peach, after the more deserving of my crew have enjoyed themselves in her. But *you*' – and Roche-Bourbon's smile sent a rod of steel through Anne's heart – 'are a different prospect. A lingering experience will be appropriate, I should think. How delicious it will be to make you scream until you think you can stand no more. But only to find that marvellous new levels of suffering are possible for you. The prospect is quite exciting.' He bowed slightly. 'But we can discuss that later. Sleep well.' And with a swirl of the velvet coat-skirts he was gone, the door latching shut and a bolt thrust into place.

Anne pulled the girl to her and closed her eyes, willing back the terror and despair.

'Oh, Edward!' she whispered into the darkness. 'Please

142

God, you will find me in time!' And she let her own quiet sobs finally take possesion of her.

The late afternoon sun was about to dip behind the low hills to the right of the mouth of the Chagrès River. Perhaps half a league at sea, Edward Mainwaring's long-boat lay hove to, its foresail brailed in, the mainsail sheeted flat while the boat rode to what apparently was a fisherman's long-hook line set out from the bows. And the figures that lay about the boat, bandanas or ragged hats shielding them from the dying sun's red light as they slept, resembled a clutch of fishermen hoping that the bounty of the sea would compensate for their sloth in bringing home a catch for their village.

But now, as the sun sank behind the bulk of the Castillo de San Lorenzo, on the bluff which marked, as they looked at it, the right-hand side of the river mouth, one of the figures in the boat stirred. He liftd his dog-eared hat, peered at the orange light flecking the wavetops, and roused the heavy figure next to him with a toe.

'Wake up, there, Mr Hooke. It's time.'

Isaiah Hooke sat up blinking like a burrowing animal routed out of the earth, and unhappy about it.

'Christ. The inside o' me mouth feels – ' and he expressed an ingenious obscenity that made Mainwaring grin at him in wonder.

'You missed your calling, Mr Hooke. With that turn o' phrase you'd have made a first-rate divine.'

''Ceptin' me thoughts are as foul as a nightsoil pit, 'alf th' time, zur. Wouldn't do.'

'That'd be true enough, cap'n,' said Evans, emerging from under a thwart. 'The Lord would strike down a chapel that'd have Mr Hooke preach in it, look you. Why, he – '

'Ye can stow that, Evans,' growled Hooke. 'I ain't no angel, an' neither is yew, y' pious Welsh cutthroat!'

Mainwaring furrowed his brows. 'Incipient mutiny, Mr Hooke? Can't you keep these men in line?'

''Tain't worth th' air o' me lungs, zur. A pack o' leadswingin' layabouts t' beat 'em I never did see.'

'D'ye think they can pull a boat, at least?'

Hooke winked. 'Damned well only one way t' find out, zur.' His voice raised to coach-horn volume. 'Stir, there, lads! Show a leg, laddies! Out of the 'micks or we cut 'em down!'

The length of the boat, there were groans of protest as the men sat up, scratching heads and peering round. They were stiff from sleeping in awkward positions on the hard thwarts, and it had been a strenuous day sailing the heavy-laden boat ahead of the wind and swell until, by early afternoon, they had reached the mouth of the Chagrès. By good luck the wind had eased, and in heaving to they had not drifted too far to leeward past the river mouth.

'Evans, ease the mainsheet,' said Hooke. 'Slade? Git that mains'l brailed in. Winton, cut away that thing off the bows. Ready? Out oars, then!'

With much thumping and splashing as the boat rocked and lifted on the swells, five oars were hauled out from where they had been lain fore-and-aft on the thwarts, and wrestled over the side until they dropped into place between their thole pins. Hooke looked at Mainwaring who nodded, pointing with his chin towards the river mouth.

'Let's 'ave a nice, steady stroke, now, lads. We've a half-league t' pull afore we gets t' th' river mouth, and Christ knows how far upriver after that. Give way, together!'

With a groan here and there, the men leaned forward, the blades bit into the rippled sea, and the longboat began to turn as Mainwaring held the tiller over. In a moment

144

the stem of the longboat was centred on the bluff that held the Castillo de San Lorenzo, and with the lugsails flapping idly in their folds against the masts, the craft began to move in towards the darkening shore.

'Stroke . . . stroke . . .' The men bent their bodies to the steady beat of Hooke's voice, sweat starting already to show darkly on their shirts. Tindall, grim-looking and darkly taciturn as ever, was stroke oar, with the muscular Evans as second stroke. Williams was the midships oar, with Winton and Sawyer second bows and bows respectively. Shanahan and Slade were the odd men out, and sat curled in the bows as lookouts, grinning and enjoying the sight of the others' efforts. Shanahan, with his warm manner and quick humour, had rapidly been accepted by the Dianas.

Now Hooke caught the Irishman's eyes. 'Yew'll get yer turn, yew two,' nodded the master, seeing their expressions. 'Handsomely, now, lads. Stroke . . . stroke . . .'

Mainwaring watched the flame colours of the sunset behind the dark shore ahead, and steered the bobbing longboat down a peach-coloured rivulet of light that led in as if to show the way. The mouth of the river was distinct, now, its water beckoning inland like a copper river between the dark masses of the shorelines.

The American could see a first pale twinkle of lantern light, a winking spot in the dark shadows farther inland on the right bank of the river. He remembered that the few miserable huts which constituted the village of Chagrès lay a short distance inland on the right bank. But closer to the mouth there would be –

'Shoal water, sir!' came Slade's cry from the bows. 'C'n see th' bottom, sir! There!'

Mainwaring cursed himself for forgetting. There was a ledge at the mouth of the Chagrès, a ledge on which Sir

Harry Morgan's ships had come to grief in his attack on Panama.

'It's the Laja Reef, Slade. We should pass over. But d'ye see breakers ahead?'

'No, sir! Clear. A bit o' pause, seein' it shoal up like that, sir.'

Mainwaring nodded. 'Aye. Sing out if it shoals again.'

But in the next instant they glided on glassy swells over the last dark grey mass under the keel, and were in deep water again.

Mainwaring peered ahead. They were barely five hundred yards off the river mouth, and he wondered if the current was strong. The longboat was still footing along at a good clip, the men sweating heavily now, their shirts wringing wet. With the mixture of bandanas and floppy, uncocked hats, they were a rough-looking lot indeed, and anyone on the bluff of San Lorenzo staring at them through a glass could easily take them for a fisherman who had drifted too far from home waters and was taking shelter in the Chagrès for the night.

Now they were into the river mouth proper, a loon flapping away in fright from before the boat, a sudden end to the sink and lift of the swells as they passed in from the sea. To the left, the shoreline was low and heavily wooded, seemingly without a break in the dense jungle wall that loomed over the river. On the right, in contrast, there were in fact three steep and rocky points of land, and in the dark Mainwaring could make out the mass of the San Lorenzo, and on the next two points, what appeared to be ruined gun batteries. Evidently Vernon's attack had been as thorough in reducing the defences here as at Porto Bello. There was no movement, no flash of light, no fluttering ensigns on flagstaffs. Close inshore to the right, a long, narrow dugout canoe was creeping along the shore, but its occupants did not even glance at the longboat as it passed.

'There's th' village, zur,' murmured Hooke. He was pointing to a cluster of thatched shacks and warehouses that were now becoming more visible, upstream on the right bank behind a strip of beach on which half a dozen dugout canoes and several European long boats were drawn up. Naked, black-haired children were splashing in the tea-coloured water beside the canoes, their shrill laughter carrying across the water. A woman in a hut doorway railed at the children in rapid Spanish, and then from the forested shore opposite a flight of brilliantly-plumed parrots swooped low over the water near the longboat, croaking gutturally.

'Steady as she goes, Mr Hooke,' said Mainwaring quietly. 'Keep the lads at it until we round that bank ahead. Past that bend, we'll be out of sight from the village, and we can ease off somewhat.'

'Aye, zur,' said Hooke. 'Steady pull, now, lads. Don't strain. Use yer backs. Stroke . . . stroke . . .'

The boat moved on, up a still and seemingly motionless river, overhung on either side by the jungle wall, out of which now came the echoing cacophony of the creatures within it. Mainwaring scanned the verdure, noting the astonishingly huge cedars that stood here and there like sentinels, surrounded by palm and bamboo, mahogany and lignum vitae. There was mangrove as well, and thorn or bramble masses under the great canopy above; cane-breaks showed at intervals, and enormous webs of creepers rose up the towering tree trunks, seeming to choke the life from the great trees. The wind had died now, the only moving air being the tickle at the back of the men's necks as they rowed. The air was thick and damp, the heat oppressive, and from the forest there came a rank odour of rotting vegetation and the gagging perfume of

147

thousands of flowers. Already, clouds of midges hovered over the water, through which the boat moved, and sandflies landed on bare skin to bite savagely and be cursed, leaving red welts that stung with the sweat.

The boat rowed on, the ripple under the bow and round the rudder the only sounds above the creak and thump of the oars. Mainwaring examined the faces of the men, seeing their dismay at the conditions inland away from the cleansing and cooling wind of the sea.

'Bear with it, lads,' he said. 'Better this than a march overland.'

The men nodded grimly and bent to their work, the boat moving up a pale river surrounded by inky black forest now that the sun had set, and reflecting in its brownish water the first of the stars to appear in the vast dome of the sky.

'What'll we do fer th' night, zur?' asked Hooke, scratching at a sandfly bite. 'Don't think the lads would fancy tryin' t' tent ashore, zur, wiv respect.'

'Nor I, Mr Hooke. We'll keep on a bit more, then find a tree that angles out over the river. Like that one, there. We'll tie on the painter and let her stream in the current. Means another night in the boat, however.'

'No fear, zur. 'Tain't any of us want t' bed down wiv all them damned bugs any sooner'n we have to, zur.'

Mainwaring wiped his sodden brow with one sleeve. 'Amen to that.'

Far astern, as the mass of the ruined Castillo de San Lorenzo vanished from sight around the turn of the river, a figure in the shadows of the ruined parapet stirred; a thickset seaman, in filthy petticoat breeches and red shirt. He grinned as he watched the boat, looking in the light of the sunset like a black water beetle inching upriver, move round the river bend and disappear from view. Then he lifted his tinderbox and set it on the parapet. With a little dried moss and twigs, he soon had a small fire crackling. As it flared, he reached into his shirt front for a round piece of polished steel, which gleamed like a mirror. Moving to stand behind the little fire, he set the steel on edge, and angled it so that it increased and reflected the flame into the distance. Aiming the invisible beam of light towards the dark hills behind which the river would take the longboat, he began a slow, rhythmic flashing.

The dawn light was still not fully developed into day, and the sun touched the top of the dense, towering canopy of trees with an orange glow that promised a sun-filled day of stifling heat. On the narrow, beaten-earth roadway that wound through the trees up the hill slopes from Porto Bello, the dozen men mounted on mules and the occasional short-legged *burro* kicked at their mounts and cursed them, tugging harshly on the lines in their hands that led other, riderless animals with empty pack frames on their backs. Behind them, two small horses carried the figures of Anne Brixham and the Indian girl, dressed now in torn and ragged cast-off seamen's clothing and riding astride, their hands bound to the high pommels of their big Spanish saddles. Already their faces were streaked with sweat, and marked with the bloody traces of insect bites. The horses jerked and trotted, tugging on the long ropes of their halters that led to the horn on the pommel of Rigaud de la Roche-Bourbon's saddle. The Frenchman rode, still in the spotless velvet, on a strong-looking white gelding that was clearly the best mount of the lot.

As the animals plodded along in the midge-filled, damp morning air, Roche-Bourbon twisted in the saddle to look back at the women.

'Enjoying the excursion, my dear?' he called. 'One has so little time for such things these days.'

149

Anne felt a retort spring to her lips, but again held it back. The time would come. But not yet.

'Dear me,' purred Roche-Bourbon. 'The little cat has lost her claws? How disappointing.'

Anne's horse stumbled over a wagon rut, and she clutched at the pommel, the bonds cutting cruelly into her wrists.

'How long does this go on?' she asked. 'And must these bonds be so tight? The girl's wrists are bleeding!'

'We ride on until the ford at the Rio Gatun, if you must know. Then we'll camp. And perhaps I'll adjust your bonds. Try to be cheerful, *hein*?'

'You bastard,' said Anne, through her teeth.

Roche-Bourbon laughed and turned forward.

When the Frenchman's eyes were averted, Anne's hands twisted over the pommel again, to where they had been working since a few minutes into the ride. Ignoring the pain in her wrists, and the blood that was beginning to run from them, she began picking at the loose stitching that held down a flap of leather, under which she had felt a curved piece of steel, perhaps a hand in length. Finally, one loop of the thread parted, and Anne managed to get the tip of a finger under the leather. With a quick look at Roche-Bourbon she began to work the piece of steel out.

The rain was falling in hard, biting torrents, startlingly cold, so much at once that the air was almost opaque with water. The surface of the river became a grey, leaping sheet, wavelets beaten flat, while behind the curtain of the downpour the jungle shoreline hung in dark, down-beaten billows of wet green. The longboat drifted, the oars trailing in the water as the men tugged at corners of tarpaulin for shelter, or sat in sodden misery, their hats battered down around their ears by the incredible, hissing force of the rain.

Edward Mainwaring squinted ahead, trying to see the point of land in the river for which he had been steering. A terrific flash and thunderclap of long, rumbling thunder made him start as the boat and the faces of the men were suddenly thrown into garish yellow illumination.

'Mr Hooke!' he cried, over the hiss of the rain. 'No damned sense in sitting out here. There's an overhung tree we can shelter under. Quickly!'

'Aye, zur! Come on, you lot! Put down them damned covers!' barked Hooke. 'Not the first time ye've been wet, an' this ain't ice off Newfoundland! Give way, there, together!'

The oars lifted and then dug in, the men cursing as the rain, driven with the force of musketshot, smarted against their backs as they rowed. And now hailstones were bouncing against the thwarts and gunwales, stinging like a small boy's stone when they struck the top of a head or a shoulder.

'Stroke! Stroke!' Hooke boomed. His grey-streaked yellow hair was plastered down over his forehead and temples, and what was left of his shirt – torn and soiled from when he had floundered ashore in the night, only to find himself armpit-deep in some frightful, stinking ooze from which he had had to be dragged by a rope – clung like wet paper to his beefy frame. The men swore and rowed on.

Then in the next moment they were gliding under a huge, overhanging branch, Shanahan reaching up to pass the painter round it as they passed beneath it. The men slumped over the oars, listening to the roar of the rain on the leafy canopy overhead, staring at each other out of stubbled, swollen faces marked with the welts of scores of insect bites. After two days on the river, the strain of the constant rowing in the terrible heat and the tormenting swarms of mosquitos and flies was beginning to tell.

'Bugger me,' muttered Hooke, slumped beside Mainwaring in the sternsheets. 'Listen t' that rain. Like the damned sea isself was up there, an' sprung a leak below th' waterline.'

Mainwaring nodded, wiping his streaming face with his hand. He looked closely at the men, who had thrown their oars across both gunwales and were slumped over them. The two nights in the cramped confines of the boat had been sleepless agonies of heat and insects, but a glance at the dark hell of the forest had dissuaded anyone from suggesting encampment ashore.

'The lads are wearing down Isaiah,' said Mainwaring, so that only Hooke could hear. 'Give 'em another tot. And tell 'em to wring out their shirts. The fever can strike if ye sit about in wet clothing.'

'Aye, zur.' Then the master cast a worried eye at him. 'In truth, zur, how much farther are we t' go?'

Mainwaring rubbed his brow and shifted his weight on the hard, wooden thwart.

'To tell the truth, we should've struck Venta de Cruces by now, Isaiah. But I could be off in my figuring. I'd swear it's no more'n a league farther.'

'Hope so, zur.' said Hooke, and spat over the side. 'We've been in the boat long enough. An' it's 'ard to be partial t' these shores, if ye know what I mean, zur.'

Mainwaring looked up, and watched a tarantula fully the size of Hooke's hand and covered in raindrop-speckled brown fur inch along the branch to which they were tied.

'You don't have to tell me, Isaiah. But the rain's letting up. Get that tot into 'em – and for Christ's sake wring out the shirts – and then get under way again.'

In a few moments the boat pushed out under leaden and glowering skies across a grey, still mirrorface that revealed its current only in the drift of clumps of plants or branches that moved slowly downstream, often perched on by the elegant forms of herons. A log floated past, a hideous iguana aboard and bound on some adventure down the growth-choked shore. The air reeked of a heavy, musk-like smell, and for a moment Mainwaring felt a pang of longing for the clean, cool air of the Massachusetts coast, with its hard, grey rock and evergreen.

Another two hours of steady rowing followed, with Hooke and Mainwaring taking their turns at the oars, when Shanahan suddenly was pointing ahead as a curve in the river broadened before them.

'Village, sorr!' he called, from the bows. 'Huts and a few bigger buildings, too!'

"Vast pulling!' ordered Mainwaring. The boat coasted round the bend of the river marked by a pair of toppling, creeper-draped cedars, and they were in full view of a small cluster of thatched huts that lay to one side of a narrows in the river. As Mainwaring watched, a *peón* in baggy white shirt and trousers rode a small *burro* splashily across, kicking it into the forest trail on the other side.

'The ford!' breathed Mainwaring. 'It's Venta de Cruces. Thank Christ!'

The men swivelled in their places, staring at the little village.

'Wot next, zur?' said Hooke.

'They'll not be expecting us. We row in as if about our business, and get ashore before they see who we are. Then we've got to find where they keep the *camino* relief horses and mules stabled. It must be on the other side of those huts. Out oars, lads. The last pull!'

With new vigour the men lay back against the oars, and the boat forged ahead over the oil-slick, muddy water. Mist was drifting through the great trees halfway to their crowns, and below it the village lay quiet, with almost no

153

life visible. A dog barked, the sharp sound echoing along the river bank but other than the cries of the birds in the forest there was no sound apart from the rumble-clunk, rumble-clunk of the men at the oars, and the little hiss of the droplets from the oar blades each time they were swept forward. The villagers would likely not know the difference at this distance between one scruffy, bearded lot of men in an unmarked boat and another. Surprise, once ashore, would be their main ally in finding the horse stables and getting themselves mounted. The stablemen, and the guards that would have to be there, would be the first problem.

But wait . . .

Something at the back of Mainwaring's neck, the old warning instinct, was tingling. Something about that line of huts towards which the boat was pulling, and now only a few hundred yards away.

'Shanahan! Slade! Break the muskets out of their oilcloth packing! Prime and load as many of 'em as you can! Keep pulling, lads! Give us a knot or two, more!'

'Zur? Wot – !' Hooke was staring at him.

'We're turning in there, Isaiah! Away from those huts! *Pull*, lads!' Mainwaring sprang to his feet and thrust the tiller bar over, steering the leaping boat for a narrow beach to one side of the hut line instead of the main beach, a muddy shelf below the huts on which a few canoes were hauled up.

'What is it, zur?' Hooke was saying, staring in surprise at the huts and then at the American. 'Do ye – ?'

'*Fuego!*'

The order was shrieked somewhere ashore, and a sharp, rippling series of musket blasts rent the air, echoing and re-echoing from the forest. From inside the doorways and behind the walls of the crude huts, pink flashes rent the dull afternoon light. The water around the longboat shot up in ball splashes that leaped man-high, and several musket balls thwacked into the wood of the boat.

And in the same half-instant, Tindall snapped forward as if struck in the back of the head. His eyes widened in astonishment, and he half-rose to his feet. Then a gush of scarlet spurted from his open mouth, and he toppled sideways over his oar into the river.

'Hooke! Take his oar! *Pull*, lads!' shouted Mainwaring.

'Hell, they was a-waitin' fer us, sir!' cried Sawyer, straining at his oar.

In the bows, Shanahan had finished priming and loading one musket. He pulled it to full cock, threw it to his shoulder. The flint sparked, but no report sounded.

'Powder, sorr!' he called aft. 'It's too damned wet! I can't – !'

'*Again!*' roared Mainwaring. 'Prime again! Three strokes, lads! Two, till we're there! Now!'

With a jolt, the boat thumped against the slick clay of the bank. Almost as it did so, another volley of musketry from the hut line split the air. Balls hummed past Mainwaring's ear and thumped against the boat or spat up little geysers in the river. But this time no one fell.

'Out of the boat and shoreward! Take a musket and box as you go! Shanahan, clear 'em away! Quickly, for your lives!'

Stumbling and splashing, falling in the shallows, the men struggled out of the boat, their cramped legs failing them, clutching at the muskets Shanahan threw at them from where he crouched in the bows. And now the Irishman was flinging himself over the side and splashing for shore, extra cartridge boxes draped round his neck, two muskets in his hands.

'Come on, Isaiah! This is no place to die!' cried Mainwaring, and he pushed the burly sailing master ahead of him in a clumsy tumble over the boat's side.

155

Mainwaring half-fell, half-rolled out, splashing down on one knee in the tepid, tea-coloured water. He fought to his feet and sloshed ashore, Hooke beside him. Shanahan was suddenly there, holding out a musket to him, and he seized it and plunged after the others.

Within a few seconds they had all thrown themselves into the wall of vegetation that began at the edge of the slick, clay beach, and fell in a group together amidst thick, dripping palmetto and creepers, and tall, knife-edged grass that reached to their shoulders. As they lay, panting and staring, another volley blasted from the hut line, the balls pinging and whizzing overhead as they cut through the bracken and undergrowth.

Mainwaring struggled to one knee, throwing a cartridge box strap over his shoulder. This undergrowth was no shelter. All the Spanish had to do was lower the fire and the big, thumb-sized balls would smash through the grass and kill them, unseen, where they lay.

'We need hard shelter. Slade, you, Winton and Sawyer form a line – there. One knee. Prime and load, and wait for my orders. If you hear that Don bastard give the order to fire again, go to your bellies! Evans, Williams, behind that palmetto clump. Shanahan, go with 'em. Mr Hooke, you follow me. Prime and load, all of you, and quickly!'

Wild-eyed, the men responded, slinging on the cartridge boxes, running and stumbling to their positions, then dropping down feverishly to prime and load the long muskets.

Hooke was crouched beside Mainwaring, shaking powder from a cartridge into his musket's pan. 'Damned paper's wet, zur. Whoreson lucky if this'll fire. Where are the Dons, zur?'

Mainwaring cuffed sweat out of his eyes and thrust his ramrod back into its pipes. 'You're right. Damned powder's so damp I wonder if anyone can fire. The Dons are there, in the hut line. Out of sight, most of 'em, but I saw one run from one hut to another.'

'Do we wait for 'em, zur?'

'No, Isaiah. They'll circle us and cut us down where we lie. Our only chance is to get to some kind of hard shelter and then fight our way out of it, when we can.'

Hooke's face was glum. 'Doesn't sound too good, zur.'

'Very perceptive of you, Isaiah. Truth is, we're in a damned precarious situation. And that means it's time to carry the war to the other bastard. Come on!'

He rose to his feet and moved forward in a rapid crouch through the heavy grass until he was beside Slade, Sawyer and Winton. Whispering to them to follow him, he continued forward, with Hooke muttering orders behind him, and in a moment he had reached the edge of the grass. Ahead, between them and the huts, lay a jumbled pile of huge cedar logs, apparently awaiting rafting down-river. With a quick glance to left and right, Mainwaring launched himself in a sprint towards the logs. As he crouched behind them, the other men followed him in quick succession, until they were all pressed together, panting, behind the low protection the logs afforded.

Mainwaring waited until Hooke, the last, had padded in and collapsed with a thump before risking a look over the top of the logs. No blast of musketry greeted him, and he saw that no more than a stone's throw away, a single whitewashed and thatched hut stood slightly apart from the others. Its low doorway was ajar.

'We'll make for that hut. Use it as a strong point until we see how many of them there are. Follow me, one at a time!'

'Wait, zur! Shouldn't we – ?' began Hooke.

But Mainwaring had left, sprinting across the hard-packed earth of the clearing. His bare feet – his shoes now a disintegrating ruin in the longboat – slipped and slithered and the cartridge box banged and clattered on his hip. He was holding the musket before him like a quarterstaff fighter, and as he ran he winced inwardly, expecting the hail of shot that in the next instant would cut him down. But he reached the hut in a sweaty lather, diving into a shoulder roll through the doorway, totally unaware of what was inside.

He struck the ground hard, fetching up in an awkward sprawl against several large cane baskets. A single chicken shrieked somewhere in the shadows of the hut and burst out of the door, making off with astounding strides and a flutter of clipped wings. Mainwaring spun to his knees, breathing rapidly. He checked the priming of his musket and then turned the butt against the wall away from the doorway. With half a dozen sharp blows he shattered the mud wattle and opened a fist-sized hole that gave him a view of the main group of huts. But again there was no movement.

Where the devil had the Spanish got to?

Behind him there was a rush of running feet, and Hooke, followed by Shanahan and Slade, burst through the door. The others arrived seconds later, pushing into the low hut to crouch panting against its walls and turn wide white eyes to Mainwaring.

'Damned odd,' said Mainwaring. 'Not a move from 'em.'

'Mayhap they've gone t' ground, zur,' said Hooke, at his elbow. 'Not sure where we are.'

'Perhaps. All the same, I don't like it. All right, ready yourselves. We'll move to the next line of huts and then through 'em, if there's nothing there. If they won't show themselves, and want to leave us an opening, then –'

The air was split by the chest-punching concussion of an artillery piece, and a cask-sized fragment of the hut wall just over the heads of three of the crouching Dianas burst in with a splattering shower of mud and wood splinters. A thick lump of the whitewashed clay struck Mainwaring violently, and he buckled, the wind driven from his lungs as if by a prize-fighter's fist. As he fell, a roar of musketry burst out around the hut, from carefully concealed positions, and balls hurtled on to the walls, flinging a mass of fragments and clay dust into the air above the heads of the stunned men within.

'Down!' roared Hooke. 'On your bellies!' The sailing master threw himself down beside Mainwaring, who was gasping for breath.

'Zur! Christ, zur, are ye – ?'

'I'll – live, Isaiah. Was that a *gun*?

'Aye, zur! It must – '

Again the terrific blast punched at them, and another portion of the hut wall exploded into flying, stinging missiles. The Dianas cowered as again a hail of musket balls tore at the hut.

Mainwaring spat, his mouth dry with dust. 'Damn my eyes, that's a bloody company of infantry volleying at us out there! Keep low, lads!'

Another thunderous blast tore at the hut until the Dianas lay under a mound of debris, not daring to stir.

Mainwaring squirmed round, ignoring the pain in his stomach, so that he could look through the door. What he saw made him freeze in shock and despair.

A small field gun, at least a three-pounder, was being feverishly served by a gun crew in the scarlet small clothes and white knee gaiters of Spanish colonial artillery. To either side of it, as far as the narrow doorway would reveal, Mainwaring saw a double row of Spanish infantry, unkempt-looking creatures in filthy linen coats, baggy trousers and straw hats. But they wore military crossbelts, and were priming and loading their three-banded Spanish muskets with a kind of competence.

159

Dear God, thought Mainwaring. *What a fool I've been. Again. Another damned trap!*

Hooke swore at his side. 'Christ, it's a bloody army.'

'Aye,' muttered Mainwaring. 'It appears we're well and truly caught.'

'But, by *who*, zur? I wouldn't 'ave thought – '

There was some kind of commotion outside that silenced Hooke. And then it was clear. A voice was hailing the hut.

'Can you hear me?' said the voice, in smooth, barely-accented English. 'Captain Mainwaring? I trust you've not been wounded. That would be a pity indeed.'

With a sickening jolt of recognition, Mainwaring stared as the speaking voice moved into view of the doorway, and stood waiting with hands on hips.

'You cunning swine!' breathed Mainwaring.

And he could see the smile beginning to form on the face of the Chevalier Rigaud de la Roche-Bourbon.

5

The prison hulk had been a brig, once, but now no lofty yards or steeving jib-boom gave grace to its otherwise squat shape. In the shimmering, windless heat of noon on the Bay of Panama, the ancient hull sat at a tumbledown jetty, looking worn and abandoned, the red and gilt paint on its sides long since faded to grey. A single lower mast, the fore, was still in place, with a yard to act as a derrick, but in all other respects the hulk was a rotting, abandoned and weedgrown castaway awaiting the inevitable moment of its destruction.

It was not without life, however; on its decks, under a patched and tattered awning, two Spanish soldiers in the ubiquitous dirty linen and straw hats of the colonial militia slumped against the rail, their muskets slung on their shoulders, idly discussed the merits of the brown body of an Indian prostitute whose services they had bought the evening before. In a while, they would stir up the two bent and crippled *peónes* who were the warders of the hulk, and supervise the ladling out of the stinking swill and weevil-ridden bread which the *peónes* prepared once a day. For in addition to the two leg-chained *peónes* and the filthy soldiers, the hulk also held, in the shadows of what had once been its gundeck, Edward Mainwaring and his companions.

The gun-deck was almost pitch black, its only light the glimmers which escaped round the closed and barred gunports. The deck had been cleared of guns and other gear years before, when the brig had seen the end of its seagoing days, and there was nothing between deckhead and deck planking. But it was not the long, open sweep of a cleared gun-deck. Rough, splintering wood had been used to make a kind of cage, hardly bigger than Stephen Pellowe's tiny cabin in *Diana*, but only three feet or so in height. Within this latticework box, in the fetid gloom of the below-decks of a dying hulk reeking of bilge, human excrement, sweat, and garlic, Edward Mainwaring and his seven men crouched in agonized discomfort.

Isaiah Hooke was jammed in one corner of the cage.

'This is bloody awful, zur. 'Tain't human,' he growled.

Mainwaring stirred, trying to ease the cramps in his legs without moving them from under Williams, who was lying across them in exhausted sleep.

'I know, Isaiah,' he murmured. 'Keep your mind tough. We've got air, and we're not chained or bound. We've got a chance.' He was trying with some difficulty to keep down the surge of claustrophobic panic and despair that threatened to break through his defences. 'Don't let the bastards win!'

'Aye, zur,' rumbled Hooke. 'Bloody Dons!'

Mainwring let his head sink back against the splintering cage bars, breathing shallowly in the stifling heat. He was drenched with sweat, and dizzy with fatigue and hunger. His breeches, torn and ripped, were loose around his waist; he knew they had all been losing weight, and with it, strength. The men, exhausted by the march over the mountains and across the dusty savannah to Panama Vieja, were for the most part in a kind of stupor that was passing for sleep.

Mainwaring felt his feet gingerly. The strips of rag that he had wrapped around his lacerated feet were dry and crusty. There was no fresh blood.

Since the capture in the hut at Venta de Cruces, when Mainwaring had realized that he had been skilfully trapped by Roche-Bourbon, his memory of events was more a blurred series of images than sharp reality. The coarse little men of the colonial infantry had pounced in through the hut door, wrenching the muskets from the Dianas' hands and driving the eight men out the door in a hail of kicks and blows, until they stood back to back in a tight knot while the exulting Spanish jeered and spat at them.

And then Roche-Bourbon had been there, immaculate and unbelievably clean, gloating in triumph as he stopped before Mainwaring and met the latter's steady look.

'I knew it was only a matter of time before I succeeded in trapping you, Mainwaring,' he had said. 'And I have. What exactly had you intended to do with this pitiful clutch of wastrels? Take a ship? Plunder Panama? *Really*, Mainwaring!'

'They are worth a hundred of these greasy little swine you lead, Chevalier. As you know.'

'Ah, yes. English sea dogs, what? Stout fellows, every one. Your identification with them astounds me, Mainwaring. Have you no sense of social distinction? But then, I forget. You are yourself a fishpot colonial, *hein*? Hardly a gentleman.'

'I might add, Chevalier, that they are certainly each worth a hundred of *you*,' finished Mainwaring, steadily.

Roche-Bourbon shook his head. 'You will persist in giving me reason after reason to punish you. As you wish.' He turned away with a shrug, issuing orders in rapid Spanish to soldiers who grinned in gap-toothed pleasure as they ran to obey.

Within minutes Mainwaring and the others had been thrust roughly into a single row, their hands bound tightly and painfully before them with grassline. A twenty-foot length of manila line had been laid out, and the bonds on their wrists had been lashed to the manila which had then been tied with great ceremony to the back of a manure-stained *peón's* cart, drawn by two fly-bitten and emaciated mules. With great gusto and swagger, several of the militiamen climbed into the cart and levelled their muskets at the prisoners, while the remainder fell in behind, in a kind of ragged company formation.

Roche-Bourbon had reappeared, mounted on a beautiful white gelding that snorted and whirled under him as he controlled it with a practised hand. The Frenchman doffed his hat in a grand gesture.

'Do enjoy your stroll to the sea, Mainwaring. If you've not seen the South Sea, it is an event not to miss. I shall see you there, when my duties are done. We shall have to think of an amusing and entertaining way of disposing of you at our leisure.'

'Go to hell, Chevalier,' said Mainwaring.

The Frenchman had snickered, rasping out something in Spanish before galloping away through the village. A whip had cracked, and the wretched mules had started forward, the rope jerking so that the prisoners stumbled over one another, trying to keep up. Mainwaring winced as his shoeless feet struck against the rocky roadway. The Spanish jeered, and the men marching behind began idly to pelt the English with stones.

The distance across the mountains on the *camino* was ten leagues from Venta de Cruces southward to Old Panama. At first the cobblestoned track, able to accommodate two carts passing side by side in places, wound through rolling high hills covered with the same dense jungle that had framed the river. Then as it twisted and turned up from Venta de Cruces to the heights before descending to the Pacific, it became a rock-strewn path of beaten earth.

For Mainwaring and his men, the march soon became a stumbling nightmare, the bloody bonds at their wrists jerking and yanking them forward as the mules plodded steadily on. The rack turned their feet into a mass of bruised and lacerated flesh, and Mainwaring gritted his teeth in agony at every step, his footprints leaving a bloody trail across the dirt and stone. From time to time the cart would stop briefly to allow different sets of the gabbling noisy Spanish to clamber aboard the cart or drink greedily from gourd-like canteens. No water was offered to the Dianas. As the day lengthened and the heat increased, the cart wheels and the mules' hooves threw up clouds of choking dust that soon coated the Dianas with a grey slime of fine clay that added to the misery of the march. The mosquitos and sandflies in swarming legions descended on bare flesh, and once Shanahan gasped as he was stung in the foot by a huge centipede, and turned pale, only kept from falling by Evans' burly arms as they staggered on.

Mainwaring found he was slipping into a dull half-consciousness, a kind of shambling stupor in which he knew what was happening but seemed to detach himself from the intense pain and weariness. His mind noted it all: the heat, the burning thirst, the caked dirt, the bloody cuts in his feet, the streaming sweat over skin tormented by clouds of hovering mosquitos and midges, the squeal of the cart's wheels, the casual spitting or pebble-tossing of the Spanish. But somehow he was seeing it as an observer, and that detached mind was noting that the roadway was angling downward, that the jungle cover was thinning, and that a broad, dusty savannah was opening ahead of them. Beyond, a thin sliver of sea glittered like a diadem on the horizon in the blazing afternoon light.

'The sea!' croaked Hooke. 'Th' whoreson South Sea, zur.'

'Aye. Damned undignified way to see it for the first time, Isaiah,' muttered Mainwaring.

In the next hours the little cavalcade wound along the straight, rutted track of the roadway across the grassland, which lay brown and charred under the furnace of the sun. Here and there, thin, long-horned cattle looked up from munching on the sparse scrub to watch the cart and its shambling train pass, or sheltered beneath the few clumps of trees with vast disinterest, chewing slow cuds. The heat and dust rose to new levels, and the Dianas were transformed into painfully stumbling spectres, their hair and skin lathered with the white dust until their eyes were red-rimmed hollows in the masks of their faces. One soldier had taken a kind of pity on Mainwaring's torn, bleeding feet and thrown him a strip of rag when the cart had stopped to allow the mules to be watered. Feverishly, the American had wrapped it round his feet, tying the bandages in place seconds before the cart squealed into motion again and the manila line snapped taut, dragging them forward once more.

The Spanish had begun gabbling anew, pointing ahead at something that Mainwaring's men, blinded by the choking cloud of dust, could not see. And then a rider had come thundering past, wheeled and turned, a man in tight, dark clothes and low, flat hat, mounted on a powerful chestnut. He had grinned at the wretched prisoners, mouthed some orders at the soldiers, and ridden off.

It had been less than half an hour later when the cart halted. As the dust settled, Mainwaring could see that they had arrived at the edge of the sea that lay in calm, glimmering quiet off a low, sand-beached shore.

'*Pacific*' *indeed*, he thought.

To either side, strange hummocks and dune-like shapes baffled him until he realized that he was looking at the ruins of a town, with all destroyed except the few, low whitewashed buildings before which they had halted. In the distance off to the west, along the low, duned shore, he could see the rooftops and spires of what appeared to

166

be a small city, shining in the sun, with ships at anchor before it.

'Aye,' he breathed. 'That must be the new town. And these' – he looked round him – 'what's left of Old Panama.'

'Yer pardon, zur?' croaked Hooke at his side.

'It's Sir Harry Morgan's work, Isaiah. They never rebuilt after he and his lads burnt it.'

The sailing master attempted to spit. 'Hell! If an' when I gets free o' these 'ere lashin's, I'll burn out a few more o' th' damned Dons. That I can promise ye, zur!'

Abruptly, a Spaniard wielding a huge *machete* appeared and came along the line, cutting the bonds from the men's bloody wrists. As the Dianas chafed at their welts, several of the colonial infantrymen appeared, their dark, hard, faces set, and began urging the Dianas forward with their bayoneted muskets.

Walking like dead men, they were pushed round the corner of a building to where a ramshackle jetty led out to a vessel. Not a ship, but the stripped, ageing remains of one, the lone yard on the stump foremast hanging a-cockbill.

'Christ save us, a bloody prison hulk,' gasped Winton, who was behind Hooke. 'Summat familiar, sir?'

Mainwaring managed a small grin. 'We seem to have a habit of being thrown in Spanish hulls as prisoners. Just remember that we got out of the last one.'

Winton spat. 'Aye, sir. I will.'

As they were thrust aboard the hulk up a narrow gangplank, they noticed the filth and rubbish about the decks, the opened deck seams, the faded paint, blistering under the savage heat of the sun. Two scrawny *peónes* in dirty white baggy trousers and shirts, heavy chains on their thin ankles, hovered to one side, while several

167

villainous-looking members of the militia appeared up the main companionway, ordering the Dianas below with a jerk of their thumbs. Once below decks in the fetid gloom of the gundeck, the sunblinded men stumbled helplessly until the short, swarthy Spanish, cursing volubly, grabbed the bigger Dianas and propelled them with kicks and punches through a low, splintery opening. Within seconds Mainwaring had realized that they were being crammed into some kind of crude, cage-like structure. A latticed door of sorts was forced shut on them, and barred with a timber before the Spanish left.

Mainwaring was keeping his breathing slow and steady, willing back the panic that was all too close to the surface by trying to make sense of their surroundings. Their pen was a kind of chicken coop, barely four feet by six feet, located on the brig's former gundeck, some fifteen feet forward of the companionway ladder. The cage door was barred by a thick wooden plank thrust into place and somehow fastened, although he had heard no rattle of a padlock. In the stifling closeness of the gundeck, the only specks of light showed round the closed and chinked gunports.

Mainwaring squirmed round. The cage was not centred in the deck, and the side away from him, where Sawyer, Evans and Slade were curled up, was almost against the ship's side, and a wedged gunport lid that seemed to emit slightly more light than the others.

'Sawyer, Evans. Change places with me for a moment, will you? And watch out for Williams. Let him sleep, poor bastard.'

With great effort the men manoeuvred on all fours until Mainwaring was pressed against the cage wall where it almost touched the gunport. He wormed his way down so that he was virtually lying on his back and could see a slim band of light that corresponded with about twenty degrees of the horizon visible to seaward.

And there was something centred in that view.

'Good Christ!' he burst out.

'What is it, sir? Can ye see somethin', sir?' Around him the men stirred.

'There's a bloody ship moored out there. A big one,' said Mainwaring.

'A Don, sir?' said Winton.

'Aye. And a sixty-gunner, or close to it.' Mainwaring squinted against the sea glare, pressing his face to the splintery wood of the cage. The ship was a vast, towering pile of Spanish red and gilt, with a swooping sheer and the characteristically high, sloping quarterdeck that marked Spanish vessels. Ship-rigged, the galleon lay low in the water, with the fat, beamy hull so favoured by the Spanish to haul the loot and plunder of half a world back to Spain. Her canvas was furled and stopped on its yards, which were braced in square, and she rode to two hawsers and a third off the stern, suggesting that the ship had been at anchor for quite some time. Huge, lazily curling Spanish ensigns drifted from the ensign staff and fore truck, and a tendril of pennant floated out from the main truck in the almost still air. The ship was alive with figures, men working on deck or aloft in the huge, old-fashioned, circular fighting tops, a flash of scarlet here and there marking the officers. And alongside, below the entry port or trailing on their painters at the quarter-booms, a clutch of boats rode, including a lug-rigged longboat not unlike *Diana*'s, her sails crudely brailed in.

Mainwaring scanned the ship carefully. A vessel like that could carry several hundred men if fought as a warship, with the usual Spanish tendency to overman. But as a plate ship, a virtual treasure galleon, she might carry few men or a vast horde; Mainwaring had no way of knowing. From the look of her, ten men, perhaps fifteen, could sail a ship that size – but if they were first-rate

English seamen. His eyes took in the enormous stern galleries, aglitter with ornate carving, the tall, fair-weather rig, and the white-and-blue figurehead of a robed woman set before the bowsprit lashing.

Ten men. But only if they sailed with reduced rig, and went watch on watch . . .

'Sink me, Mr Hooke,' he said, suddenly. 'I think we've found our quarry. That's the Manila Galleon, by God!'

There was a sudden stir in the cage, with not a few curses as elbows met ribs, and muttered warning to 'watch yer bloody feet'.

'The one yew was a-talkin' of, sir?' said Sawyer. 'Loaded wiv booty, an' swag, an' all?'

'Booty and swag and all. I can feel it in my guts. That's her, lads!'

'Christ!' said Winton. 'Bloody lot o' good it does us. Beggin' yer pardon, sir. Trapped like stoats in a sack, an' a bloody prince's ranson o' bullion a pistol shot away!'

Mainwaring levered himself up. Now, thank God, there was something he could focus the men's attentions on. And build their resolve for what had to be done.

'Take turns having a look at her, all of you,' he said. 'Crab around clockwise – this way, Winton. Trapped stoats we may be, but we're going to get out of here. And *she* is where we're going!'

It took considerable patience and tolerance, but the men wrestled and inched and crawled their way around in good discipline until each had had his moment of savouring the sliver of light and the view of the great ship, so near and tantalizing. Mainwaring could see that already their minds were turning away from the reality and suffering of the march and the cage, and focusing on the alluring quarry which rode to its hawsers such a short distance away.

'What *can* we do, sir?' asked Williams. 'In this damned rathole, is there a way out?'

Mainwaring looked at their faces, the sweat-streaked dust masks now becoming visible again as their eyes adjusted to the gloom after the brilliance of the look outside.

'We've been in corners as tight as this before, lads. Winton. Sawyer. Slade. Remember the cable tier in *San Josefe*? You too, Mr Hooke. And we've been in worse. Mark me, we'll get out of here, if you follow orders and we work together. We'll get out, and the Dons and that bastard Frenchman will know we've been here, by God!'

There was a growl of assent, confirming that spirits and a willingness to fight, to survive, were strong again.

'How, zur? How c'n we do it?'

'I don't know yet, lads,' replied Mainwaring grimly. 'But I promise you we will!'

On the quarter-gallery of *Nuestra Señora de Granada*, sheltered by its canopy from the blistering heat of the airless anchorage, Anne Brixham paced, her hands working together in worry. She still wore the man's rough shirt and rope-fastened breeches which had been her costume for the ride across the *camino*. Now she and the half-Indian girl, whose name she had found was Maria, were locked in the stuffy opulence of the admiral's great cabin of the *Granada*, after Roche-Bourbon had made an elaborate, mocking show of rowing them out to the ship. They had been granted access to the quarter-gallery – Roche-Bourbon doubting that either woman would risk the shark-infested water or could even swim – and so Anne was pacing, barefoot, along the incongruous luxury of the gallery, still aware that only the completion of the work of unloading the riches with which the ship was crammed was delaying an unthinkable fate at the hands of Roche-Bourbon.

Suddenly her pacing stopped. There was activity ashore, on the deck of the loathsome, stinking hulk tied at the jetty, which Roche-Bourbon had identified as a prison. The grubby white linen coats of colonial infantry flashed, and bayonet tips. And then half a dozen or so figures, markedly taller and heavier than the Spanish were being prodded ahead of those bayonets.

One tall figure with a certain set to his shoulders and a particular way of walking sent a surge of recognition through Anne.

'Oh, dear God!' she breathed. '*Edward!*'

She clutched at the rail and watched as the bigger men were thrust below out of sight. Her mind was already racing. The work of unloading the bullion and other stores from the galleon had not yet begun. The galleon's crew, a slack bunch of layabouts who, to Anne's experienced eye, were lucky to have survived the Pacific voyage, had refused to help in the shifting of the cargo. The work would have to be done by Roche-Bourbon's men off the *Esperanza*, and the Frenchman was finding the captain of the *Granada*, a cunning but astonishingly lazy *hidalgo* named Monteria, disinclined to accept either his letters of authority or his insistence that he, Roche-Bourbon, assume virtual command of the ship. It all meant, as Roche-Bourbon had seemingly delighted in confiding in her, that there was about two days of negotiation pending before the work would begin – and four to five days of preparing the pack animals and wagons for the trek back to Porto Bello.

Anne bit her lip, staring at the prison hulk. That meant no more than seven days of life. For her, and likely for Edward Mainwaring. She turned and went into the cabin, crossing to the box bunk where the *cimarrone* girl lay sleeping.

'Maria!' said, with gentle urgency. 'Maria, wake up! There is much to do!'

The dusk fell with suddenness, the blazing orb of the sun hovering for a moment above the horizon to the west before dipping like a sphere of molten iron into the farrier's quenching bowl of the sea. The light around the anchored galleon and the hulk inshore dimmed, and lanterns appeared on the ships. The anchor watch changed; the colonial infantry ashore drank small beer and grabbed at the giggling women of the *cantina* in one of the huts; the seamen in the galleon wolfed down their garlicy beef and bitter wine; Rigaud de la Roche-Bourbon and Monteria duelled with their egos over a light dinner in the cabin above Anne Brixham's; and in the hulk, Edward Mainwaring and his men hunched in the stinking darkness and did their best to eat the bucket of repulsive swill which had been thrust into their cage at bayonet point.

In her cabin, Anne Brixham watched the light of day slowly fade until the shore was a shadowed line, and the prison hulk a dark mass distinguished only by the single feeble lantern which flickered at its stern. She turned to the *cimarrone* girl who was dressed in the ragged gown Anne had been wearing when Roche-Bourbon's attack had struck at Modego.

'You look – the way you should, Maria. Thank you,' said Anne.

The olive-skinned girl smiled, a flash of even white teeth. Her hair was brushed back behind her ears, and glowed like a raven's wing in the light of the cabin's single deckhead lantern. She had done her best to wash off the dirt and grime of the ride, and the neckline of the gown swung low enough from her strong, square shoulders to reveal a curve of fullness from a high, rounded bosom.

'It will be nothing, señora. *Nada*. If you can help him escape. Do you think you can?'

Anne shook her head. 'I don't know. But we've got to try. It's either that, or – ' She did not finish.

Maria shuddered. '*Sí. Eso es*. We have no choice.' She threw back her hair, tugged down the neckline so that more of her breasts were revealed. A determined look came into her eye. 'How do you want me to do this?'

'There's a sentry on this deck, outside our door. He regularly looks through the sidelights to see if anyone is on the quarter-gallery. The light from the lantern is enough for him to see any movement there.'

'*Sí?*'

'Maria, listen to me. I need as close to an hour as I can get – a turn of the glass. And the sentry shouldn't want to look out at the quarter-gallery during that time. Do you – ?'

A knowing look came into the girl's eyes. '*Sí*. I know what you want.'

'Maria, I can't think of any other way – ' began Anne.

'*Yo lo creo*. It is all right. Do what you must do. He will be busy.' She smoothed her hair. 'How soon?'

Anne looked out through the stern lights as she began to strip off her breeches. 'In a few minutes. Do you think you can?'

The girl shrugged. '*Espero que sí*. It is better to try than wait to die.' She took a deep breath and rose, moving towards the cabin door.

'Be ready, señora!'

Anne reached under the ticking mattress of the bunk and found the braided cord and the curved piece of saddle steel. Then, from within a slit in the mattress itself, she pulled a coil of light, strong grassline which she had found

174

lying on the gallery. Quickly, she tied a rolling hitch with the braided cord round the piece of steel, made a large loop in the remaining cord, and dropped it over her head, stuffing the dangling steel inside her shirt. It felt cold and cruel against her breasts, and she shivered. Picking up the grassline coil, she looked for Maria.

At the cabin door, Maria jerked a thumb towards the quarter-gallery and nodded. Anne ran lightly to the low, rounded doorway that led out on to the gallery, paused, and then slipped out, feeling visible and naked in the light of the quarter lantern that flickered over her head. Behind her, she heard the cabin door open, Maria's voice in low, musical notes, and then the Spanish sentry's leering, expectant chuckle. She heard the slap of his roped-soled sandals on the decking of the cabin, the clunk of his musket being set carelessly aside. With quick, deft fingers, Anne tied one end of the grassline coil firmly to the quarter-gallery rail, and tested the knot with a few hard tugs. Then she dropped the coil over the side, hearing a faint splash as it reached the water. Her heart pounding, she grasped the rail and was up and on it, her bare legs flashing in the dim light. She glanced over her shoulder into the cabin. She could see Maria's back, and facing the girl a swarthy infantryman, dark stubble mottling a fat chin. His straw hat was thrown aside and, as Anne watched, he reached forward with pudgy hands and pulled the gown from Maria's shoulders. As it fell about her ankles, the man bared a gap-toothed smirk and roughly pulled the naked girl against him, burying his mouth against her neck. From where she crouched Anne could see the shudder of revulsion that coursed through the girl.

'You've done your bit. Dear God, I must do mine!' she breathed, and looked below. A sudden determination took her, and with quick agility she grasped the grassline, dropped her legs over the rail, and sank towards the black water. Within minutes she was swimming strongly towards the hulk's jetty, trying not to think of what might be lurking in the inky depths below her.

Edward Mainwaring was crouched in his corner of the cage, feeling the ache in his legs but unwilling to move them. It was Hooke, this time, snoring in exhaustion, who lay across them. The others were propped one against the other, or lay curled in a tight, cramped ball, all trying to sleep away the rigours of the march.

He rubbed his face with his hands, feeling the grit and sweat. Once again he forced his mind to go over the situation. They had no knives or tools – not even belt or shoe buckles – that might have allowed them to break out of the cage. The door was only opened, once so far, when one of the crippled *peónes* came below with a lantern and a bucket of the foul slop. There were at least two sentries on deck at all times, as careful listening to the footsteps had revealed. The other militiamen likely were ashore in the huts. That meant that at any one time there would be the two *peónes* to deal with – by the look of them, not a difficult problem – and two armed sentries, who were a far more serious matter. It might be possible to seize, somehow, the *peóne* who brought the swill, and then –

His eyes, accustomed now to the pitch blackness of the gundeck, had caught a flicker of movement forward, where the companionway came down from the weatherdeck. Little more than starlight shafted down the companionway, but it was enough to see by. A small, bare foot came into view on the companion steps. Then a second. Then a pair of slim white legs, climbing cautiously down the companion. As he stared, pressed against the cage, the legs were resolved into a slight, curved, womanly figure wearing a shirt which reached very little past her hips and clung wetly to the contours of her body. As the figure turned, peering fearfully into the dark, her hands held against her breasts, Mainwaring felt a jolt of recognition.

'*Anne!*' he burst out, in a hoarse whisper. 'Dear God, girl! Over here!'

Anne's figure crouched, as if for flight, and then moved out of the light, feeling her way aft. For a moment Mainwaring lost sight of her in the darkness, and his heart raced wildly. He was just about to cry out for her when suddenly she was there, wet and shivering, her breath coming in quick gasps, water dripping from her as she crouched by the cage.

'Edward? You're – in *this*? What is this thing?' she panted.

Her fingers reached for his, and their hands met through the grill. Mainwaring felt a surge of emotion that was hard to hold down.

'What in the name of all that's holy are you – ' he began.

'Please, Edward! Please be quiet! I've only a moment!'

'How did you get here?'

'I'm in the galleon. Let myself down by a line from the stern galleries. The Frenchman is trying to get the ship's bullion out to take back to Porto Bello.'

'What? You *swam*?'

'Yes. Climbed up on the jetty and got aboard. There're two guards, and they're in the cabin drinking. *Will* you let me finish!'

Mainwaring could not resist grinning at her through the cage. 'All right. Go on.'

'They can't get the galleon's captain to agree, so the work is held up. But the crew are a sloppy, lazy lot of oafs, and won't help. So it'll take at least a week. They plan to pack it all over to Porto Bello – '

'I know. To a ship, there. The same one they used

177

when they raided you on Mondego. I'm sorry, Anne. I got there too late. Your father . . .'

He saw the tousled head sink, heard the half-sob bitten back. 'It – it's too late to talk about it. I can't. Oh, Edward, that man is a monster!'

'Has he touched you? Has he – ?'

'No, no. Not yet. But he will, and worse, when they finish the offloading. And he plans to kill you, too!'

In the cage the Dianas were stirring, groaning. Hooke sat up.

'*Miss Anne?*' he croaked, incredulous. 'Wot th' deuce – !'

'Please be quiet, Isaiah. Let her talk. The rest of you, stay silent! Go on, Anne.'

The small figure shuddered. 'He plans to torture and kill you. All of you. You've got to get clear!'

Mainwaring was crouching upright now. 'Not without you, m'love! The bar on the door of this thing. It's on the side. Can you get it off?'

The girl padded quickly around, and inside the cage the men were alert now, their eyes alive with new hope. In the next instant she was feeling for, then tugging at the door's bar.

'It's jammed . . . can't get it . . . There's a lock! A kind of wooden peg lock. I can't get it free!'

The sudden memory of the hated little guards came to Mainwaring's mind. 'Anne, get out of here. We'll find a way to escape. You mustn't get taken by these swine! Get back to the *Granada*. Will you have to climb a line into her?'

'I've done that before. Here! Take these. I managed to hide them!' She pulled the looped cord from her shirt and pushed it through the grillwork into Mainwaring's hands, her fingers lingering on his.

'Please, my love, get out. And come for me!'

'I shall. I shall. Now get going. God, through the bloody sharks and all. You mad, beautiful – !'

'I love you, too,' whispered Anne. 'Please *do* get yourself and your lads out of there. A gentleman really should do the calling!' And in the next instant she was gone, vanishing silently up the companionway.

'God, let her succeed,' breathed Mainwaring.

'Amen t' that, zur!' growled Hooke, the other men murmuring assent.

Mainwaring worked the cord free of the steel, and passed it to Slade.

'Here, Slade. You're the knife artist in this lot. Be ready to use it if we get out of here.'

Slade's teeth flashed in the dark. 'Thankee, zur!'

'That a knife, sir?' asked Winton.

'No. Piece of curved steel. Why?'

Winton was up on his knees. 'The roof o' this damned pigpen, sir. Ain't nailed. It's lashed.'

'What?'

Mainwaring reached up, fingering the overhead grill. Winton was right. The long strips of wood were lashed at their crosspoints, with what felt like tarred marline.

'Damme, you're right. Where's Evans?'

'Here, sir.' A dark shape rose beside him.

'Slade, let Evans have that piece of steel. I promise it'll be returned to you.' Mainwaring turned to Evans. 'You've got the best strength of us all. See if you can cut through that marline.'

'Sir.' The Welshman hunched into position and began sawing away vigorously at one of the cross lashings.

'The rest of you, stand ready to take your turns. Keep sawing till we cut through.'

'Aye, zur!' growled Hooke. 'I be next, Taff.'

Mainwaring sank back, looking over his shoulder instinctively to where the sliver of light would have

179

showed had it been day. He prayed briefly that Anne was somehow back aboard the galleon, and safe, if but for the moment . . .

Had he been on deck in the hulk, he might have seen the faint phosphorescence that flashed in the water, stirred by a small, sturdily swimming figure that moved in frightened determination across the gap of dark water between the ships, to grasp and monkey up the line that hung from the quarter-gallery, and pull herself over the gallery rail to the safety of its shadows with almost the last of her strength.

The lashings proved tougher than Mainwaring hoped and after twenty minutes or so of sawing, the sweat running off him in streams, Evans had ended his third turn and sank down, panting like a run-out dog.

'Bloody cord's . . . made of iron, look you . . . Can't get through.'

Hooke reached for where Evans had been cutting.

'Hell, Taff, ye've done better'n ye thought. Ye've cut through almost all of it, an' were sawin' on th' wood! Give us that piece o' steel.'

Hooke took the tool and began sawing away at a different angle. Within a few minutes he grunted in satisfaction.

'That's done for it.'

Mainwaring knelt beside him. 'Can you pry that wood apart? How much space do we get with one lashing cut?'

Hooke tugged at the wood. 'No more'n a hand's width. Have t'slice more lashin's away.'

'Right, then. On with it.'

It took, in the event, almost three hours of working in turn with the maddeningly small and dull bit of metal before eight lashings had been cut. The last one parted as Sawyer was toiling away in the last frenzy that comes just before the muscles grow too full of pain and fatigue to continue.

The Vineyard man slumped to the deck, gasping. 'Did it, sir! Cut the last 'un. Ye . . . can pry open th' slats . . . I'd warrant!'

'Help me, Mr Hooke!' Mainwaring rose to the half-crouch the cage permitted and, with Hooke beside him, grasped the rough, slivered wood and strained against it. Hooke swore, throwing his weight against the next slat, pulling it in the opposite direction. For a moment, nothing happened, the two men straining in taut silence, at the limits of their strength.

'Damn you!' gasped Hooke. '*Move!*'

In the next instant, with a squealing, snapping crackle, the two slats parted, sending both men sprawling atop the others.

'Good on 'ee, zur!'

'That's our Hooky, by Christ!'

'Quiet, all of you!' barked Mainwaring. 'We'll have those damned sentries down here in an instant!'

He paused, listening for any movement above, any step of rope sandals on decking that meant the dirty little men had heard.

Nothing.

'Come on, lads. Quietly, now, and one at a time. You first, Slade, and get to the foot of the companion as a sentry. Here, take your "knife".'

'Zur!' The little man clutched at the slats, wormed his way up through, and dropped lightly to the deck. Without a sound, he flitted to the foot of the companionway and crouched there watchfully.

'Out you go, the rest of you. You next, Mr Hooke!' whispered Mainwaring.

Within a few minutes all of the men were out of the cage, dropping to the deck and hobbling on stiff and cramped muscles. The deckhead on the brig was little more than five feet in height, but it was palatial compared with the cage.

'Everyone all right?' asked Mainwaring quietly. 'Anyone not able to keep up?'

Shanahan was standing with his weight on one foot. 'It's me foot, sorr. The bloody beastie bite. Can hardly put my weight on it. Sorry, sorr.'

'No matter. You'll not be left behind.'

'I'll look after 'im, sir,' said Evans.

'Good. Now let's get –'

He stopped as Hooke held up a silencing hand in the gloom. There was a scuffle of feet overhead, and then the slap of rope sandals heading for the companionway.

'In under the companion, all of you!' hissed Mainwaring. 'And keep out of sight! Slade, are you – ?'

''Ere, sir. But this ain't no knife t' kill wiv, zur!'

'Then take this braided line. But do it!'

Slade's teeth flashed. 'Aye, zur!'

The others behind him, Mainwaring moved in quick, bare-footed silence to the deeper shadows under the companionway ladder. He looked round for Slade as the rope sandals slapped down the ladder within inches of his eyes.

Slade was in the shadows to the left of the companionway, the braided line Anne had made looped in his small, quick hands. He inched forward, ready to spring.

The guard, short and squat in baggy white pantaloons and torn shirt, clumped heavily to the bottom of the ladder. He was hatless, with a wicked-looking *machete* dangling in one hand. He spat productively into a shadow at the foot of the companionway, wiped his mouth with the back of his free hand, and turned towards the cage. A reek of stale beer reached Mainwaring's nostrils.

The guard had taken two steps when Slade was on him

like a mongoose. The cord whipped around the fat Spaniard's throat, and Slade dragged him down, the *machete* clanging to the deck, the man wheezing horribly as his thick hands clawed at his throat. Slade twisted in terrible effort, and the Spaniard made a queer, popping gulp, and suddenly was still. Slade stood up over the body, and pulled away the cord.

'There's for one o' th' bastards, sir!' His teeth gleamed in a feral grin.

Mainwaring looked down at the blackened, goggling face, the eyes staring in clouding horror, the tongue protruding from the grimacing fat lips. He forced down a feeling of mixed pity and revulsion.

'Williams, get his *machete*. Well done, Slade.'

'Done pigs as was 'arder, zur. Thankee.'

'Follow me on deck, now. And not a sound, if you want to live!'

Mainwaring started up the companionway, creeping silently a step at a time, alert for the faintest alarm. Then a waft of sweet, fresh air struck him, and he was looking up at a sky brilliant with stars.

Cautiously he peered over the lip of the companionway. A quarter moon threw its pale beams across the deck of the prison hulk, and in one swift glance Mainwaring saw that the deck was empty. Aft, the doorway that led in under a half deck was ajar, revealing the flickering light of a guttering candle. Ashore, a few lamps showed along the coast towards the new town, and an orange glow came from the window of one of the low buildings in from the jetty. A babble of voices, a few in song, joined with the clink of glass and pewter to suggest that the building was serving as a *cantina* for the soldiery. To seaward, the galleon rode, anchor lanterns shining in the foreshrouds and above the stern. Warm squares of light showed along the ghostly blue sides, where gunports were open to the cooler night air, and the Spanish seamen within swilled their wine and drunkenly played at cards or dice over their mess tables. The galleon lay in a river of silver that the moon threw across the still waters of the Pacific Ocean, the great South Sea, but now was not the time to be lost in appreciation.

The war. The bloody war, thought Mainwaring, and shook his head.

With a final quick look around, he was out of the companionway and sprinting soundlessly under the half-deck, out of the moonlight. Within a few moments Hooke and the others had emerged like black wraiths from the lower deck and moved to join him, Shanahan hobbling energetically with Evans beside him. As they all pressed in under the half-deck, flattening themselves against the bulkhead to either side of the slightly open door, the *machete* glinted in Williams' grip.

Hooke's whisper was at Mainwaring's ear.

'There were two o' th' buggers, zur. 'Tother must be in there.'

'Aye.' Mainwaring motioned to Williams.

'Sir?'

'You'll have one chance: when he comes through the doorway. Kill him quickly and quietly with that thing. Follow?'

Williams nodded, hefting the evil-looking blade.

'The rest of you, as soon as the man goes down, get in there and see what arms you can find!'

'Aye, aye, sir!'

'Stand ready, then.' Mainwaring inched closer to the door. Then he pursed his lips, and gave a low whistle.

'*Diego? Diego, mi compadre. Qué pasa?*' The voice from within was slurred, and heavy with wine.

Mainwaring whistled again. A chair scraped back, and

then fell to the deck with a thump. Feet scuffed towards the doorway.

Williams' fingers tightened on the *machete*.

In the next instant the Spaniard was stepping out, and Mainwaring had a glimpse of a thin, stooped figure in shirt sleeves and baggy trousers, a pistol in one hand and a straw-wrapped wine bottle in the other. The man was hatless, and his thinning hair blew in the faint breeze above low brows and a long, hooked nose.

'*Ay! Diego? Qué – !*'

Williams' vicious backhand cut of the *machete* struck the man squarely in the throat. Without a sound, he pitched backwards through the open half-deck door and fell sprawling in the passageway. The bottle spun near one outstretched hand, dark wine running to mix with the darker blood that pulsed from the hideous gash across the thin throat.

'Inside!' barked Mainwaring. He leaped over the doorway coaming and over the body, the Dianas at his heels. The aft cabin doorway was ahead, and Mainwaring kicked it open.

'Lor' bless me, what a mess!' said Slade, at his elbow. 'Lived like pigs, they did!' He stared around at the rubbish of wine bottles, bits of food, discarded clothing and equipment.

'There's what we need!' Mainwaring pointed to a musket rack in which twelve long, three-banded Spanish infantry flintlocks were locked, with a clutch of cartridge boxes and bayonets hanging on hooks beside. 'Break the lock, Williams!'

'Aye, sir!' A few ringing blows sent sparks flying as Williams struck at the padlock with the *machete* until the lock shattered and fell to the deck.

'Good! Arm yourselves, lads. Check those cartouche

boxes t' see they've got rounds in them. Prime and load as soon as – '

'Sir!' It was Sawyer, at one of the small sidelights of the cabin that faced shoreward. 'The Dons, sir! A company of 'em! Comin' out o' that hut, an' makin' fer us at th' trot!'

'God damn and blast. On deck, all of you!' barked Mainwaring. '*Move!*'

The men dived for the muskets and the crossbelts, and burst out of the cabin at the run, thundering down the narrow passageway and leaping over the body of the slain guard and the spreading pool of wine and blood.

With Mainwaring leading, they emerged on deck and peered into the darkness ashore.

'Oh, Christ! Now we're for it!' muttered Hooke.

A group of men, the white coats bright in the faint light, were moving at a shambling half-trot towards the jetty, their muskets held high in the ready position known as the 'recover'. At their head was a man whose tricorne marked him an officer, holding high a slim sword. As the officer saw the Dianas appear on the hulk's deck, he shouted an order, and with guttural cries the men came on faster.

'Damn!' swore Mainwaring, and spat over the side. 'Shore sentry must've seen us. Mr Hooke!'

'Zur!'

'Take Williams, Evans and Winton, and get to cover behind the quarterdeck rail! Sawyer and Slade, on the foredeck! Shanahan with me here in the waist! And don't fire until I give you the word!'

In a wild scramble the men moved to their posts, still pouring cartridge powder down barrels or thumping home rammers as they ran. Shanahan, left with Mainwaring, hobbled to the rail and sank to his knees, levelling his musket and drawing it back to full cock.

'Sweet Mother, look at 'em come, sorr!' he said.

In feverish haste Mainwaring finished ramming down the cartridge in his own musket, thrust the ramrod back in its pipes, and pulled the lock to full cock. To either side he heard the other musket locks click.

'Hold till I call!' he cried again.

There was a sudden thunder of feet as the Spanish reached the planking of the jetty. The officer was trotting in front, exhorting his men in a voice rising almost to a shriek, the sword whirling above his head.

They're not going to fire! Mainwaring thought. *They're rushing us with bloody bayonets!*

'Wait . . . wait . . .' He forced his voice to be steady.

The Spanish thundered closer with a chorus of panting oaths and insults, the officer's face smug now, sure the English were going to die in fright. Had they not been an easy mark in the hut at Venta de Cruces? But what of those levelled muskets . . . ?

'At the leading ones, lads! *Fire!*' cried Mainwaring.

He threw his musket to his shouder, took aim at a dim white figure in the bobbing mass on the jetty, and jerked the trigger. With a bright pink flash and shoulder-punching *ftoom*, the big weapon responded. Almost in the same instant, Shanahan fired, and then in a rippling discharge, the other Dianas. The blasts were close, and ear-splitting, the pink flames leaping from the musket barrels blinding in the night gloom.

As the half-dozen heavy lead balls struck home, the officer spun round as if pirouetting, his mouth an open circle of surprise, and then fell in a sprawling heap, his sword clattering down on the jetty. Behind him, several men went down like dumped bundles of laundry on the planking. One man screamed as he fell, a thin, high sound.

Mainwaring coughed in the acrid smoke that billowed

round, pushed back at him by the land breeze. He was priming and loading his musket as fast as possible, hearing the cursing and clink of ramrods as Hooke and the others did likewise. If the Spanish rushed them now, it would have to be the bayonet . . .

But from the jabbering, hesitating men on the jetty, several musket blasts sounded, the sudden punch of smoke and pink flash heralding a few balls that hummed past or struck the hulk with dull thwocks. The death of the officer had thrown the company into confusion, and they milled about, voices at high pitch, fear and uncertainty now visible in their actions.

'Again, lads! Hit 'em!' cried Mainwaring, and again the Dianas' muskets barked out, Mainwaring's among them. More Spanish were punched back and down, their shrieks sounding over the echoes of the gunblasts and the yelling rage and panic of their comrades. For several moments, the Spanish stared about wild-eyed, as some of them fired badly-aimed shots at the sheltered Dianas. And then, as if on signal, the white-coated figures turned and ran in stumbling disorder back along the jetty, a few falling to rise and crawl, ignored by the rest in a pell-mell rush for shelter.

Mainwaring felt the grit of black powder between his teeth. He took aim at a fleeing figure and fired. As the weapon bucked against him, the man threw up his musket, cartwheeling in the air, and fell on his face as if struck down by an axe.

'Cease firing!' coughed Mainwaring.

'They're goin' to shelter, zur!' Hooke bellowed. 'Keep low, zur!'

Even as Hooke spoke, a single musket banged from inshore, and the ball struck the rail several inches from Shanahan's face, sending a small cloud of wood splinters and chips pattering over the deck.

Mainwaring swore luridly and crouched low behind the rail. He squinted inshore as the musket smoke dispersed, trying to see what the Spanish had done. On the jetty, some seven or eight bodies sprawled, dark blotches spreading on the grubby white cloth. The survivors had rushed back to the beach line, where a haphazard stacking of barrels, hogsheads and discarded rigging from the hulk was strewn. Hidden behind this shelter, the Spanish were yelling at one another, and beginning now to snipe at the Dianas.

A second musket flashed inshore, and a ball ticked at Mainwaring's sleeve before glancing with a whine off a mainshrouds deadeye.

'Down, sorr!' said Shanahan. 'They ain't fools with their guns, if ye'll pardon th' liberty!'

Mainwaring dropped to his stomach on the deck, cursing quietly. 'Sweet bloody hell. A musketry skirmish, with us pinned on this damned barge, and making enough noise to rouse half of bloody Spanish America!'

Hooke, working along the quarterdeck like some kind of grovelling bear, had heard Mainwaring. He was pointing seaward now.

'One thing's sartin, zur. The bloody Frog heard us. He's got th' Dons t' put to sea!'

'What?'

Mainwaring squirmed round to stare at the *Granada*. The great ship was alive with activity. But not the activity Mainwaring would have expected and feared, of hordes of armed men cramming into the ship's boats to come inshore, under the run-out guns of the galleon. Men were swarming up the ratlines and out along the yards, casting off the gaskets on the carefully-furled canvas. Already, the fore-t'gallant had been pushed off its yard; a partially opened shape ready to be sheeted home, after its yard was raised, into a working set. On deck, men were at the pin rails, while from below came the muffled but distinct clink of the pawls as the anchor cables were hove short.

'Sir!' Williams was pointing, calling, ignoring a musket ball that shattered against the lip of a lazarette coaming inches from him. 'She's setting sail, sir! She's running!'

'I see it, Williams! For Christ's sake, keep your head down!'

Crushed and with a sinking heart, Mainwaring watched the galleon turn slowly to the wind as its canvas was unfurled. He had had no idea how he was going to deal with the great ship; just a certainty that Anne had to be recovered, and Roche-Bourbon's plans thwarted. It had been a forlorn hope, from the beginning, and he had been stupidly foolish to think that, with a handful of men, he could penetrate the bowels of Spanish America and hope for anything other than death or imprisonment. He thought of the little figure that had stolen down the companion, dripping wet from that incredibly courageous swim, and felt her slipping from his grasp. In listening to his heart and not his duty, he had already killed poor, dour Tindall and had brought Hooke and the others here to die in a preposterous musket skirmish on a rotting hulk in Panama Bay, while the woman he loved and the quarry he had been pursing were sailing away, out of reach for ever.

Hooke had risen, and in a low crouch, rushed with surprising speed and agility down the short ladder from the quarterdeck, his musket at his side. Cries sounded anew ashore, and several muskets banged, the balls whizzing by the ursine form as Hooke slumped to the deck beside Mainwaring, pointing with his free hand at the galleon.

'Lookee thar, zur. On the stern galleries. C'd be these 'ere glims o' mine ain't trimmed proper, but ain't that – ?'

Mainwaring stared. The galleon had turned seaward, now, the great anchors dripping at the catheads, the topsails, and courses dropping with rippling thumps into place, the chants of the men at the braces carrying over the water. The stern lantern glowed orange above the high transom carvings, and the great ensign was floating out in the land breeze that was bearing the ship out to sea. Most of the clutch of boats that had ridden alongside the ship, or astern, had been streamed out on long lines, and were turning obediently, to be towed out to sea and brought aboard when it was felt safe to heave to.

But as Mainwaring looked, he could see the line that secured the lugsail longboat. It led, not up to a boom or a fairlead farther forward, but to the after rail of the stern gallery itself. And there, a small figure with long, dark hair and a billowing white chemise was working at the line which held the boat. Working, even as a tall figure in red suddenly appeared at one end of the gallery and rushed towards her. In the next instant, the figure in red had seized her, a hand cuffing round in a blow, the small figure sinking, dragged back along the gallery and thrust roughly in through a doorway.

But not before the longboat's line snaked over the gallery rail and splashed into the sea, leaving the longboat with its badly brailed-up lugsails turning in the wake of the galleon as she gathered way to seaward.

'Anne!' choked Mainwaring. 'Roche-Bourbon, you foul *bastard*!'

And then, in a rush, he had leaped to his feet, thrown down the musket, and was flinging the cartridge box from him as he sprinted across the deck. In the next instant he was up on the rail, the dark sea-face seemingly hundreds of feet below. Without a pause, he launched himself into a long, arrowing dive, falling for what seemed like an eternity, the wind rushing through his hair.

Then he struck, the tepid water like a wall as it met his head and arms, and he was sinking down, down, the bubbles roaring in his ears, the fear of some unspeakable creature in the depths rising under him making his legs and arms flail out. And then with a gasp he was on the surface, the salt stinging his eyes. The galleon was huge before him, and behind, a rattle of musketry echoed from the shoreline, and closer muskets on the hulk spat back in reply.

The boat!

The longboat swung to its drifting painter, farther to the left than Mainwaring had thought, the land breeze pushing at it now. Mainwaring kicked out strongly, remembering the swimming lessons of old, toothless Obomsawin in the frigid waters of Vineyard Sound. The water roared about his ears as he stroked and kicked, squinting up for the boat. It seemed to recede; was he not moving towards it? If it dirfted seaward faster that he could swim . . .

Then suddenly, it was there above him, his hands banging against the rough, painted wood of the lapstreaks, and he was kicking hard, reaching up, scrabbling for a grip on the gunwale. One hand caught, and then the other, and with cursing effort he fought himself up and over the gunwale, the boat heeling alarmingly – why had he not tried to board over the stern? – and he was collapsing in shin-banging indignity, dripping, into the floorboards.

He sat up, looking around, trying to get his bearings. The galleon was a quarter-mile to seaward now, all plain sail set, her boats behind her like obedient goslings. The hulk loomed, black and stump-masted, behind him, and again the sharp bark of muskets sounded, the white smoke drifting over the rail of the hulk and low over the dark sea towards him.

The boat contained a jumble of ill-stored gear, but

several long oars lay along the thwarts. Mainwaring pulled in the long painter, and then wrestled two of the clumsy oars into their thole pins. Planting his feet against the footboards, he worked the ungainly oars until the longboat bore on the hulk. With a grunt he threw himself into rowing, the loosely-brailed lugsails flapping over his head as he strained, looking over his shoulder for the hulk, the galleon tantalizing and infuriating as she dwindled in lantern-lit, full-sailed elegance to seaward. Swearing volubly, Mainwaring pulled at the oars, sending the heavy boat footing through the lightly rippled water.

''Ere, zur! Throw me yer line!' It was Hooke, high above him at the hulk's seaward rail. Mainwaring was there.

'Never mind that, Isaiah! Get the lads down the battens to me, one by one! Keep some firing going till everyone's here. What are the Dons doing?'

'Gatherin' for a rush, zur! More of th' buggers showed up from inland!'

'Then move! Quickly!'

In the next minute, as Mainwaring manoeuvred the longboat under the battens on the hulk's side, Williams had come tumbling down, eyes wide, his musket banging against the ship's side as he half fell into the boat. His cheek was bloody from a long, wicked-looking wound, and he saw Mainwaring's eyes find it.

'Don ball, sir. Just lucky,' he panted.

Shanahan was next, Evans helping him over the side. Muskets barked somewhere above, and the Irishman swore as he struggled down the battens, his musket slung over his shoulders. With a crash he fell into the floorboards.

'Sweet Mother of Christ!' he burst out.

'Holy Mother Church wouldn't like such talk, Paddy,' said Evans good-naturedly, hauling him up.

'And what a bloody Protestant like you would know about – !' began the Irishman.

'Not *now*, both of you!' rasped Mainwaring. 'Stand ready to help the others!' He looked up, seeing no movement, hearing only another discharge of musketry. 'Come on, come on!' he breathed.

And then they were there, all of them. Hooke standing and snapping off a blast at the rail, the others tumbling and falling down the battens in a heap into the rocking, heeling boat.

'The bastards are makin' their rush, sir!' puffed Winton.

Mainwaring worked the oars furiously, turning the boat so the transom faced the hulk's battens. 'Winton! Clear away the foresail brails! Williams, find the sheets! Shanahan, get up here beside me and take the larboard oar! Quickly!' He looked up, seeing Hooke crouched at the hulk's rail, reloading his musket. A burst of firing sounded, and balls crashed around the sailing master.

'Mr Hooke! In the name of God, *get down here*!'

'Aye, zur!' boomed Hooke. He threw his musket to his shoulder and fired, then turned in savage satisfaction as a shriek followed the sharp crack of his musket and, with startling agility, leaped down the battens and into the boat, a huge grin on his face.

'Got the bugger, zur!' 'E'd tried half a dozen times t' – '

'Isaiah, this is not time for a chat! Clear away the damned mainsail brails! Slade, if you and Sawyer will stop smirking at one another like newlyweds, there's sheets to tend! *Pull*, Shanahan!'

In the general silence that followed the men attended to their work, and with the Irishman following his stroke, Mainwaring leaned into the oar with a will. The boat surged away from the hulk, swinging from side to side as

Mainwaring's more powerful stroke unbalanced Shanahan's.

'Rudder an' tiller 'ere, sir!' Slade cried. He was on his knees on the floorboards, reaching under the aftermost thwart.

'Evans, take my oar! Williams, give those sheets to Shanahan and take his oar. Smartly, now!' He looked up, hearing shouts from the Spanish, and the thump of feet on the gangway. They were still hanging back, uncertain if the Dianas were merely under cover.

Slade was wrestling the heavy wooden rudder over the stern. Mainwaring joined him, and they managed to lower it so that the pintles dropped into their gudgeons. A tiller bar materialized in Slade's hands, and he thrust it into place on the rudder cap and forced in the pin.

'Steerage, sir!' he beamed.

'Well done!' Mainwaring grasped the tiller, working it with a strange thrill of pleasure. 'Pull steady, now, you two! Get us free o' the lee of this hulk. Clear away those brails yet, Mr Hooke?'

'Soon, zur! Damned Dons knotted 'em all t' hell an' gone!'

The two Welshmen strained at their oars, the boat moving fairly quickly now out from under the loom of the hulk. Above, the stained, flax canvas sails were beginning to shake out from their yards as Hooke untangled the fouled line, but the longboat was still too much in the wind shadow of the hulk to feel the breeze yet.

Mainwaring's fingers were white on the tiller bar. If they could only get away before the Spanish fired down at them, and they died like rats in a trap.

Shanahan was looking astern. 'They're on to us, sorr! Aboard the hulk, an' pointin' us out!'

'*Pull*, lads!' urged Mainwaring. He twisted round to

195

look aft. They had moved no more than a hundred yards off the hulk, still close enough for muskets.

Then the Spanish soldiers saw them, realizing that the boat stealing out to sea was the Dianas. Shouts of anger and a welter of orders rang out and white figures lined up along the hulk's seaward rail, the faint light glittering on the musket barrels as they came level.

'Oh, Jesus!' murmured Evans, and closed his eyes.

Mainwaring looked up at the sails. They were stirring now, flapping gently. Could it be that the wind – ?

The pink flashes rippled along the hulk's rail, and there was a hum and whistle in the air. Man-high jets of water spat up around the boat, and overhead a small neat hole pierced the mainsail.

'Missed us, sir!'

'Better luck next time!' said Mainwaring. 'We're still too damned close. Mr Hooke! Bear out the foot of the fores'l to starboard with the boathook! Winton, come aft here and use that bearing-out pole to wing out the mains'l foot to larboard! Lively, now!'

The muskets were coming level again on the receding hulk, the voices loud in anger and frustration. But the wind was freshening, now; the land breeze that had borne the galleon out to sea, and made her a faint, lantern-marked shape on the horizon, was now lifting and carrying them.

'Christ!' said Hooke, clambering aft over the thwarts. 'A breeze, to take us t' seaward!'

The next volley flashed at the hulk's rail, this time more distantly. One ball hissed into the water several feet from the boat's stern. But that was all. The wind was building, firm now, the twin lugsails arching suddenly before it, their reef points tapping happily, the sheets cracking and popping as the strain built, the boat lifting under the

196

exhausted men as a rush and gurgle began to sound under the bows and round the rudder.

'Done it, by God!' exulted Winton. The others grinned and laughed, relief written large on the dirty, smeared faces.

Mainwaring grasped the tiller firmly, aware of the gnawing hunger and the thirst that made his mouth dry as parchment. Relieved as he was to see the last of the hulk and the Spanish muskets, he realized that he was steering this boat off into the middle of the Gulf of Panama in pursuit of a fully-manned and armed Spanish galleon, not knowing if the boat carried so much a single biscuit or drop of water. And if, by some miracle, they survived the next days at sea and came up with the galleon, what in the name of heaven was he going to do then?

Gripping the tiller bar yet more resolutely, Mainwaring relished the lift and rush of the little boat, and the feel of the wind in his hair. He looked at the faces of his men, carefree and beaming at one another as if they entrusted the outcome wholly to him.

Be damned to questions that could not be answered, he thought. Ahead was a ship carying away the woman he loved more than anything in existence, and a man who had become more than a sworn enemy, representing a kind of coldly intelligent evil that threatened every human value and ethic that Mainwaring cherished. And around Mainwaring, in the boat, were seven men who had followed his word and leadership through all the pain and anguish, and who still obeyed and followed him in faith and discipline, ready to try the impossible if Mainwaring but told them he believed it could be done. The galleon standing away on the horizon was not simply an imposs-ible objective; she was there to be pursued, and eventually dealt with. There was no other option. Death would have to be risked again, as in the past, without question.

Play the game, said Mainwaring's mind. *Play the game, and to the very end, my man.*

And with a firm set to his mouth, he took a fresh grip on the tiller bar, and steered in pursuit of the galleon.

6

Edward Mainwaring lay in the tall dune grass that fringed a line of low sand hills on the north shore of the small, sunbaked island of Perico. The bloated red sun had sunk away to the west over the Gulf of Panama, vanishing behind the purple mass of Punta Chame on the mainland. The sky was clear, with a pale evening moon in its darkening blue clarity. A light onshore breeze, the first stirrings of air after a windless day, riffled the grass around the American where he lay.

Mainwaring looked at his hands, red and blistered with saltwater sores. They were trembling slightly, and he felt the weakness lying in his bones like some kind of dread lethargy. He knew he looked, as did all the Dianas, like an apparition of seawreck; hair matted and thick with salt; face sunburnt, the lips cracked and sore, chin and cheeks stubbled with beard; clothing torn and in stained rags; bare feet scarred and scabbed. The last two days, with no food save the powdery biscuit found in the longboat and no water except what they had caught during a pre dawn rain squall that had struck a day before, had seen his strength and that of the others deteriorate to the point where now was the time for the last, desperate gamble: the gamble that would win all – or lose all.

He hugged the hot metal of his musket closer to him, lowering his head to his arms to shake off a wave of faint dizziness, and then forced his bleary, red-rimmed eyes to concentrate on the scene before him.

Nuestra Señora de Granada lay moored by bow and stern anchors in the flat, sandy cove, huge and imposing mass against the low, featureless shoreline. Her canvas was clewed up, and a procession of her boats was under way, rowing in to the dusty beach which fronted the stunted palmetto bushline. Each boat was crammed with noisy, gesticulating men, who splashed ashore to join a growing crowd of their fellows around an enormous, crackling fire over which the crisping carcass of a steer was being slowly turned. Mainwaring had lain in the grass all afternoon, faint with the sun's heat and the swarming insects, as the steer had been forced over the side of the ship, led swimming to shore, and then slaughtered and skinned in *boucanier* fashion for the great fire. As the men waded ashore, the boats pushed off again, returning to the ship to take aboard more of the guffawing, bottle-wielding men that lined *Granada*'s rail.

Emptying the ship for a swill-up ashore, thought Mainwaring. *That lessens the odds*.

The smell of the roasting beef, wafted on the fitful breeze, made him almost cry out in hunger. He bit his lip, forcing the control to return. Of Roche-Bourbon, nothing could be seen. Mainwaring found himself wondering if the galleon's captain had run in panic from the fight in the hulk; it seemed unlikely that the Frenchman would have done so, given the overwhelming force at his command. And Roche-Bourbon was no coward. But how long would the *Granada* hide in this fly-infested, miserable islet in the Islas de las Perlas before putting back in to the Panama Coast – some twenty leagues to the northward – and offloading the treasure cargo? Mainwaring had an image of the galleon's captain and Roche-Bourbon locked in an exchange of wills. And in such an exchange it would be only a matter of time before the Frenchman's icy resolve would win. For that reason, and for the more evident one that Mainwaring and his men would soon lose their capacity to fight, Mainwaring had to act, soon.

He looked at the stern lights of the great ship, a knot of anxiety in his throat. Where, behind those leaded windows glinting golden in the setting sun, was Anne? Was she still alive, still well? The thought of the alternative, and of Roche-Bourbon's vicious cruelty, was almost too much to bear.

The boats were surging towards the beach again, laden to the gunwales with more hooting Spanish, already drunk. And ashore, the voices were louder, the yells and laughter growing as the fire lit the scene more brightly now the sun had set. Bottles clinked and smashed, and an odd, guitar-like instrument was being strummed, a chorus of surprising harmony rising spontaneously in a minor-key song.

Mainwaring looked at the ship closely. He could see no one aloft; one man, apparently unarmed, was pacing the foredeck in sullen duty; another two stood on the quarter-deck, with slung muskets, talking under the curl and snap of the floating great ensign; and in the waist, three men leaned over the rail and shouted at the toiling boatmen in evident desire to join the happenings ashore.

Mainwaring narrowed his eyes in thought. Presumably the boat's crews would become part of the developing bacchanal ashore. That left three men on deck, and perhaps a few more below, including Roche-Bourbon and the galleon's captain. By the flash of red and feathers ashore it would appear the officers of the great ship had not been reluctant to join the festivities. There would never be a better time to act – and likely never a better chance to succeed.

Keeping himself low, Mainwaring squirmed back through the sand and grass until he was out of sight of the ship. Then he rose to his feet, and loped back along the shoreline of the narrow, palmetto-edged beach, until he came round into the narrow creek inlet where the long-boat lay, dragged up on the beach. He stepped in under the hanging branches, and was among the sprawled bodies of the Dianas.

'All right, my lads,' he said. 'Turn to. It's time for action. Mr Hooke!'

Isaiah Hooke, his features burnt fire-coal red, sat up and scratched his matted thatch.

'Christ,' he croaked, 'thought I'd slipped me hawser, an' wuz gone.'

'You're very much alive, Isaiah. And we've got to rouse them.' Mainwaring moved among the men, shaking the tattered, sleeping figures. Slowly, with groans and much effort, they began to sit up and peer at him with strain-reddened eyes.

Sawyer got shakily to his feet and leaned his hands and forehead on his long musket.

'Damn me for a dog, I'm weak!' He looked at Mainwaring. 'Wot's th' do, sir? Beggin' yer pardon. Is the Spanisher there?'

'Aye, she's there, Sawyer. You were right, Winton. She put in and anchored in the bay, instead of standing on towards Isla del Rey. If she had, we'd have lost her in the night.'

Winton was sitting up, rubbing his stubbled chin. 'Figured as much, sir. Flukey winds an' all, this'd be the only shelter, an' Commodore Anson'd be sure t' strike Isla del Rey or th' other bigger islands.'

Slade was on his feet now. His thin features were cruelly sunburnt, and his lips were cracked and bleeding.

'What've the Dons done, zur?' he asked.

'They've left the ship, most of them,' said Mainwaring. 'Got a steer on a spit over a fire ashore and deep into their wine while the Frenchman tries to convince their captain to go back to Panama, I'd think.'

202

At the mention of the beef the men's eyes took on a hard look.

'Damn the bastards. Let 'em choke on th' beast!' muttered Sawyer.

Hooke looked thoughtful. 'That'd mean they've little left but an anchor watch, 'ceptin' thems as may be left below, zur.'

Mainwaring nodded. 'Aye. I could see three watchmen on deck.'

'What is it ye plan t' do, zur, then?' asked Hooke.

Mainwaring looked round the group. 'How many here can't swim?'

'Oh, Christ!' murmured Hooke.

The men looked at each other. Shanahan and Winton held up their hands.

'Me, sorr.'

'Me neither, sir.'

Mainwaring's eyebrows shot up. 'And all the rest can? Bloody marvellous. Usually there isn't a man jack who can swim a stroke.'

Hooke's look was incredulous. 'Is that it, zur? D'ye plan t' *swim* to 'er?'

Mainwaring grinned at the grizzled master's look of dismay. He squatted in the sand and picked up a twig, scratching out a quick sketch.

'Partly,' he said. 'Look. The main cove is here, the galleon's anchored – here. And the ship's company are ashore on the beach – here. And we are here.'

'Not that far from 'em zur,' said Hooke.

'No, it isn't. Surprised we can't hear the bastards carousing, in fact. But here's what we're going to do.'

The men moved in closer around him.

'Four of us – you, Mr Hooke, Slade, and Sawyer, with me – are going to get into the water just behind this point, and swim to the ship, approaching her from the seaward

203

side. There's no appreciable current, and almost no swell. Even so, it'll be a fair swim. Can the three of you do it?'

Hooke exchanged a quick glance with the two little men before nodding. 'Aye, zur. We c'n do it wiv yew.'

'Good. Our job will be to get aboard the ship and secure the upper deck. It'll be completely dark by that point, although the moon will be giving some light. We'll be visible to you others if you know where to look.'

'What'll our job be, sir?' said Winton.

'You, with Shanahan, Evans and Williams, will bring the longboat round. Brail the sails tight as you can, to reduce the chance of being seen. They're dark canvas, and against the horizon won't stand out, likely. Bring the muskets, and wait behind the point, where you can see the ship, but where you're masked from the shore. The moment you see us go over the rail, pull for the seaward side. By the time you get there, we should have taken care of the anchor watch. Get on board, and bring arms for us as well, as quickly as you can.'

'And then, sir?' said Evans. 'I mean – '

'We proceed from there, Evans. Have you no interest in trying to take the ship?'

'Well – er – yes, sir. Of course, sir. But sort of thought of going about it in a ship, see, sir. Not with four matelots in a boat.'

''Ere, Taff,' growled Hooke. 'Don't forget us swimmers.'

Mainwaring grinned. 'All the more challenge, Evans. Remember, it's the last thing the bastards will be thinking about – or expecting!' Then he looked round the gaunt, burnt faces.

'Look, lads. You've given your best. But without food or water we can't go on much longer. We've come this far, and now we've got a chance to finish the job. For Christ's sake, let's not let the Dons win this!'

There was a growl of assent, and Hooke spoke.

'Ye needn't ask, zur. We'll stand by ye.'

Mainwaring looked into the exhausted eyes, seeing there the loyalty and self-discipline.

'Thank you,' he said hoarsely. 'Now, let's do it!'

An hour later, a star-dusted night had settled across the island, transforming it into a floating wraith of moonlit humps and dark shadows set on the surface of the still sea. The fitful Gulf of Panama winds had died away again, and the moon made a still rivulet of light upon which the majesty of *Nuestra Señora de Granada* rode in stately, shadowy grandeur, the orange beam of her great stern lantern adding its own reflection to the water. Ashore, the blazing fire roared ever higher, and above it the figures of the Spanish seamen cavorted or staggered, bottles held high and dripping slabs of roast beef waved about at knifepoint before being devoured. The guitar thrummed, and the harmonies, thickened and slurred now with drink, still rose in the plaintive songs of distant Valencia and Catalonia.

Ashore as well, at the point of land that marked the beginning of the galleon's cove, four other figures, stripped to torn breeches, were moving stealthily. They waded into the tepid, still water and then struck out in steady, quiet swimming for the galleon.

Mainwaring kicked towards the ship, which seemed huge from water level. He tried not to think of the dark shapes of sharks that might be circling under them. Beside him, Hooke was puffing and blowing as he paddled on.

'Looks . . . like a proper castle, don't it . . . zur!' he panted.

'Aye! And I'm wondering how in hell we're going to get aboard that thing!'

'Must be a line or somethin' o'erside, zur. There'll . . . be a way!'

Feeling naked and vulnerable, Mainwaring swam on, looking round every now and then to see that Hooke and the other two were keeping up. The water was cool, now, cooler than Mainwaring had expected, and he found his senses sharpening through fatigue and hunger. It had been sand bottom where they had waded in, but all was dark and deep beneath them, and he shared with the others a reluctance to be the first to speak of the fear he felt prickling at the back of his neck.

The galleon loomed closer, huge and towering. Exposed in the open water, Mainwaring felt certain they were visible, four heads bobbing in the moonlight's path, phosphorescence sparkling round their chests as they swam. His heart was pounding, more from tension than from the strain of the swim. And his mind was full of racing anxieties. How *were* they to board the great ship? And if once aboard, what weapons could they find in time to use? Belaying pins? Would it be bare hands, again?

There was a gasp and a curse behind him, and he swung in the water, to see Slade grimacing and clutching his shoulder.

'What is it, Slade?' hissed Mainwaring.

'Jellyfish, sir! It – just touched m'arm a bit. Hurts – bloody terrible, sir!'

'Can you make it?'

'Aye, sir! No – wish to stay out 'ere, sir!'

'Good man. Come on, then. Sawyer, watch him!'

Puffing and blowing, glancing at the raucous party ashore with white eyes in the darkness, the men swam on towards the ship, the ornately carved stern looming hugely over them, its black-shadowed gilt intricacies touched by the blue moonlight. They could hear the slap-lap of water under the counter, and a gentle swirling slosh around the weed-grown rudder.

Suddenly, the angled, slivery and beslimed column of

206

the aft mooring line was before them, like a snake rising from the seabed. Hooke clung to it, looking up to where in the shadows far above them, it led over the transom rail. The master grunted as he scrabbled at the thick, bar-hard rope, then slid back with a curse.

'No good, zur!' he whispered. 'Slippery as an eel. Can't grip it nohow!'

'All right. Let's move round to the seaward side. And for God's sake don't splash now!'

Cautiously, the four men emerged from the gloom of the counter, edging along the barnacled wale above which towered the wooden wall of the hull. They came round to the side Sawyer pointed with his chin.

'Look, sir! Boat alongside, at th' battens!'

'Come on!' hissed Mainwaring. He led the way, swimming close against the ship's side until the waving seaweed tendrils brushed his forearms and feet. The tumble-home of the hull might hide them from the eyes of the men pacing somewhere above. Then he was at the jolly boat which was tied fore and aft to the distant rail, riding below the battens which led, like projecting steps, to the entry port in the rail above.

'Hooke! Slade! Hold her, either side. Watch you don't bang against the ship's side, Slade!' Mainwaring remembered his shin-barking tumble into the *Granada*'s long-boat. 'I'll go over the stern. Hold her, now!'

When the two men had a grip, Mainwaring reached for the top of the transom, seized it, and hauled himself over and in, gasping and dripping.

He sat up, looking aloft. No inquiring face peered over the rail.

'Right. You next, Sawyer!'

In a moment, the skinny Vineyard youth was aboard and, seconds later, both Hooke and Slade had struggled like seals into the little craft. All four crouched, panting

207

and blowing, waiting for their strength to return. It was obvious to Mainwaring that the men were fast approaching complete exhaustion unless food could be found, and some sleep snatched on anything other than a boat's hard and splintery thwart.

'Follow me up. Slade, you and Sawyer have these men aft. Christ knows how you'll do it. I have the foredeck man. Mr Hooke, you've the waist to secure. Clear?'

The men nodded.

'All right. In the order I told you. Come on.'

The American rose cautiously to his feet in the little boat, and then paused. His voice had a hard edge to its harsh whisper.

'One other thing. No quarter! If we fail at this, we're dead men ourselves!'

The others looked at one another, and then nodded grimly.

'Up we go, then.'

Making sure of his grip, Mainwaring began the long climb up the battens. As he emerged from the shadows, he threw a glance to his right. Back inshore, Evans and the others should now be able to see him, and should be pushing off in the longboat. But he could see nothing.

Upward he went, feeling dreadfully alone, a fly on a wall, the rapid thumping of his heart so strong in his throat that it threatened to choke him. Slade was a few feet below. Mainwaring looked up to the entry port a bare six feet above. If he arrived at it in full view just as the anchor watch's eyes fell on it . . .

And then, in the next minute, he was there, the vast expanse of the galleon's waistdeck before him, and he was scrambling through, to crouch in wide-eyed, pounding silence in the shadow of a high-trucked long gun that sat at its gunport to one side of the entry port. He risked a quick look to either side, saw no one, and in a low crouch ran noiselessly the ten paces needed to hide behind the coils of line hung on the mainmast fiferail. Looking back, he saw Slade and Sawyer slip through the entry port and vanish in a swift, soundless sprint aft into the shadows of the short companion ladder that led up to the quarterdeck. As they did so, Hooke rolled his burly frame through the port, sank down behind the same gun where Mainwaring had hidden, and then in a low scurry remarkable for a man of his bulk crossed into the shadows beside Mainwaring.

'Where th' deuce are th' buggers, zur?' he panted. 'Can't see any of 'em!'

'Christ knows. Perhaps – ' Mainwaring froze. From the half-deck, mere inches from the crouching Slade and Sawyer, two seamen had appeared, muskets slung on their shoulders, talking volubly in breathy Spanish as they went up the ladder to the quarterdeck.

'Time for me to go, while their heads are turned!' whispered Mainwaring. 'Keep low!'

Dodging to the far side of the mast, Mainwaring glanced quickly forward to where the foredeck sentry was leaning against the ship's belfry, staring at the noisy party ashore. His eyes fixed on the sentry. Mainwaring ran swiftly taking care that the mainmast blocked him from the sight of the two men on the quarterdeck. The quick sprint brought him to the side of the larboard foredeck ladder, and he stooped there out of the moonlight.

In the next instant, the silence was broken. As Mainwaring spun round, the bare-backed figures of Slade and Sawyer rose from the shadows, were up the ladder in a few bounds, and rushed the two figures who stood lounging against the starboard mizzen shrouds. A brief cry issued from one of the Spanish, and then the four bodies crashed to the deck in a furious, soundless struggle. Such was the speed and force of the attack that neither Spaniard had managed to unsling his musket. Mainwaring saw fists rise and fall, heard choked-off grunts. And then the two little Dianas were rising to their feet over the prone forms, pulling the muskets' slings free.

On the foredeck, the single sentry had turned and gaped in astonishment. He was unarmed, but in the next instant had dived for the larboard pinrail, reaching for an unencumbered belaying pin.

At that moment, Mainwaring vaulted up the half-dozen steps of the ladder, lowered himself, and tackled the man about the legs in mid-run.

Both men hit the decking hard, the Spaniard yelping in surprise. He was a big man, in baggy petticoat breeches and a coarse, stinking shirt torn open to the waist. Swearing in a burst of garlicky breath, the man lifted his knee in a violent thrust at Mainwaring's groin, while his hands clawed womanishly at the American's face. But Mainwaring had sensed the coming blow and twisted, taking its force on the hard bone of his hip. A sudden fury rose in him at the hands digging into his face, and he smashed them aside with a sweep of his left arm.

'D'ye never fight like *men*, ye bloody – !' he raged, and drove his bunched right fist with all his strength into the man's stubble chin. The Spaniard's head snapped back against the deck with a report, and he was still.

Mainwaring sprang to his feet, looking around. Slade and Sawyer were leaping down into the waist, the Spanish muskets in their hands.

'What'll we do wiv 'em, zur?' Hooke muttered from the waist, pointing at the slumped forms on the foredeck.

'I said no quarter,' said Mainwaring, feeling the claw marks on his face. 'Over the seaward rail with 'em!' And he seized the shirt front of the unconscious man he had felled, dragged him to the rail, and pitched him over. The body hit with a splash, the other two a second later. In

210

the next minute, all four men were standing together in the waist.

'Anyone else visible?' asked Mainwaring. 'What about below?'

'No sign, zur,' Slade shook his head. 'An' th' Dons are noisy buggers, usual, ain't they?'

''E's right, zur,' said Hooke. 'They be all ashore, 'ceptin' an officer or two below, I'd reckon!'

And Anne! said Mainwaring's mind. *Oh, God, grant she's here and alive . . .*

A thump and scuffle sounded at the rail, and Mainwaring turned to see Evans, musket in hand, vault in through the entry port.

'Reportin' as ordered, sir!' he grinned.

'Good man! The others?'

'Followin' me up, sir. Boat's tied up just aft o' that jolly boat. Jammed the painter in a split in one o' the battens. Didn't see us a-rowin', sir?'

Mainwaring shook his head. 'And neither did the drunken swine ashore.'

Hooke spat over the rail, and hitched up his torn breeches.

'What's next, zur?'

'Get yourselves armed. Ah, Williams, and Winton. You've the cartridge boxes too? Good!'

The other men had struggled up through the entry port, laden with weapons and staring around them at the moonlit expanse of empty deck.

'Christ, sorr!' marvelled Shanahan as he limped over. 'She's abandoned!'

Mainwaring took a musket from the Irishman and threw a cartridge box over his shoulder. He began priming and loading the weapon rapidly as he spoke.

'Not bloody likely, Shanahan. Now listen, all of you. We've got to move quickly. Mr Hooke, you'll take Slade and Sawyer and go forward. Search the for'rard companionway and find out if any hands are left aboard. If you find any fight in em', kill 'em. If not, secure 'em somehow and report to me back here. But work your way aft. Winton, you'll come with me down to the cabin area. Evans, I want you and Williams to go below. Find the gunner's stores and break into 'em if you can. I want one of these landward sixpounders loaded and shotted, somehow, facing that beach and those boats! Clear?'

'Aye, sir. What if we meet Dons?'

'Make sure it's you who comes out alive. And don't worry about noise. The uproar ashore will mask that.' He turned to the Irishman. 'With that foot, Shanahan, I want you on deck, here. If the Dons ashore make a move to the boats, fire at 'em. We'll know, and come on deck. And if anyone else shows at that entry port, put a ball into him!'

Shanahan set his jaw. 'Aye, aye, sorr!' he said, and hobbled to the rail.

'Right, then. Away you go, lads! Winton, with me!'

His heart pounding, Mainwaring brought his musket to full cock and held it close against his chest. He moved aft, to where a door led in under the half-deck. Winton padding behind him, he crept to the door and peered within. Light was coming from somewhere inside. He stepped silently in, and saw that ahead, at the end of a narrow passageway, light gleamed around the edges of a cabin door.

'Capt'n's cabin, sir!' whispered Winton.

Mainwaring nodded. Their feet making no noise on the decking, the two men advanced until they stood just outside the door.

'No sentry,' breathed Winton. 'Every one of 'em *must* be ashore, sir!'

'Expect perhaps here,' whispered Mainwaring. *Anne,*

where in God's name are you? cried his thoughts. And with a nod to Winton, he kicked open the door and leaped through, Winton at his heels.

'Good Christ!' burst out Winton.

In the middle of the cabin, sprawled on his back, lay a fat Spanish *hidalgo* with white-powdered, queued hair and a lace-fronted shirt, stained scarlet by the long-handled *stiletto* that rose from the middle of the man's chest. The pudgy face was wide-eyed in surprise, and the white, beringed hands were clutched around the blade that had brought death by an accurate thrust to the heart. Below the shirt, the body was naked, and the white, froglike flesh and dark hair looked obscene in the light of the single guttering lantern that hung over the cabin's bunk.

In the middle of the cabin, over the body, her shoulders heaving with sobs, stood a striking young girl with Indian features and long, black hair, her fists clenched tight against her stomach, oblivious of the gown that had been torn down to her hips, baring heavy, pointed breasts that shook with her weeping.

She looked up, tears streaming down her cheeks.

'I – I saw your boat,' she said, in lightly accented English. 'You are coming for the señora. She knew you would. And I – I knew it was time to take my revenge.' She bowed her head, and the sobbing took command.

'*Anne? Miss Brixham?*' Mainwaring whispered. 'You know where she is? Where – ?'

'*Sí!* Below. The – the cabin below this one. Hurry, *señor*! The other one, the cruel one, has her! And he – ' She could not go on.

Mainwaring spun round. 'Look after her, Winton. And see if there are keys in here. Magazine keys. Then get both of you back on deck!'

'Aye, sir!' Winton was a rough, hard-bitten man, but

213

there was sympathy in his eyes as he looked at the miserable girl. 'I will. Watch your back, sir!'

Mainwaring hurled himself through the door and sprinted forward to the short companion leading below, fear and anxiety gripping him. He vaulted down the narrow ladder and landed with a slap of his feet on the deck below. Ahead was the great cabin's door. In a headlong sprint, Mainwaring rushed down the passage-way, lowered his shoulder and, with a grunt, smashed through the door in a cloud of splinters.

He landed hard, rolled to his feet like a cat, and levelled the musket. A kind of red haze blurred his eyes at the scene before him.

Anne Brixham, her dark hair tumbling in waves down her back, with bruises and welts on her cheeks, and a thin line of blood running from the corner of her mouth, was stretched up taut on tiptoe by thongs that lashed her wrists to the low beam that centred the cabin's deckhead. Her body shook and trembled above the rumpled pile of her clothing, gleaming naked in the light of four candles that had been carefully placed to illuminate her. A fifth candle burned in the hands of a shirt-sleeved Rigaud de la Roche-Bourbon, who was heating the thin sliver of a slender knife blade in its flame.

For a split-second, these figures froze: Anne, her eyes wild with rage and pain, seeing Mainwaring in a kind of unbelieving joy; Roche-Bourbon, disturbed as if from a rubber of whist, eyes featureless in astonishment; and Edward Mainwaring, barely able to speak with the fury that now possessed him.

'You . . . *bloody* . . . *bastard!*' and with those words he fired the musket from the hip.

The weapon went off with a thunderous, deafening detonation, the flame a brilliant flash, the smoke a reeking cloud that filled the chamber. The ball hummed past the incredulous Frenchman, and smashed one of the great stern lights in a crash of breaking glass.

But Mainwaring had not waited to see if the ball had struck home. With savage, killing instinct, he launched himself across the space between them, shouldering into the hard, wiry body of the Frenchman and crashing to the deck with him. Mainwaring's hands intercepted the knife that was arrowing for his throat, twisted the wrist hard, and heard Roche-Bourbon curse in a kind of little shriek as something snapped. In the next half-second, the Frenchman's knees came up, hard and accurately, between Mainwaring's legs, and as the American buckled, eyes misting with nausea, Roche-Bourbon was rolling and scrambling away, clutching his broken wrist with the other hand, eyes on Mainwaring and teeth bared in black, cold fury.

'You are too lucky, Mainwaring!' he shrieked. '*Sacristi*, I should have killed you!'

Mainwaring wavered to his feet, and lunged towards the Frenchman, the nausea still overpowering him. With his good hand Roche-Bourbon seized a chair and threw it at Mainwaring's face. The American took it against his upraised arms, pausing as the impact struck him. Roche-Bourbon sprinted like a cat for the cabin door and was gone through it, screaming in Spanish for the sentries.

The cabin was filled with smoke, more than the musket had produced, and Mainwaring could see that the candle in Roche-Bourbon's hands had landed at the foot of the heavy draperies framing the box bunk; already flames were licking up towards the deckhead, crackling and roaring.

'Anne!'

'Edward! Oh, God, Edward!' Anne Brixham was sobbing uncontrollably.

In a bound, Mainwaring seized the hateful little knife

215

and cut her wrists free, gathering her tightly against him as she fell, her tears streaking his cheeks, her hands holding his face.

'He was – I thought – Oh, Edward, I – '

'Hush! We must get out of here!' He scooped up her clothes – pathetic scraps of a seaman's shirt and breeches – and they stumbled coughing through the smoke. Mainwaring slammed the cabin door shut and then helped Anne struggle tremblingly into her clothes.

'Where is he?' Her eyes were suddenly wild. 'Where is he? I'll *kill* him!'

'Not if I get to him first. On deck for us, now, my love!' Grasping her firmly to him, they rushed up the companionway to the upper deck.

The scene that met their eyes was dramatically different from when Mainwaring had gone below. In the shadow of the foredeck, half a dozen Spanish seamen, in various stages of undress, huddled together, staring at the levelled muskets of Slade and Sawyer. Winton was standing with the girl in the torn gown, who ran to Anne when she saw her and embraced her tearfully. Evans was furiously ramming a short ramrod down the bore of one of the waistdeck guns, while Williams knelt by Shanahan, wrapping a strip of cloth around the Irishman's forehead. Shanahan was pale, and blood from his head wound had made dark rivulets down his face.

Mainwaring knelt beside him.

''E's all right, sir,' said Williams. 'Took a blow from a pin, is all.'

'The Frenchman?'

Shanahan nodded, wincing. 'Aye, sorr. Burst up out o' somewhere an' struck me! Would've done for me, but Taff and Willy here came on deck. The Frog went off at a run somewhere, screamin' somethin'.'

'Trying to find more guards, likely. He – '

'Sir! Sir!' It was Sawyer, pointing landward, holding his musket with the other hand like a huge pistol. 'The Dons, sir! They're comin' at us!'

'Damn!' Mainwaring spun, staring shoreward. On shore, a group of the Spanish were pointing and yelling at the *Granada*, while almost a dozen were shoving at the largest boat on the beach, a launch by the look of it.

'Evans! That gun! Will it fire?'

Evans threw down the rammer. 'It's loaded, sir! Ball and wad! But I've no match! I was damned lucky to find – '

'Never mind! Williams, Winton! Use your muskets as handspikes, here! Move!' The two seamen ran to either side of the gun. Mainwaring rasped quick orders until they had levered the long six-pounder round so that it bore on the launch on the beach.

'Good!' Mainwaring scrabbled in his cartridge box for a musket cartridge.

'Sir! We're *afire!*' Shanahan yelped, and with a *whoosh*, an enormous tongue of flame leaped from the half-deck doorway, illuminating the scene in a ghastly orange glare.

'Over the side with the Dons, Slade!' cried Mainwaring. 'Make 'em swim for their lives! The rest of you, into the longboat! Quickly, Anne!'

The girl was pulling at him. 'Edward, leave the gun! You'll never hit them!'

'I must! They could pursue us with that one boat! *Get over the side!*' he roared, and thrust her towards the entry port.

Overhead, the mizzen rigging was starting to catch alight, and now the heat was building on their faces as the scene was lit ever brighter by the lurid glow.

'Come on, lads!' boomed Hooke, leading a rush to the rail.

'All the swag an' booty in this ship! Spanish gold fer all

of us! All goin't' burn an' be lost! It ain't Christian!'
Evans wailed.

Forward, Sawyer and Slade pushed the last shrieking
Spaniard over the landward rail and then sprinted aft.
Evans picked up Shanahan as if he were a child and ran
to the port, Winton and the Indian girl already making
their way down the battens to the waiting boat. In a
moment, Mainwaring was alone on the blaze-lit deck,
swirled round with smoke.

Coughing as the fumes tore at his throat, he looked
along the gun, seeing that it bore dead on the launch. The
big boat had been shoved clear of the shore, and it was
jammed with seamen wrestling out oars, shaking their
fists at the lone figure illuminated on *Granada*'s deck.
Pouring the musket cartridge on to the gun's vent, he
stepped to one side, inverted his musket over the vent so
that the lock almost touched the little black mound of
gunpowder, and pulled the weapon's trigger.

The gun fired with an ear-splitting bang, leaping back
against its breeching line, the twenty-foot tongue of flame
bright even in the furnace-like glare of the roaring wall of
flame behind Mainwaring. The gout of smoke swirled up
and away, and Mainwaring squinted, peering inshore.

The boat lay half awash, packed with struggling,
screaming figures, the gaping hole clearly visible at the
waterline where the ball had smashed in through the
sternpost and ploughed a bloody path through the massed
flesh within. In the flickering light of the fire, the faces of
the struggling men were so many blobs of white in the
inky darkness of the water.

'A lucky shot, by Christ!' Mainwaring exulted. And
then he heard her calling from overside, the voice clear
and clean through the roar of the flames.

'Edward! Edward! The fire!'

Mainwaring looked up, feeling the heat searing his face,

218

the bubbling tar under his feet. He was surrounded by leaping, roaring flame, the heat mounting unbearably each second. He flung his musket aside and staggered coughing to the rail. Shielding his eyes with his arms, he clambered on to the rail.

Then, with a push of his legs, he launched himself out in an arcing dive towards the dark water below.

The water struck at him like a fist as he hit it, and he sank into its cool depths, the bubbles roaring in his ears. Then he was bursting to the surface, gasping in lungfuls of air, stroking away from the vast, roaring pyre of the burning galleon. It seemed to tower behind him, the burning yards and masts like huge flaming crucifixes that, in the next instant, would topple and smash him into the black depths.

His hands struck wood, and other hands were reaching for him, hands that included hers, soft on his face, and he was being hauled into the longboat, to crumple as a gasping heap in her arms in the sternsheets.

'Right, lads! Let's get to sea, where we c'n sail away from *that*! Give way, t'gether!' cried Hooke.

The oars creaked in the thole pins, Evans and Winton and all the rest doubling up on the oars, their eyes on the towering, enormous blaze that lit them and the sea-face with eye-searing brilliance.

'Must be all that gold, an' such,' said someone. 'All them lovely riches . . .' They pulled steadily to seaward.

Mainwaring sat up, Anne pressed close against him, and stared at the burning ship.

'Damn my eyes, not the end for her I had hoped.' He looked down at Anne. 'But thank God we found you. Nothing else means as much. Nothing!'

Evans, at the stroke oar with Shanahan, spat over the side.

'The Frenchman, sir. Did he – ?'

Hooke nodded. 'Got clean away, seems like. The jolly boat was missin'. Must've gone over th' side when I was for'rard.'

Anne shuddered. 'He's alive. Oh, God. Edward, I can't bear to think – '

Mainwaring hushed her, holding her close.

'He'll have his hands full staying alive, Anne. And the Dons will not think kindly of him. They can hold him responsible for the loss of the ship and all she had in her. He'll be lucky if they let him live.'

'Pray God he does die!' breathed Anne, and pressed closer.

'Look thar, sur!' said Hooke, both hands on the tiller. 'She's goin'!'

Mainwaring looked astern, Anne with him. The men stopped rowing and stared. The Indian girl was curled at Winton's feet, and one of her hands stole into his as they watched.

In the next moment, as if waiting for its audience, the flaming galleon settled lower in the water, clouds of steam hissing up around the flames, and then with a rumbling roar it lifted the flame-wreathed finger of its bowsprit to the night sky, and sank away into the darkness of the bay.

Epilogue

Lieutenant James Howe, acting commander of His Britannic Majesty's Ship *Diana*, paced the quarterdeck in morose resignation. *Diana* was standing along the Darien coast under reduced sail – topsails and headsails – but in the orders that Howe had received from the clearly distraught Admiral Edward Vernon, *Diana* was to break off her patient vigil in one more day. That meant an end to the hopes of all aboard, from the double-up lookouts scanning the shoreline to the dignified, grey-haired gentleman whose slim figure had joined Howe on the quarterdeck at the latter's request. Now Howe met the clear eyes of that gentleman and shook his head.

'I'm – sorry, sir. The lookouts report nothing. We shall have to go about presently.'

Richard Brixham sighed and lowered his eyes, a sad resignation coming over his features for the first time since joining *Diana*.

'I still cannot accept that she is gone, Mr Howe. I still feel that the same Providence which allowed me to lie wounded yet hidden from the Spanish, but be seen and rescued by you, would have protected her. I cannot accept that she is gone. I will not.'

Howe looked at his shoes. 'I understand how you feel, sir. We all wish to believe that she, and Captain Mainwaring and the others, are alive. But I fear that there is less and less chance that – '

'Deck! Deck, there!' came the cry from aloft, not from one of the lookouts, but from the hawk-eyed Jewett, in the maintop.

'Deck, aye?' replied Howe.

'Canoes, sir! Dugouts, by the look of 'em! Paddlin' out. Ye c'n see 'em wiv th' glass, sir!'

A tingle arose at the back of Howe's neck. 'Where away?'

'Just abaft th' beam, sir!'

With quick strides Howe was at the binnacle box, pulling the great telescope from its leather sheath. He snapped it open, searched for a moment, and then steadied the glass.

'Dear God!' He turned to Brixham, a strange expression on his face. 'Sir, I believe – '

But Richard Brixham had taken the glass from him and was peering through it at the two dugout canoes paddled by seven shaggy-haired, bearded men in rags, and two women. One, Indian-looking, with long, straight black hair – and the other with tousled, curly hair, and a wide, happy grin that shone across the water towards him.

Brixham lowered the glass and then turned to Howe. He saw that the tears in his own eyes were matched by those brimming in Howe's.

'Mr Howe,' he whispered, 'I believe you are about to get back your captain. And I my daughter.'

'Quite, sir,' said Howe, a lump in his throat. 'I believe we are!'